The Evolution of Stars

THE MACMILLAN SKY AND TELESCOPE LIBRARY OF ASTRONOMY

With the advent of space exploration the science of astronomy enters a new phase—that of practical application significant not only to scientists but also to the public at large. The rapid critical developments in astronomy that preceded this new phase are presented in this unique library of astronomy made up of articles that first appeared in the prominent journals *Sky and Telescope, The Sky,* and *The Telescope.*

The Evolution of Stars

HOW THEY FORM, AGE, AND DIE

Edited by Thornton Page & Lou Williams Page

volume 6 *Sky and Telescope* Library of Astronomy

Illustrated with about 100 photographs, drawings, and diagrams

The Macmillan Company

Collier-Macmillan Limited, London

Contents

3. The Ages of Star Clusters

4. Star Formation

5. The History of Spinning Material

6. Stellar Explosions

7. Changes in Chemical Composition

8. Peculiarities in the Lives of the Stars

Epilogue   305

Illustrations

Tables

Preface

The changes implied by "evolution" are strongly associated in most minds with the biological species and Charles Darwin. How can the word be applied to the "changeless stars"? A previous volume in this series, Starlight, shows how the stars are changing in many ways, although the changes are generally too slow to be apparent in one man's lifetime. Variations in brightness were first recognized in the western world about four hundred years ago. Then, about two hundred years ago, it was realized that the tremendous energy output of a star implies a change like that which takes place in the burning of coal. About eighty years ago it was proposed that the stars provide their radiant energy by slowly contracting, and by 1910 it was realized that mass is converted to energy in stars. Not until 1940 was it recognized that this conversion takes place in nuclear reactions that slowly alter the composition and structure of each star.

Now, in 1967, astronomers use high-speed electronic computers to calculate how the stars evolve. Most of the computer programing, the formulas, and the ideas on which they are based were developed in the past thirty or forty years, and much of this was recorded as it happened in The Sky, The Telescope, and Sky and Telescope, magazines read by professional astronomers and by many others interested in astronomy. This volume, the sixth in the Sky and Telescope Library of Astronomy series, is a collection of articles arranged in a logical sequence, with a few explanatory notes and connecting remarks by the editors. It is intended to show how current ideas have developed and what astrophysical research is going on today. Subsequent volumes will deal further with nebulae, our Milky Way, and distant galaxies.

Each of the articles in this volume is reproduced essentially as it originally appeared in Sky and Telescope or its predecessors, The Sky and The Telescope, with minor modifications for consistency of style. One article comes from the Monthly Bulletin of the Hayden Planetarium, predecessor of The Sky. In order to maintain continuity, some tangential material has been cut. When the deletions are short they are not indicated, but omissions of one or more paragraphs are designated by ellipses. Occasional minor changes have been made in the wording to improve clarity or to eliminate repetition. A few explanatory additions have been made, usually within brackets.

Selections for which there is no author credit were prepared by the staff of the applicable magazine. Footnotes supplied by the editors bear the initials TLP, as do the passages of editors' comments interspersed throughout the volume.

Of course, the few articles reprinted here are only a small fraction of the record. For more details the reader is referred to bound volumes of The Sky, The Telescope, and Sky and Telescope, available in most libraries. The Introduction to this volume gives a broad description of stellar evolution and a tribute to Otto Struve, who was long involved with the study of it. The following three chapters outline developments in the study of stellar structure and in the collection and presentation of statistical data on individual stars and on clusters. Chapter 4 deals with the formation of stars from clouds of gas and dust, and Chapter 5 with the effects of rotation of such primordial clouds. Chapter 6 describes the "explosive end" of some stars, and Chapter 7, the effects of nuclear reactions. As in most research, the studies and conclusions have raised many new questions; some of these are described in Chapter 8.

THORNTON PAGE

LOU WILLIAMS PAGE

January 1967

About the Editors

Thornton Page is now Fisk Professor of Astronomy at Wesleyan University, Middletown, Connecticut, and director of the Van Vleck Observatory. After studying at Yale University he went to England as a Rhodes Scholar; he received a Ph.D. from Oxford University in 1938. He then spent two years at the Yerkes Observatory and the University of Chicago. Starting in 1940 he worked for the U.S. Navy on magnetic sea mines, first in the Naval Ordnance Laboratory and then as a junior officer in the Pacific, ending up in Japan studying the effects of atomic-bomb explosions. After the war he returned to the University of Chicago and observed galaxies with the new 82-inch telescope of the McDonald Observatory in western Texas. In 1950 he was called back to military service with the Army's Operations Research Office; he spent two years as scientific advisor in the U.S. Army Headquarters, Heidelberg, Germany, and several months in Korea during the war there. Since 1958 he has spent four summers at the Lick and Mount Wilson Observatories in California, taught astronomy courses at the University of Colorado, UCLA, and Yale. During 1965, 1966, and 1967 he has been NAS Research Associate at the Smithsonian and Harvard Observatories.

Mrs. Page received her Ph.D. in geology from the University of Chicago. She is the author of A Dipper Full of Stars, and has collaborated with Mr. Page and others in writing a three-volume text, Introduction to the Physical Sciences. More recently, she has served as editor of the Connecticut Geological and Natural History Survey, taught a science course at Wesleyan University, and written a book on geology for young readers called The Earth and Its Story. The Pages also collaborated with others in writing the high-school text for an earth-science course sponsored by the National Science Foundation and have, individually, produced several research papers in their widely separated fields.

Introduction

Stellar Evolution[1]

BART J. BOK

(*The Sky*, December 1938)

It is a dangerous undertaking for a research astronomer to write a popular article about stellar evolution, and while I do not wish to apologize for my choice of topic I feel as though I should at least try to justify it. The study of stellar evolution is scientifically justifiable since it is in principle only an attempt to correlate more or less isolated observed regularities. But I do not believe that that is the whole story; one cannot neglect the human element. Many of us, who like to think about man's place in the universe, will at least wish to make an attempt to find out if there is not some reasonable scheme for the past development of our universe. Some of my readers may consider this a case of unpardonable curiosity, but human curiosity is one of the main driving forces for scientific research, and should never be prevented from extending itself beyond the observed facts into the realm of the dim past.

The primary task of the astronomer and astrophysicist is to describe and interpret the universe as it is today. It is true that we can boast of many triumphs, but still we should admit that our factual descrip-

[1] Based on notes for a lecture to the Junior Astronomy Club, New York City, delivered on November 19, 1938.

tion of the universe is by no means complete and that the more difficult task of interpretation lags necessarily behind. The study of evolution deals with unobserved changes in present conditions, and we are clearly inviting trouble if we undertake to worry about evolution before we have completed our tasks of description and interpretation of the present.

In 1927 Russell, Dugan, and Stewart wrote what is still the best general textbook of astronomy in the English language. Eleven years after the first publication of the book the authors decided that it was time to bring up to date the second volume, which deals with astrophysics and the sidereal universe. They did not rewrite the entire volume, but added instead a supplement of thirty pages in which they reported on recent advances. It was, however, felt necessary to rewrite completely one chapter, that on the evolution of the stars. The situation seemed hopeful in 1927, inasmuch as the titles of two sections in the chapter on evolution were "Resulting History of a Star" and "The Course of Stellar Evolution." In the 1938 edition the title of the first section is judiciously changed to "Possible History of a Star," and the second one has disappeared entirely.

These changes are symbolic of a change in attitude. In 1927 we realized that we knew little, but we were hopeful of being on the right track; in 1938 we feel that we have learned a great deal in the past eleven years, but we are frank in admitting that at the same time we have become entangled in conflicting views on the subject.

Considerations of the probable age of our universe are basic for all theories of stellar evolution. How long have stars and galaxies existed in more or less their present forms? How old is our sun? Ten years ago the answers to those two questions would have been 10^{12} to 10^{13} years. The proofs that were at that time given, for what is now generally referred to as the "long time-scale," were based on not only an assumption of apparent equipartition of energy of motion among the stars but also on studies of the orbits of double stars and on speculations about the degree of stability of star clusters. Each separate proof seemed valid in 1927, but all these have since been shown to be in error. Because of the importance of stellar-age estimates in discussions of stellar evolution, we shall examine briefly each of these three proofs.

First comes the equipartition argument. The giant stars with total masses of five to ten times the mass of our sun were found to be mov-

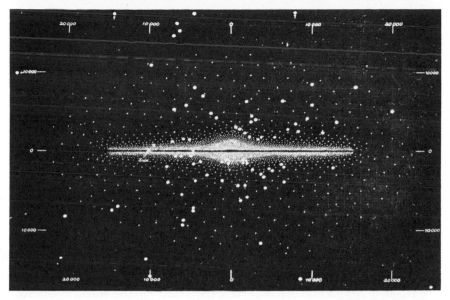

FIG. 1. A model of our galaxy constructed in 1935 by J. S. Plaskett shows a great central disk of stars irregularly distributed in groups or clusters but probably with an underlying field of stars and possibly with a spiral arrangement. The effective diameter is 30,000 parsecs, and its thickness from 1000 to 2000 parsecs except at the center, where there is probably a great spheroid enlargement 5000 parsecs or more in thickness The large dots are globular clusters. Far from the center of the disk is the location of our star, the sun. (From *Dimensions and Structure of the Galaxy* by J. S. Plaskett, Oxford University Press, 1935)

ing very much slower than the dwarf stars of small mass. Computations of the energy of motion indicated that the average amount of energy per star was identical for stars of different mass. This was generally construed as a proof that the stars had had enough time to exchange considerable amounts of energy. Some simple calculations showed that sufficient exchange of energy would probably take place during 10^{12} or 10^{13} years. The equipartition argument had to be discarded when additional observations revealed the presence of fast-moving massive stars.

The double-star argument was disposed of when it became evident that the basic theory for the origin and development of double-star orbits was incorrect.

The original computations for clusters of stars like the Hyades and the Pleiades had showed that these clusters would very slowly "loosen up" because of the irregular gravitational pulls of passing field stars. These computations, which indicated that most clusters would be safe for another 10^{12} years, were based on the assumption that our sun is not very far from the center of our Milky Way system. We now know, however, that our sun is somewhere in the outer parts of our Galaxy, where, according to the theory of galactic rotation, it whirls around the galactic center at a rate of 150 miles per second. When the shearing forces of galactic rotation are taken into account, it is readily shown that a cluster like the Hyades could not be expected to last for as much as 10^{10} (or ten billion) years. It then became apparent that our Milky Way system could hardly have existed in its present form for more than ten billion years.

The past ten years have brought forward several new arguments for the "short time-scale," which is of the order of ten billion years. The theory of the expanding universe has yielded an estimate of 3×10^9 years; if we accept the observed red shifts of the spectral lines of distant galaxies as evidence of real outward velocities, we find that 3×10^9 years ago all galaxies must have been very close together. A second argument came from studies of the distribution of spectra and brightnesses of stars in clusters. In many cases clusters are found to contain some extremely bright stars. These supergiant stars radiate energy at such a rapid rate that they must still be extremely young, ten billion years being an upper limit for their possible age. All stars of a cluster presumably came into existence at the same time, and we can hardly escape the conclusion that the cluster as a whole has existed approximately as long as its most luminous members.

It seems that less than ten billion years ago our universe went through some major catastrophe in which stars, clusters, and galaxies were formed in a volume of space that was small compared to that occupied by luminous matter at this moment. The short time-scale allows the universe only one one-thousandth as long to reach its present stage of development as did the long time-scale in which most of us believed around 1927. That factor of one-thousandth has made it necessary to abandon our 1927 views on stellar evolution entirely and start over again.

All stars are continually losing energy in the form of radiation. That energy must somehow be generated somewhere in stellar interiors, and we wonder if the energy supply will "dry up" in a million years, a billion years, or if it will hold out over a thousand billion years. We can evidently not hope to make relevant remarks about stellar evolution unless we make a detailed study of the mechanisms by which stellar energy is supplied.

Some simple calculations show that chemical transformations of the types that go on in our home furnaces when we burn coke or fuel oil cannot yield sufficient energy to keep a star radiating for as much as a couple of million years. It was at one time thought that the star might draw its energy of radiation from the gravitational energy that would be released as it gradually became smaller and smaller, but it was soon found that this source of energy would also not last for any appreciable length of time. We have to call on more powerful energy sources and it is natural that astrophysicists have considered the possibility of energy generation through nuclear transformations. We can in this connection call on three different types of processes: first, radioactivity; second, annihilation of matter; third, atomic synthesis. Radioactivity of the variety that we know from experiments in the physical laboratory proves to be not a powerful enough source, and our only remaining hopes are processes two and three.

The process of annihilation of matter would yield a very powerful source for stellar energy, if we could only be certain that conditions in stellar interiors are such as to encourage its taking place on a grand scale. We know from modern physics that mass and energy are equivalent. Under certain conditions it should be possible to change the nucleus of a hydrogen atom during a collision with an electron into an energy wave of very short wavelength. This energy wave could then be passed on to the outer layers of the star through a continued process of absorption and re-emission, and the energy would finally be radiated out into space. If such phenomena were actually taking place, most stars would have enough energy to keep on radiating at their present rates for billions upon billions of years. We have learned, however, a good deal about the pressures and temperatures in stellar interiors. The central temperatures, which are most important for our purpose, range apparently from ten to a hundred million degrees. A temperature of a hundred million degrees may seem hot enough for most purposes, but it is not sufficient to start the process of annihilation off on a grand scale; temperatures of the order of ten billion degrees are apparently needed before annihilation will set in.

The only active process on which astrophysicists are agreed is that of atomic synthesis, the process by which heavier elements are built through collisions of lighter particles. Ten years ago the atomic nucleus was still much of a mystery, but by now we know a good deal about the behavior of these nuclei. At the temperatures which prevail in stellar interiors the nuclei of light atoms will collide with such speeds with other nuclei, and electrons or neutrons, that new and heavier nuclei will come into existence. The same kinds of atom building that can now be produced artificially in the physical laboratories are apparently going on on a grand scale inside the stars.

How can the process of atom building be the source of stellar energy? It is a well-established fact that the mass of a heavy nucleus, formed through a collision, is less than the combined mass of the two particles which unite. The small amount of mass lost in the encounter is liberated in the form of radiant energy, and it is this energy which keeps the star's supply up to par during millions after millions of years. We abandoned the hypothesis of the complete transformation of mass into energy because the temperatures in stellar interiors are apparently not high enough for the process to occur. Instead we are now led to a hypothesis in which only a small fraction of the total stellar mass is being "burned up." It is estimated that hardly more than 1 per cent of the total mass of a star will have been changed into radiant energy in the course of the entire process of evolution.

Today there appears to be substantial agreement with respect to the general character of the source of stellar energy. A star will presumably in the beginning consist largely of the lightest element, hydrogen. A small fraction of the available hydrogen will be transformed into helium, and part of the helium supply will take part in the formation of the elements with heavier atomic nuclei. Current estimates suggest that 60 per cent of our sun's mass consists of hydrogen, 36 per cent is probably helium, and the remaining 4 per cent is accounted for by the heavier elements. It is for the present still extremely difficult to predict which specific nuclear transformations will take place at a given temperature and pressure. Numerous suggestions have been made, but I would hesitate to write down the formulas for the nuclear reactions that are most active in the interior of a red-giant star like Betelgeuse or in a more modest dwarf star like our sun. Another ten years may however tell the rest of the story. . . .

If we compare the present situation with that of ten years ago, we find that the short time-scale has replaced the long one and that the

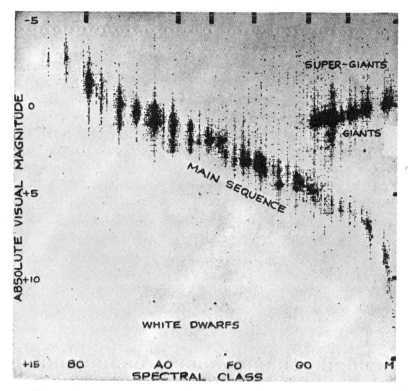

FIG. 2. The relative frequencies of stars of different luminosities (absolute visual magnitudes, M) are demonstrated in the Hertzsprung-Russell diagram, using statistical studies by P. J. van Rhijn. (After Gyllenberg, Lund Observatory; from *Astronomy* by Robert H. Baker, D. Van Nostrand, Princeton, 1964)

uncertainty about the source of stellar energy has been removed by the suggestion, supported both by theory and by experiment, that large amounts of energy are released as a by-product of the process of atom building. With these changes has come a radically different outlook on the problem of stellar evolution.

There is one diagram that plays an important part in all theories of evolution and which we should discuss briefly as an introduction to our remarks on stellar evolution. Twenty-five years ago Russell and Hertzsprung brought together the evidence on the distribution of spectra and absolute magnitudes, or *luminosities*[2] of the stars, and

[2] Figure 2 is a plot of absolute magnitude (or luminosity), M, which is about 5 for the sun, 0 for stars 100 times more luminous than the sun, 10 for stars 100 times less luminous than the sun, and so on.—TLP

embodied it in a diagram that is generally referred to as the Russell-Hertzsprung diagram. Figure 2, which is taken from a paper by the Swedish astronomer Gyllenberg, summarizes our present information on the subject. We know, roughly speaking, of four different types of objects—supergiants, giants, dwarfs, and white dwarfs. The average supergiant is a star whose luminosity exceeds that of our sun by a factor of one thousand, whereas the average giant is fifty to one hundred times as bright as our sun. The giants and supergiants fill the upper portion of the diagram; it is significant to note that all spectral classes, *i.e.*, all surface temperatures, are represented among the giants and supergiants. The vast majority of the stars in our galactic system belong, however, to the main sequence of the dwarf stars, which runs diagonally from upper left to lower right in the diagram. There finally remains the group of the inconspicuous white dwarfs, for which plenty of reserved space is still available in the lower left corner of the diagram.

Some of my older readers are probably acquainted with the picturesque theory of stellar evolution of twenty-five years ago in which a star was supposed to begin its life as a red giant, in the upper right corner of the diagram. In the course of its development it was then supposed to shrink and grow hotter at its surface until finally it became a blue-hot B or A giant [see p. 16]. After that it would gradually cool again, on its way down the main sequence, pass through a stage of development where it would resemble our sun (absolute magnitude +5; spectral type Go), and finish by becoming a very red dwarf of low luminosity and eventually a cold body.

The theory that we have sketched above was replaced around 1925 by one in which account was taken of the recent discovery of white dwarfs, similar to the companion of Sirius, and of some facts about the compressibility of stellar gases, which were unknown in 1913. I need hardly enter into detail about the 1925 theory, which has recently been abandoned, but I wish to point out that in all earlier theories it was assumed that the time which had elapsed since the beginning of things was sufficiently long to render it possible for a single star to have passed through several stages of development from a giant to a dwarf. The acceptance of the short time-scale of cosmic development makes it necessary to look now at the same problem from an entirely different viewpoint.

Let us consider a star like our own sun. Its loss of mass through radiation is so small as to be negligible for an interval of ten billion years. The great majority of the stars are dwarfs that are no where near as bright as our own sun, and we would expect all of them to have hardly changed their positions in the Russell-Hertzsprung diagram during the last ten billion years. It was generally supposed that a dwarf star would follow the main sequence in the course of its evolution. At the moment, the opposite view prevails; a dwarf star, which uses part of its hydrogen for the building of heavier atoms, will probably change its position in the Russell-Hertzsprung diagram very slowly in a direction perpendicular to that of the main sequence [toward the upper right]. The change would be so slow as to be hardly perceptible in our diagram over an interval of ten billion years.

The energy output of the massive giants and supergiants is much more rapid than that of the dwarfs. If atom-building processes are the only source of stellar energy, some of those stars must have undergone considerable changes during the past ten billion years. The supergiants lose energy at such a terrific rate that it is difficult to imagine how a star which is a thousand times as bright as our sun could possibly have existed for more than ten billion years. We have already pointed out that the coexistence of massive supergiants or giants with normal dwarf stars in certain clusters is strong evidence against the long time-scale. Nowhere among existing observations have we any indications that stars are still being "born" today, and we can, at least for the present, not escape the conclusion that all stars were probably formed at an epoch when conditions differed radically from what they are today. The presence of youthful supergiants speaks strongly for the comparative youth of our entire universe with its vast array of stars and stellar systems.

Where does it all lead to? For many years astronomers had thought of our universe as in an advanced evolutionary stage. The advent of the short time-scale has spoiled that picture of quiet dignity. We shall all have to become accustomed to thinking that we are probably living within ten billion years of the beginning of things, which, cosmically speaking, is only a short interval. The universe as we know it today is probably not so very different from what it was shortly after the stars and stellar systems had passed through the great catastrophe that may have marked the beginning of our present expanding universe.

Some of the "short time-scale" theory described by Bok will be further explained and substantiated in this book, and some of it will be modified as a result of observations and theoretical work since 1938. For example, red shifts in the spectra of galaxies now indicate that the age of our "expanding universe" is over ten billion years; many star clusters are much younger than ten billion years; and a few seem to be somewhat older. A great deal more is known about the nuclear reactions going on in stellar interiors and about the evolutionary tracks on an H-R (Hertzsprung-Russell) diagram. Both observation and theoretical calculations show that some stars did not begin life composed entirely of hydrogen.

Fairly definite evidence has come to light of stars now in the process of formation, condensing from interstellar material that probably either was spewed out by older stars or is the debris of an earlier generation that died off in violent explosions. In fact, the idea of two generations of stars—young "Population I" stars and old "Population II" stars—has been extended; there are now thought to be five generations of stars. Of course, it is easy to cite these results of thirty years' research; later chapters will show how such conclusions were reached and provide a better basis for understanding them. Also, it is likely that some of the present ideas accepted by astronomers will be modified during the next thirty years.

Several terms are basic to any discussion of stars. Absolute luminosity (L) is a measure of the intrinsic brightness of a star—the energy radiated per second—usually given in multiples or fractions of the sun's luminosity (about 4×10^{33} ergs/sec). Since stars and clusters of stars have luminosities from 1/10,000 of the sun to 10 billion suns, it is convenient to use the magnitude scale based on the logarithm of L; on this scale the absolute magnitude, M, equals $4.9 - 2.5 \log L$. Spectral class or type is an indication of the surface temperature of a star and is obtained by visual inspection of the star's spectrum. As noted in Chapter 2, it can be replaced by the star's color (ratio of its brightness in red light to that in blue light, or the logarithm of that ratio on a magnitude scale). Spectral type is designated by letters: "O" (for hot stars, about 50,000°K), through "B" (20,000°K), "A" (10,000°K), "F" (7000°K), "G" (5500°K), "K" (4500°K) and "M" (3000°K). These types, and the measurements made to get them, are defined more completely in Volume 5 of this series, Starlight.—TLP

....

Dean of American Astronomers

HARLOW SHAPLEY

(*Sky and Telescope*, April 1957)

Many pages would be needed to give a full account of Henry Norris Russell and his work. In brief space, however, I can record what seems to me of most significance, including his unswerving personal friendship, which was always spiced with useful criticism. But first of all, I should mention his impact on astronomical developments the world over. This may have been even more fruitful than his interpretations and theories.

No one individual in American astronomy has ever equaled his influence throughout five decades as consultant on problems and programs. He grew up with astrophysics. At Princeton, at the Bureau of Standards, at Harvard, and at the Western observatories, he advised, computed, speculated, incited. He also grew up with eclipsing-star theory, with modern thinking on planetary origins, and with the deduction of the masses of the stars; in fact, he fathered these developments.

Russell was at Princeton, except for two years in England, all his adult career. "I had the good fortune," he once remarked, "to have a breakdown early in life." The consequence was that he knew his physical limitations and took care of his health for the succeeding five decades. Although he systematically had vacations by the sea and enjoyed traveling in Europe, his active mind was never far from the stars. His intellectual precocity was acknowledged by his amazed college instructors, who in 1897 graduated him *insigne cum laude*— the only time in recent Princeton history that this ultra-maximum honor has been granted.

To his students Russell was a terrific pacesetter, especially when it came to analysis. And what a memory he had—a quick glance at a page and he retained all its essential content. It would have been discouraging to the rest of us had he not kindly pretended not to notice our limitations.

FIG. 3. Henry Norris Russell, 1877–1957. (Courtesy Princeton University Press)

His early postdoctorate years in England (1903–1904) were devoted to work on stellar parallax, which was continued on his return to Princeton as an instructor. The studies of eclipsing-variable stars began at about the same time that he was promoting his discoveries about giant and dwarf stars and producing the famous diagram showing for the brighter stars absolute magnitudes plotted against spectral types. His name is permanently associated with that of Hertzsprung in this magnitude-color array, which is the most used plot of data in current astronomical research. Russell admitted in my student days that he didn't know exactly the meaning of this H-R relation, and later enjoyed the student howler that "the H-R diagram is the plot of H against R."

Throughout his early years the work on stars and spectra was infiltered with considerations of the planets. One of his first published scientific notes dealt with the atmosphere of Venus. His planetary thinking was synthesized in a lecture series at the University of Virginia and in his very influential book *The Solar System and Its Origin* (Macmillan, 1935). But gradually his interest in the details of spectra grew into a permanent concern. . . . The culmination of this work

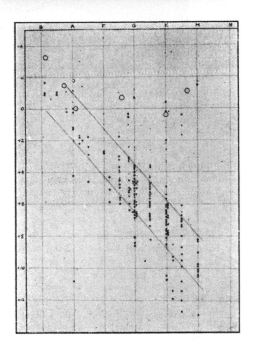

FIG. 4. The original basic Russell diagram of the spectrum-luminosity relation, plotting spectral types against absolute magnitudes of stars for which trigonometrically measured distances were then known. The main sequence is outlined. (Reproduced from *Popular Astronomy*, 1914)

is in his classical paper *"The Composition of the Sun's Atmosphere"* (1929), which gives spectroscopically derived values for the abundance of fifty-six elements. . . .

All the appropriate medals and degrees, and other honors, came to Russell in due course, including the presidencies of the American Astronomical Society, the American Philosophical Society, and the American Association for the Advancement of Science. He didn't like these administrative assignments very much "not my métier," he would say. It was more in keeping with his desires to sit across a table from a few eager students or associates and scribble ideas and make lightning-quick calculations. For several years he was a research associate at Mount Wilson Observatory and at Harvard Observatory. "He is the most important reflector in our whole equipment," one of his beneficiaries observed. . . .

The Yale citation in 1951 on the occasion of awarding him an honorary degree properly summarizes Russell's place in American science: "Dean of American astronomers, profound student of the physics of the stars and the structure of the atom, master in the interpreting to us of the whole domain of astronomical research, philosopher of cosmic evolution and man's place in the universe."

The "eclipsing variables" Russell studied are pairs of stars so close that they appear as single stars in even the largest telescope. As one star moves around the other in such a pair it comes between us and its companion, causing a decrease in brightness by this eclipse. The way in which the masses of the stars in an eclipsing binary (and other pairs of stars) can be determined is described in Volume 1 of this series, *Wanderers in the Sky*. Masses of stars range from 1/10 of the sun's mass to about 100 suns (2×10^{32} gm to 2×10^{35} gm). As might be expected, the more massive giant stars are many times more luminous than the less massive dwarfs. This "mass-luminosity law," together with the H-R diagram, is basic to the study of stellar interiors discussed in Chapter 1.

The many double stars, some of which ("visual binaries") are widely separated and can be tracked in orbit, also provide evidence about stellar evolution, and raise a question of origin: How can a cloud of gas condense into two stars?—TLP

Double-Star Evolution

(*Sky and Telescope*, November 1952)

G. J. Odgers and R. Stewart, of the Dominion Astrophysical Observatory and Pacific Naval Laboratory respectively, have investigated the action of gravitation upon vast bodies of low-density gas and dust as a means of forming double and multiple stars. Double stars are so common in the universe (about one in four) that their existence poses an important problem for which no entirely satisfactory theories have been found.

It is unlikely, for instance, that fission can give rise to a star at all, and the accretion hypothesis runs into the difficulty that there is no correlation between the mass and the period of a binary system. Odgers and Stewart point out that the components of binary stars are in the great majority of cases normal single stars.

There does not seem to be any physical force able to bring enough matter together to form a star except gravitation, and Odgers and Stewart show that masses so formed have stellar dimensions. The density fluctuations in a gaseous medium, consequent on the turbulent character of the motions involved, cannot as such give rise to stars; the very violence of the motions will prevent the matter from coming together sufficiently. But once a star has begun to form, there is a finite probability that it can impose such a pattern of movement on the adjacent material as to give rise to a second stellar mass within its gravitational influence. Thus, under favorable circumstances, a binary system would originate, and multiple systems would form with only slightly less probability.

..

Origin of Binary Stars

DORRIT HOFFLEIT

(*Sky and Telescope*, July 1956)

Fission as a mechanism for the formation of spectroscopic binaries appears to be finally ruled out, according to G. P. Kuiper, Yerkes and McDonald Observatories, in the *Publications* of the Astronomical Society of the Pacific (December 1955).

Kuiper favors a single mechanism for the origin of all types of double stars, spectroscopic as well as visual. Citing recent work on the dimensions of globules [protostars], he believes that a number of condensations in a single protostar could result in a multiple star, though systems of more than two components would ordinarily not be stable unless the distances between the members permitted them to survive under their mutual gravitation.

There is no evidence for two classes of binaries, close and wide, as often supposed in the past. The apparent division into visual and spectroscopic binaries is caused by observational selection. Fission cannot take place in bodies having as strong a density concentration toward the center as is now known to exist in stars.

Kuiper finds that his model for the formation of double stars from protostars gives predictions in reasonable accord with observation for the relative numbers of binary orbits of different sizes.

There is a good deal more about the mechanical problems of double and multiple stars in Chapter 5. A theory of stellar evolution must account for their large numbers and the difference in physical charac-

teristics between two or more stars formed at the same time. As indicated in the two articles above, it was first thought that one rapidly rotating star could split in two ("fission"). Another possibility might seem to be capture of one star by another that happened to pass close by. Calculations show that capture is almost impossible because there is no way to absorb the large energy of motion of one star speeding by another.

In the discussion of rotating stars and double stars, a key concept is that of "angular momentum," a measure of the spin of material about the center of mass. Unless a twisting force is applied from outside, the angular momentum of the material in a nebula condensing into stars must remain constant. Since double stars in a pair go around each other in orbit, the cloud from which they formed must also have been spinning (though more slowly, because of its larger size). So the existence of double stars and rotating stars today implies that there were eddies (vortices) in the earlier clouds of gas and dust. It may be that the original sizes of such eddies determined the sizes of stars formed.

These ideas about birth are linked with ideas about the death of a star. Of course, it might just exhaust its nuclear fuel and cool off to a cold, nonluminous body. But if there are generations of stars, as concluded over thirty years ago, how can one generation provide for the birth of the next?—TLP

•••

Ageing of Stars

(*The Sky*, April 1939)

Professor George Gamow of George Washington University has suggested recently that stars grow old by burning up their supply of hydrogen and getting hotter and hotter. After this first stage in the star's evolution there follows a progressive contraction in which the star's radiation comes from gravitational energy alone. Gamow further suggests that at the point between the two stages the mass of the star must be redistributed, and that during this period of redistribution gravitational energy is liberated, which may result in the additional brightness we observe in so-called exploding stars, or novae.

....

Red Giant to
White Dwarf

DORRIT HOFFLEIT

(*Sky and Telescope*, May 1945)

According to George Gamow of George Washington University a white dwarf may be the remains of a former red giant star, one in which the outer layers have been lost and the white dwarf core exposed. Gamow is the recipient of the award of the Washington Academy of Sciences for achievement in the physical sciences in 1944. The award was made "for distinguished service in theoretical physics, particularly in the understanding of atomic nuclei and of stars."

A normal main-sequence star, evolving in accordance with the carbon cycle of energy production [see p. 36], may eventually consume all of the hydrogen in its central region. Then the surrounding shell of gas must expand, and the star will become a red giant. Surmounting difficulties previously encountered, Gamow reports briefly in the *Physical Review*, February 1945, on a revised stellar model he describes thus:

"The stable state of a star with a core exceeding 10 per cent of the total mass will consist of three different regions: (1) degenerate nucleus, (2) isothermal layer of ideal gas, and (3) radiative envelope." The size and luminosity of the star are determined by conditions at the boundaries between the successive regions.

This stellar model leads to interesting and far-reaching conclusions. "It may be expected that with the gradual approach of the energy-producing shell to the stellar surface, the star will begin to eject its outer layers. . . . The resulting loss of a large part of the stellar mass must lead finally to the unveiling of the white dwarf, which was gradually growing in the center of the star during the red giant part of its evolution."

....

Tycho's Star

DORRIT HOFFLEIT

(*Sky and Telescope*, May 1946)

Tycho's supernova, known as B Cassiopeiae, is invisible because it is at least a billion times fainter than when it shone as bright as Venus in 1572, but it is as laden with interest now as it was then. Its history has been studied by Walter Baade of Mount Wilson Observatory. Two other supernovae of similar type have appeared in our own Milky Way system in the past nine hundred years. Their positions are found from the still visible expanding nebulosities caused by the stellar explosions of 1054 (the Crab nebula) and 1604. Baade states that the supernova star B Cassiopeiae "is of particular interest because it throws new light on the final state of a supernova." No star which could have been the supernova can be found on Mount Wilson plates showing stars to the nineteenth magnitude.

"If the shell [of ejected gas] is unobservable today," Baade writes in *The Astrophysical Journal*, "the reason must be that the excitation provided by the stellar remnant is insufficient." In the case of the Crab nebula, the central exciting star has all the earmarks of a white dwarf except that its bolometric absolute magnitude [its radiation over the entire spectrum] is -1 instead of $+10$. According to the theory of Chandrasekhar, of Yerkes Observatory, the end product of a supernova is a white dwarf; but the fully developed white-dwarf stage (degenerate matter throughout the star) is achieved only after some finite time. The implication is that B Cassiopeiae having an absolute bolometric magnitude probably fainter than 5, is much closer to the final white-dwarf stage than are the other two stars. Although the remnant of the star is too faint for discovery with the 60-inch and is too far north for the 100-inch telescope, Baade says, "there is every prospect that it will be found when the 200-inch telescope at Palomar Mountain comes into operation."

A core of "degenerate matter" forms in the center of a star where nuclear fuel (hydrogen) has run out; there is no more heating, and the pressure and density become very large. The word "degenerate" means that the material no longer behaves like a gas. The nuclei and electrons are jammed so close together that they lose their ability to move freely and to resist compression by exerting outward pressure as a gas does.

The collapse of this degenerate core probably causes the explosion of a supernova, throwing a large fraction of the star's mass out into space and leaving the rest in the form of a white dwarf—a degenerate mass about equal to the sun's mass packed into a volume the size of a planet. These modern concepts of a star's life—from birth in a nebular eddy to death in a collapsed dwarf—are briefly summarized in the next article. A fuller description of how they developed is presented in the rest of this book.—TLP

....

Ages of the Stars

OTTO STRUVE

(*Sky and Telescope*, September 1960)

The stars that make up our Milky Way system differ greatly in age. Very luminous hot blue objects, like Vega, are comparatively young; their enormous outflow of energy cannot have been continuing for more than a few million years. Because such stars are observed in large numbers, the supply of them must be replenished, and some are being formed at the present time.

At the other extreme, the oldest stars are now believed to have ages of the order of 20 billion years, perhaps five times greater than the best estimates of astronomers a few years back. This far-reaching finding is based on studies by many scientists, notably Fred Hoyle in England, Martin Schwarzschild and Allan R. Sandage in the United States.

The breakthrough was made possible by a much improved knowledge of the thermonuclear reactions that are the sources of stellar energy and by a more refined understanding of the internal structure of stars. It became feasible to trace by calculation the manner in which a star evolves, as well as the time scale involved. Using a large electronic computer, today's theoretical astrophysicist can follow, step by step into the remote future or past, the changes of a model star in radius, luminosity, mass, and chemical composition.

If, then, the properties of suitably chosen model stars are compared with the observed characteristics of actual stars, much can be learned about stellar ages. Particularly suitable for this comparison are stars that belong to open clusters. The members of such a cluster are objects of similar ages, which have evolved at different rates, primarily because of differences in mass from star to star.

Three years ago, Sandage presented a paper on the color-magnitude diagrams of star clusters at the Vatican symposium on stellar populations. His basic observational material is summarized in Figure 5A, which gives for each of ten open clusters the relation between the absolute magnitudes and colors of its stars. The lower parts of the main sequences coincide, but for each cluster the upper end of the sequence turns to the right. The most luminous stars on these "stubs"

FIG. 5. A. In this 1957 color-magnitude diagram, by Allan R. Sandage, the ages of stars in galactic clusters may be read on the scale at the right, valid for the upper end of each main sequence. The globular cluster M3 and the sun are also included for comparison. (Courtesy Mount Wilson and Palomar Observatories) B. The color-magnitude diagram as replotted with the horizontal scale converted to temperature in degrees Kelvin (top labels), and the vertical scale to intrinsic luminosity. The clusters to which different features refer can be found in A. Hot stars are at the left and very bright ones near the top. The largest stars, with radii about 1000 times the sun's, are in the Double Cluster in Perseus (upper right). (From *Stellar Populations*, Vatican Observatory, 1958)

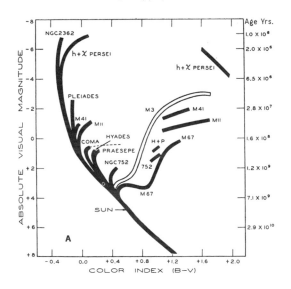
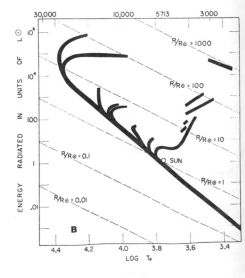

are of absolute magnitude —7 in NGC2362 and the Double Cluster in Perseus, but only about +2 in NGC752.

Sandage gave the same cluster data in a different form in Figure 5B, where the vertical scale is stellar luminosity in units of the sun, and the horizontal scale is effective surface temperature. The dashed lines show the radii of the stars in terms of the sun's as unity.

Sandage told the astronomers gathered at the Vatican symposium, "Current ideas of star formation and subsequent evolution (due principally to early work by Opik, Schönberg and Chandrasekhar, Gamow, and later by Schwarzschild and his school) require that stars are formed from the interstellar medium and contract toward the main sequence. . . . The central temperature rises during contraction, until, at a certain critical value, thermonuclear reactions begin, contraction stops, and a stable star is born. The luminosity of the stable star depends upon the mass of the initial condensation. Because there were many different masses in the initial condensations, stars are spread continuously along the main sequence at the time of stellar birth.

"The first result of the nuclear reactions is to convert hydrogen into helium in the central regions of the star. This causes a readjustment of the stellar structure so as to compensate for the increase in the mean molecular weight. Detailed computations of this structural change were first made by Schönberg and Chandrasekhar and later by many other authors. The general result is that the evolving star remains close to the main sequence until a critical fraction, q_c, of its mass has been exhausted of hydrogen, at which time the star rapidly expands and moves redward [rightward] in the color-magnitude diagram into the region of the yellow giants.

"These theoretical considerations find direct support in the color- and temperature-magnitude diagrams [Fig. 5]. When a cluster has been in existence for a time, 'T', all stars brighter than a certain luminosity will have exhausted the critical mass q_c and will have left the main sequence. Stars only slightly fainter than this limit will have exhausted a smaller fraction q_1 [which is less than q_c] and will have evolved only slightly from their initial stellar structure on the main sequence. The details of the theoretical evolution explain rather well the observed change of slope of each galactic cluster main sequence near its termination point.

FIG. 6. The very young cluster NGC2362 surrounds fourth-magnitude Tau Canis Majoris. This five-minute exposure photograph was taken with Harvard's 60-inch Boyden Station reflector on November 23, 1939. (Courtesy Harvard College Observatory)

TABLE 1. AGES OF GALACTIC CLUSTERS

Cluster	Constellation	M_t	Age in Millions of Years
NGC2362	Canis Major	<-7.0	<1
Double Cluster	Perseus	-7.0	1
Pleiades	Taurus	-2.5	20
M41	Canis Major	-1.5	60
M11	Scutum	-1.3	60
Coma	Coma Berenices	$+0.5$	300
Hyades	Taurus	$+0.8$	400
Praesepe	Cancer	$+0.8$	400
NGC752	Andromeda	$+1.9$	1000
M67	Cancer	$+3.5$	5000

"The age of each cluster follows immediately if we identify the main sequence termination point with the stage when a star has exhausted q_c of its mass of hydrogen."

In this way Sandage obtained the cluster ages in Table 1. They can be read off directly on the scale at the right side of Figure 5A, at the level of the absolute magnitude, M_t, at which the upper end of a cluster's main sequence terminates. For M67 there is no gap between the main-sequence stars and giants, but $+3.5$ can be taken as the brighter limit for the former.

Thus the galactic cluster NGC2362 in Canis Major (Fig. 6) consists of very young stars, less than a million years old, while M67 in Cancer has an age of five billion years, according to Sandage's 1957 work.

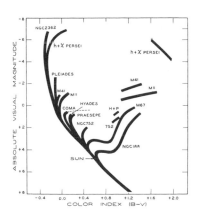

FIG. 7. This is Figure 5A, with the addition of Allan R. Sandage's data for NGC188, whose position in this diagram indicates its extreme age, even greater than that of M67. (Mount Wilson and Palomar Observatories diagram)

During the three years since, several important advances have been made. The time scale of stellar evolution has been more accurately calculated by several astrophysicists, most recently by Hoyle and his associates in England. These computations enabled him, in 1959, to revise the age of M67 upward to 9.2 billion years and to find that the nearby subgiant star Delta Eridani may be as old as 15 billion years! Hoyle and J. Crampin also deduced an age of 50 million years for the Pleiades, although the member star Pleione might be even older.

On the observational side, Ivan King had called attention in 1948 to the odd open cluster NGC188, noting that although it is 14 minutes of arc in diameter, its brightest stars are only about apparent magnitude 14. This cluster is in Cepheus, at right ascension $0^h39^m.5$, declination $+85°04'$ (1950), and is about 3000 light years distant.

In 1956 S. van den Bergh, at David Dunlap Observatory, noticed that the luminosity function (relative number of stars occurring at different levels of luminosity) of NGC188 resembled that of M67. He therefore suggested to Sandage that NGC188 might be as old or older than M67.

The California astronomer undertook a detailed investigation of the cluster in Cepheus, measuring the brightness of its stars in two colors on photographs taken with the Mount Wilson 60-inch reflector, in terms of sequences obtained photoelectrically with the 200-inch Palomar telescope. Figure 7 is from the discussion he plans to publish in *The Astrophysical Journal*, adding the data for NGC188 to Figure 5A.

There is a remarkable similarity in the color-magnitude patterns for M67 and NGC188, but clearly the latter cluster is considerably older, because its turn-off point from the main sequence is at absolute magnitude +5 instead of +4. Using Hoyle's dating process that gave an age of nearly 10 billion years for M67, Sandage finds that NGC-188 is perhaps 24 billion years old.

Sandage cautiously remarks in a letter, "I do not much believe this large age and hope other theoretical people will compute additional models." But there is hardly any doubt that the *relative* ages of the galactic clusters are reasonably correct.

These new estimates of the ages of the oldest stars by Sandage and Hoyle run up to five times greater than the five billion years suggested not long ago for the entire galaxy. This longer time scale is consistent with some other kinds of astronomical data. For example, the age of the earth is fairly reliably known to be between four and five billion years; it is not unreasonable that the galaxy may be several times older. Furthermore, W. A. Fowler and Hoyle's recent calculations on the formation of chemical elements in the Milky Way system give an age of between 12 and 20 billion years.

Another argument can be based on the red shift of the galaxies. Present data indicate that the velocity of recession increases by 75 kilometers per second for each million parsecs of distance, though this value of the so-called Hubble constant is highly uncertain. On simplified assumptions, its reciprocal—11 billion years—represents the lapse of time since the expansion started. But this age should not be taken too seriously because the red shift of galaxy spectra is still not fully understood.

On the other hand, the very long time scale of the oldest stars contradicts some other results. In a discussion of Sandage's paper at the Vatican symposium, the Dutch astronomer J. H. Oort pointed out that only a few galactic clusters have hottest stars of spectral class A1 or later. Out of seventy clusters, ten have stars between O and B2; the hottest stars of fifty-one are between B3 and Ao; and only nine clusters have no stars earlier than A1. Yet if we assume that clusters were born at a uniform rate during the last few billion years, there should be many more of them in the third group than in the first two combined, because cool stars evolve so very much more slowly than do hot ones.

Oort raised the following question: Can any galactic cluster resist for longer than five billion years the disruptive action of tidal forces exerted by other stars, cosmic clouds of dust and gas, and the galaxy as a whole? Even assuming that a cluster is dissolved only by gravitational interaction among its member stars, Chandrasekhar found that the Pleiades will have broken up after three billion years. He derived similar maximum ages for other clusters.

Furthermore, if as some astronomers believe, the internal motions of cluster stars exceed their velocities of escape (as they do in some stellar associations), these stellar groups would disintegrate even more rapidly, perhaps in a few tens of millions of years. Oort expressed his belief in "halfway long" ages of the order of 500 million years for the oldest open clusters.

Other evidence against extremely great stellar ages comes from Su-Shu Huang's very recent study of the masses of stars within 10 parsecs (32.6 light years) of the sun. P. van de Kamp had listed these nearby stars, which, with very few exceptions, are on the main sequence, being predominantly red dwarfs. There is a striking lack of stars with masses less than 1/20 of the sun's in this sample, although current ideas about star formation suggest they should be very numerous.

Why have so few such small stars been detected? Huang proposes that it is because they are not yet shining by thermonuclear reactions, but are still in the contracting stage of their evolution. Hence they would in most cases be too faint to be detected.

This would suggest that the age of the Milky Way is roughly equal to the time interval required for a star of about 0.08 solar mass, such as Ross 614B, to have contracted from a globule to a main-sequence M star. This time is about six to eight billion years. All stars of smaller mass would still be contracting, not having reached the main sequence. Huang also suggests that other dwarf stars are unevolved stars of this kind.

•••

Otto Struve

(*Sky and Telescope*, May 1963)

One of the world's greatest astronomers died on April 6 in Berkeley, California, at the age of 65. Otto Struve deeply influenced the course of twentieth-century astronomy by his discoveries and far-reaching

FIG. 8. Otto Struve, 1897–1963.

suggestions, and by being the teacher of a whole generation of American astrophysicists.

Otto Struve's family background was very remarkable. During the last 250 years his German and Russian ancestors included distinguished historians, mathematicians, chemists, soldiers, diplomats, and social reformers. No fewer than five of his immediate forebears were directors of important observatories in Germany and Russia. When he was born, in Kharkov in 1897, his father, Ludwig, was professor of astronomy there. His grandfather Otto and his great-grandfather Wilhelm had both been Pulkovo directors. Early in the present century Hermann Struve (his uncle) was in charge at Königsberg Observatory, and Georg (Hermann's son) at Berlin-Babelsberg.

In 1921 Otto Struve came to the United States, and two years later he obtained his doctorate at the University of Chicago. Quickly he attained dominating stature as an astronomer. He became the director successively of Yerkes and McDonald Observatories (1932–1947), Leuschner Observatory (1950–1960), and the National Radio Astronomy Observatory at Green Bank, West Virginia (1959–1962). Among the many honors that came to him were the presidencies of the American Astronomical Society (1946–1949) and the International Astronomical Union (1952–1955).

In 1944 he received the high distinction of the Royal Astronomical Society's gold medal. The universities of six countries gave him honorary degrees.

Otto Struve's passing is a special loss for *Sky and Telescope* readers. His monthly article on astronomical research is missing from this magazine for the first time since 1949.

In the intervening years, he wrote for us 152 articles, fourteen of them in two installments. Despite his heavy administrative burden, his extensive observational work and technical writing, he found time to build in this journal an invaluable bridge between astronomical researchers and the scientifically minded public.

While Struve's articles were appearing, astronomy was developing faster than ever before. Many of its advances originated in his own work. The realization that a vast cloud of gas pervades our galaxy and the establishment of its properties was one of his contributions. His discovery that many stars are rotating very rapidly and his brilliant studies of close binary stars are among the foundations of the modern science of stellar evolution.

*In addition to his research and writing (several books, as well as the articles for Sky and Telescope), Otto Struve stimulated many astronomers in the U.S. and in other countries. He attracted to Yerkes Observatory (of the University of Chicago) a prominent group of astronomers, founded the McDonald Observatory in Texas, and helped to educate a sizable fraction of American astronomers. His own work in stellar spectroscopy, and his encouragement of others, were involved in much of what is reported in this book. On May 28, 1966, a group of his colleagues dedicated the 82-inch reflector at the McDonald Observatory as the Struve Telescope after a two-day discussion of astronomical research he had initiated.—*TLP

1

Inside
the Sun
and Stars

In order to study evolutionary change, it is first necessary to describe a star with sufficient precision that changes can be detected. The obvious characteristics are mass, luminosity, radius, and surface temperature. These are found to be related (when the values are tabulated for many stars) in the mass-luminosity law (Fig. 11) and the H-R diagram of luminosity versus temperature. Of course, it might be possible that two stars with equal masses, luminosities, radii, and surface temperatures could differ in some other way; they might, for example, have different central densities, or different chemical compositions. Other possibilities are covered in Volume 5 of this series, Starlight; they include differences in rotation, pulsation, magnetic field, conditions where one star is the companion star in a pair, where its surrounding nebula differs from that of another star, and where it has other peculiarities, such as flares.

The theory of stellar interiors was developed from 1890 to 1930, largely by European astronomers, many of them British. It turned out to be fairly simple to fit the characteristics of ordinary stars by "models," each a sphere of gas of assumed characteristics and an assumed energy source (equal to the luminosity) at the center. Each model star is worked out in accord with the law of gravitation, the relations between pressure, density, and temperature of a gas, the relations between temperature and the energy radiated by hot material, and the estimated opacity of hot gas (absorption of light passing through it). By 1938 astronomers were fairly confident that they knew the conditions inside the sun and stars.—TLP

....

What's Inside
the Stars?

C. A. FEDERER, JR.

(*The Sky*, July 1938)

It might seem a superhuman task for astronomers situated upon this small earth of ours to imagine what is going on inside of one of those tiny points of light which we call the stars. Perhaps not quite so remote seems the possibility that we might learn something about the interior of the sun, for of all the stars it is the only one near enough to present a sizable disk to us. However, problems of this kind are not new to modern scientists, and for many reasons astronomers are interested in knowing about stellar interiors.

First, what is a star? The sun is the nearest star to the earth. If it were as remote as the rest of the stars, it would appear just like one of them, or if another one of the stars were brought as close to us as the sun is, it would probably appear very similar to the sun. Tremendous mass (of the order of 10^{33} to 10^{35} grams), enormous size (of the order of a million miles in diameter), the lavish output of energy (7000 horsepower per square yard for the sun), which includes both light and heat, and a gaseous condition, are the distinguishing characteristics of a star. It is incorrect to think of the sun as being on fire, for it is so hot, even at its surface, that the chemical combination which we call fire cannot take place. It obtains the tremendous energy which it radiates from deep in its interior, and this is the chief reason we are so interested in the composition and construction of that interior. Stars might well be called powerhouses of the universe, for they are the original sources of practically all of its available energy.

Telescopic and spectroscopic observations have furnished us with considerable information about the atmospheres of the sun and the stars. The atmosphere of the sun is all that portion of it outside of or above its photosphere, which is the surface that we commonly see through the telescope or in ordinary photographs of the sun. The photosphere has some thickness; from beneath it no radiation escapes directly into space; from above it very nearly all the sun's energy passes outward without further change. Nevertheless, above the photosphere, there is absorption of a very small percentage of the outgoing radiation, and the material which produces this absorption constitutes the atmosphere of the sun.

Analysis of the dark lines in the sun's spectrum produced by such absorption shows that the solar atmosphere contains about two thirds of the ninety-two chemical elements, and there is no reason to believe that the others may not be present as well. Hydrogen, helium, and calcium are present in comparatively large quantities. The temperature of the atmosphere is lower than that of the photosphere and continually decreases with increasing height above the photosphere. The photosphere itself is at about 5800° absolute. This is usually referred to as the surface temperature of the sun. Some stars have surface temperatures as low as 1000°, while others are as high as 50,000°. Stars may be classified by their colors or spectra. The sun is a yellow star of class Go. Both color and spectral type vary with surface temperature. As told by William A. Barton, Jr., in the May [1938] *Sky*, the stars range tremendously in brightness, size, and density, from the dense companion of Sirius (a white dwarf) to the enormous and puffed-up companion of Epsilon Aurigae (infrared giant).

Now let us turn from a consideration of the largest bodies to the smallest—from the stars to the tiny atoms of which all matter is composed. There are ninety-two different kinds of atoms, which enter into chemical combination to make millions of different kinds of molecules. The atoms themselves are composed of smaller particles, which may be considered pieces of electricity. If they are units of positive electricity, we call them positrons; if neutral, neutrons; if negative, electrons; there are also heavy positive particles, called protons.

Each atom is thought to be constructed of a central nucleus formed by a compact combination of several of these fundamental electrical particles. The nucleus has a net positive charge. For each element the number of particles in the nucleus is different, and so is the positive charge. For hydrogen the positive charge on the nucleus is one. For helium the positive charge is two, and for each succeeding element it increases by one, until uranium is reached, for which the positive charge is ninety-two. The charge on the nucleus therefore identifies the atoms of each element to the exclusion of all others.

But if the atom is to be electrically neutral, it contains more than just the nucleus. In order to counterbalance the positive charge, there must be negative charges, or electrons, outside the nucleus. Although present-day physics has necessitated sweeping changes in the theories regarding the structure of the atom (which no longer permit us to picture it and liken it to larger things), it will serve our purposes in considering stellar interiors to make use of the now old Bohr theory of atomic structure (1913). According to this theory, the electrons outside the nucleus are called "ring electrons." They are thought to revolve around the nucleus in the same manner that the earth and other planets revolve around the sun. These ring electrons are equal in number to the amount of the positive charge on the nucleus, so that for hydrogen there is only one ring electron, for helium there are two ring electrons, and for uranium there are ninety-two electrons outside the nucleus. . . .

An atom which has the full number of ring electrons will be neutral as far as its electric charge is concerned. But if by some process, usually requiring considerable energy, one of the ring electrons is knocked off or removed, the atom will have a positive charge of one unit, and we call it an ionized atom, or simply an ion. It is also possible to remove more than just one ring electron, and in that case we say the atom is doubly or triply ionized, or more, as the case might be. It is not impossible to conceive that all of the ring electrons can be stripped from the nucleus, so that nothing is left but the nucleus. In the heavier elements, however, this requires such a great amount of energy that physicists are still occupied in trying to strip these larger atoms of more than a few of their outermost electrons.

The astronomer comes to the assistance of his brother in the laboratory by pointing out that in the sun and in the stars we have a workshop where conditions exist which cannot be produced on the earth. By the study of these distant objects much can be learned about the properties of the atom.

Let us try to imagine what matter inside a star is like in terms of our knowledge of the atom. It is thought that as we descend into our own earth the temperature increases very rapidly. The same is true of the sun and all stars. The temperature at the photosphere of the sun is about 5800°K [5527°C or 9980°F; absolute temperature (°K) is measured in centigrade degrees from absolute zero, −273°C], but as we go into its interior the very weight of the overlying material causes a continual increase in the temperature, because of the increasing pressure. At the center this pressure must be of the order of a million tons per square centimeter. At such a pressure the temperature must be at least ten million degrees and it may be actually two or three times this amount.

This is not an amazing figure to the physicist, for he thinks of temperature in terms of speed of motion of the particles composing the gas. Nevertheless, this is no reason for thinking of the inside of a star as not being a very hot place. At such high temperatures the particles of which the star is composed are flying about so fast that they are coming into collision very frequently with one another, with the result that they are all rather badly damaged. The impacts are so violent between the atoms that the ring electrons are knocked loose, and in many cases the atomic nuclei are entirely stripped of their ring electrons. Thus in the interior of the star we have a laboratory which can bring about a condition of the atoms difficult, if not impossible, to obtain on the earth.

The *neutral* atom, with its *complete* number of ring electrons, is composed mostly of empty space. One of the problems of astronomy has been to explain how the stars could contain so much matter, be so dense at their centers, and still remain entirely gaseous. Ordinary terrestrial atoms, if subjected to too great pressure, will have a tendency to jam, and the matter changes to a solid or liquid state, even though the temperature is high. But in the stars, where most of the ring electrons are lost, the size of each atom is probably tremendously diminished, and it is possible to have matter in a "degenerate" state several thousand times the density of platinum, if we can strip the atomic nuclei of almost all their ring electrons. The famous companion star of Sirius is an example, for it is definitely known that a cubic inch of the matter of that star, if brought to the surface of the earth, would weigh about a ton; it is 50,000 times as dense as water.

But matter is not the only thing inside a star. It also contains a tremendous amount of radiant energy. The light which comes out is only a very tiny fraction of this energy which has managed to leak out from inside the star. The interior energy is mostly in the form of X rays, which are the same as light rays but of a much higher frequency and shorter wavelength. These X rays are continually passing through the material inside of the star in all directions, being absorbed by the atoms and re-emitted by them, and gradually passing from the hot center to the cooler outside. We can now understand how a star retains its size, for if only gravitation were active in it, it would surely collapse to very dense and solid material. The pressure of gas at high temperature and the pressure of the radiation are the two factors which counteract gravity and keep the star puffed up and expanded, like a balloon.

One of the important facts about the stars is that their masses range from about one tenth to about one hundred times that of the sun (from 10^{32} to 10^{35} grams). It has been shown that in a body less massive than 10^{32} grams, radiation pressure is practically negligible and the luminosity very low, while in a body more massive than 10^{35} grams, radiation pressure becomes so great (in comparison with gravitational force holding the gas down) that the body is unstable. Apparently, then, too massive a star would explode or be disrupted by radiation pressure, while those not massive enough do not shine at all.

Why does the star contain radiant energy at all? Again we must rely upon the tremendous temperatures which prevail in stellar interiors to explain this. The hotter a piece of iron in a forge becomes, the brighter it shines. Laws of electromagnetic radiation show that the total amount of energy emitted increases with the fourth power of the temperature. Furthermore, the frequency of the radiation of maximum intensity increases with the temperature. Thus stars of high surface temperatures have bright surfaces and are white or blue, while cool stars are dull and red. Inside the stars the temperatures are so high that the radiation of maximum intensity is soft X rays, of shorter wavelength than ultraviolet light. The total amount of such energy inside a star is immense.

Naturally astronomers have endeavored to determine the source of the energy which a star so profusely radiates. The theory of the contraction of the sun and the consequent increase in its temperature from the loss of gravitational energy does not permit the sun a life-time as long as that of the earth [four billion years]. Neither can radioactivity supply sufficient energy. It has been suggested that meteors falling into the sun have supplied the energy it radiates, but there are not enough meteors near the sun to do this. The only present theory which seems to fit the facts is that the stars are giant converters—changing matter into radiant energy. In fact, according to the theory of relativity, each gram of matter in the universe repre-sents 10^{21} ergs of energy. This means that the total mass of the sun is equivalent to 2×10^{54} ergs. Just how the annihilation of matter inside a star is taking place has not been established, but even at its present rate, converting five million tons mass to energy each second, the sun can keep on shining for many times its present age, which is thought to be about five billion years. The sun is thought to have lost only one fifteen-thousandth of its whole mass in the past billion years.

Our newspapers daily attest to the fact that research physicists everywhere are devoting the greater portion of their efforts to the problems of the structure of the atom and the release of subatomic energy. The interior of a star, as Eddington and others have shown, assumes a position of major importance in their considerations, since it provides unique conditions for study.

···

Source of the
Sun's Energy

DONALD H. MENZEL

(*The Telescope*, July–August 1937)

Astronomers are missing something if the following excerpt from a story in the Chicago *Daily News* is reliable: "So, alternately talking and dozing and eating bananas, the sun sank slowly behind the mountains and the air grew fresher."

Perhaps some of those faint lines as yet unidentified in the solar spectrum are due to banana oil. The rumbles and squeaks we are getting on the radio these days may be due simply to solar snoring, and not to sunspots!

And now we know where the sun gets its energy. In fact we can calculate the number of bananas the sun must consume daily in order to keep going. According to the diet handbooks, an average banana is equivalent to 170 calories. The sun's energy output per day is 7,730,000,000,000,000,000,000,000,000,000 calories. Dividing this latter figure by the former, we calculate that the sun consumes 45,470,588,-235,294,117,647,058,823.53 bananas per day.

To determine the weight of the fruit, we first consulted the observatory secretary, who told us that when bananas are three pounds for a quarter she can purchase four bananas for ten cents. One banana, therefore, weighs three tenths of a pound. Since in scientific research experiment is always advisable, your editor borrowed a banana and weighed it on the postal scales. The answer was, again, three tenths of a pound, a result that proves our calculations correct up to this point and provides correlative information about the grocer's honesty. Thus reassured, we multiply the above number by 0.3 and divide by 2000. The weight of the daily banana intake is 6,820,588,235,294,-117,647,058.8 tons, approximately. By a curious coincidence, this figure is almost exactly equal to the mass of the earth. We can be reasonably sure, therefore, that the sun does not get its bananas from terrestrial sources. The sun now weighs 329,390 times as much as the earth, and since the sun is adding to its mass at the rate of one earth per day, we easily figure that it sprang into existence 329,390 days, or 900 years, ago. A more refined calculation, with a slide rule, places the date of creation as April 27, A.D. 1075 at 4:32 P.M., Eastern Daylight Time. This result is probably as reliable as some others that have been given.

The foregoing calculations are not without true scientific interest. Substitute coal, kerosene, or illuminating gas for the bananas. Since the caloric value of these commodities is at most three or four times higher than that of bananas, it follows that if combustion were the source of solar energy, the sun would burn to ashes within a few thousand years. There is no evidence of replenishment of fuel from without. No ordinary chemical reaction could maintain the solar heat. The earth has been in existence for at least a thousand million years. Hence astronomers still search for more powerful energy sources and theorize about subatomic chemical reactions that involve the hearts of atoms.

Menzel's humor is intended to cast ridicule on the idea of chemical reactions (digesting bananas or burning coal) as a source of the sun's luminosity. Note that in the late thirties both Federer and Menzel were convinced that the sun's energy comes from conversion of mass, but that neither one knew of a specific process by which this could be done. One of the speculative "subatomic processes" mentioned by Menzel was worked out by Hans Bethe in 1938—a series of nuclear reactions, now called the carbon, or C-N, cycle, that can account for the rate of energy output from the sun. See Volume 3 of this series, The Origin of the Solar System, for a discussion of this. By 1948 Bethe's C-N cycle was fully accepted by astronomers, and another cycle (the "proton-proton reaction") was soon to be announced.—TLP

....

The Energy of the Sun and Stars

LAWRENCE H. ALLER

(*Sky and Telescope*, February 1948)

The sun is larger than a million earths and has about 330,000 times as much mass as the earth. Insofar as the surface composition can be regarded as typical of the sun as a whole, we may say that it is composed mostly of hydrogen and helium, with liberal amounts of impurities such as calcium, carbon, iron, magnesium, oxygen, and sodium.

The energy output of the sun is enormous by our standards. We can measure the amount of energy reaching the earth by the rate at which the sun heats water or warms a blackened silver disk exposed to its rays. The earth and other planets intercept only a tiny fraction of the energy of the sun—all the rest passes out into space and is wasted, as far as we can judge. The total radiation of the sun is equivalent to 5.08×10^{23} horsepower. If we paid for this at the rate of one cent per kilowatt hour, then the entire cost of the Second World War—one trillion dollars—would purchase the sun's energy for but a hundred millionth of a second!

Whence is this vast energy output derived? If the sun were made of pure coal and enough oxygen were supplied to burn it, the sun would burn out in 6000 years, a tiny fraction of the time man has existed on the earth. The sun is not burning—its power derives from some other source. Many years ago, Helmholtz, a German physicist, suggested that the contraction of the sun and the consequent heating of the gases of which it is composed supplied the solar energy. A shrinking of a few hundred feet a year would suffice to supply the observed energy output, hence no change in the apparent size of the sun would have occurred in historical time.

But even by contraction the sun could not have supplied energy at its present rate for more than 20 million years, and the geological record in the rocks reveals that life has existed on the earth's surface for at least a thousand million years. Since life is a fearfully fragile phenomenon, this means that the sun must have been shining at very close to its present rate for a million millennia. No chemical or mechanical process will do; we must turn to subatomic or nuclear processes wherein the very atoms themselves are transformed.

Our first guess might be that the sun is made almost entirely out of uranium. Under natural conditions this element disintegrates into lead with the emission of high-energy radiation, electrons (beta rays), and helium nuclei (alpha particles). The process is very slow. It would take 2000 million years for a pound of uranium to change half into lead. A uranium sun would last long enough, but the energy output rate would not suffice to prevent the oceans on the earth from freezing solid.

Next we might inquire whether the high densities and temperatures that exist in the center of the sun could play a role. The nuclear physicist can tell us the temperatures we must have for the atoms themselves to be transformed. Fortunately, this question is not as difficult to answer as one might suppose. The sun is gaseous throughout, even though its average density is greater than that of water— about that of soft lignite coal. Through most of the solar interior the temperature is so high that the electrons are stripped off the atoms, and the gas may be compressed to a very high density and still retain the properties a physicist or chemist associates with the term "gas."

In some way energy is generated in the interior and passes to the surface of the sun and other stars, whence it escapes into space. The way in which the energy flows is determined by the rate of temperature increase as we go into the star. If this rate is high, the energy transport takes place by large-scale convective currents, much as a room is heated by air currents rising from a hot stove and circulating about. Throughout most of the star the energy is passed from point to point by light waves—the material is hot and absorbs and emits radiation—and the energy, mostly in the form of soft X rays, gradually works its way to the surface. The rate of flow of radiation will depend on the temperature of the material and on its composition. In the deep interior, where the temperature is a million degrees or more, iron will be much more effective at blocking radiation than will hydrogen or helium.

Furthermore, the star must be a permanent affair and therefore in balance. At each point the pressure of the gas must offset the weight of the overlying layers, just as the pressure in the earth's atmosphere equals the weight in the atmosphere above a unit area at any given altitude. The pressure of a gas is proportional to the temperature and to the number of particles per cubic inch. A pound of hydrogen completely ionized into its constituent electrons and protons supplies more particles than a pound of, say, iron which has been completely ionized into iron nuclei and electrons. To produce the same pressure, the iron must have a higher temperature than the hydrogen.

The pressure within a star is determined by the weight of the layers above, that is, by the mass of the star, and hence the temperature in the interior will depend on the mass and, as we have seen, on the composition as well. Therefore if an astronomer is given the mass, luminosity, radius, and composition of a star, he can compute the temperature and density in the deep interior with the aid of the aforementioned physical considerations. In this way it is found that the central temperature of the sun is about 20 million degrees absolute (K), and the central density is about 100 times that of water

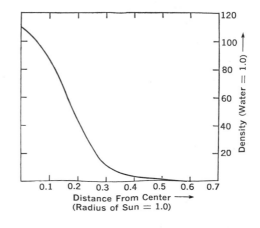

FIG. 9. The internal densities in the sun, in terms of the density of water, are here plotted against distance from the center (sun radius equals 1.0). (From *Atoms, Stars, and Nebulae* by Leo Goldberg and Lawrence H. Aller, McGraw-Hill, Blakiston Division, 1943. Permission, Harvard University Press)

Density (Water = 1.0)

Distance From Center ⟶
(Radius of Sun = 1.0)

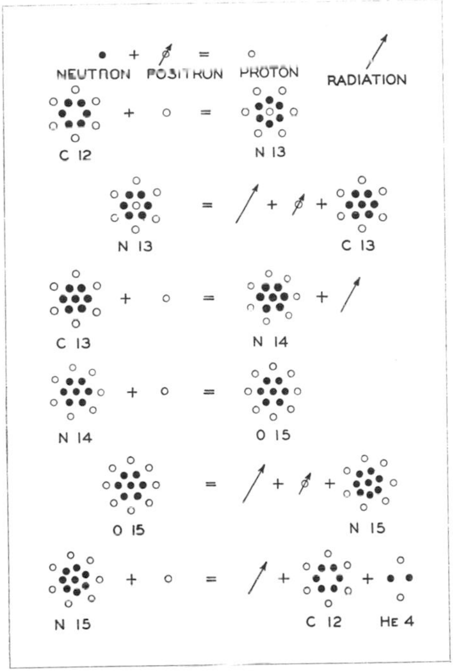

FIG. 10. The carbon cycle, proposed by Hans Bethe to explain the energy generation in the main-sequence stars. The key to the symbols is given in the topmost equation: neutron plus position equals proton. Note that the end product of the carbon cycle is the original carbon 12 atom and a helium atom.

● NEUTRON + ∅ POSITRON = ○ PROTON   ↗ RADIATION

C 12 + ○ = N 13

N 13 = ↗ + ∅ + C 13

C 13 + ○ = N 14 + ↗

N 14 + ○ = O 15

O 15 = ↗ + ∅ + N 15

N 15 + ○ = ↗ + C 12 + HE 4

(Fig. 9). The vast bulk of the interior of the sun is hotter than a million degrees.

At these temperatures the stripped atoms are jostled violently against one another. The impacts may be so severe that the nuclei of the atoms themselves are transformed. Thus a proton (hydrogen nucleus) colliding with a carbon nucleus under conditions prevailing in stellar interiors may be captured by the latter to form a nitrogen nucleus of atomic weight 13. A high-energy X ray is emitted in the process. Subsequent changes in the nitrogen nucleus caused by further bombardment by protons may turn it into oxygen, which in turn breaks up into carbon and helium, as shown in Figure 10. Thus, the energy of the sun and similar stars appears to be generated in a very special process called the carbon cycle, wherein four hydrogen nuclei are cemented into helium while carbon acts as the catalyst, that is, as a necessary participant in the process although it itself is not used up.

On the scale of the relative weights of atoms, a hydrogen atom has a mass of 1.00813, while a normal helium atom has a mass of 4.00386. Therefore, four hydrogen atoms have a mass of 4.03252 and exceed the mass of a helium atom by 0.02866, or one part in 141.

This excess mass is converted into energy in accordance with Einstein's formula $E = mc^2$, where c is the velocity of light in centimeters per second and m is the loss of mass in grams. In order to shine at its present rate, the sun must annihilate four million tons of matter every second [or convert 141 $\times$ 4 million tons of hydrogen into helium every second]. But the mass of the sun is so great that it can go on shining for thousands of millions of years to come before it exhausts its supply of hydrogen fuel. Bethe found that at the temperature and density of the center of the sun, energy generation by the carbon cycle would suffice nicely to account for the observed energy output and to insure its continuance throughout all of geological time.

Although the carbon cycle gives an excellent explanation for the energy output of the sun and similar stars, difficulties appear when we attempt to apply it to giant or very luminous stars. The troubles are of two kinds. If, with the methods followed for the sun, we calculate the internal temperatures and densities of a giant star such as Capella, we find that the internal temperatures are too low for the carbon cycle to operate. Other nuclear processes might work, but they all involve light and terrestrially rare elements such as heavy hydrogen (deuterium), lithium, boron, or beryllium, and it is difficult to conceive of the giant stars as being composed primarily of them. If gravitational contraction plays a role (as Helmholtz had suggested for the sun), the life of a giant star must be unduly short.

Among the most interesting objects in the sky are the Cepheid variables, pulsating stars many times larger than the sun. The periods of pulsation of these objects depend on their respective densities—the greater the density the shorter the period. If these stars were contracting, their densities would slowly increase and their periods would shorten. The best known of these variables, Delta Cephei, has been observed for two hundred years and no shortening of period has been found. Hence gravitational contraction appears not to be the source of energy generation, at least in the Cepheids.

The carbon cycle explains energy generation in very hot blue stars, although the energy output per pound must be a thousand times greater than in the sun [in agreement with the mass-luminosity law; Fig. 11]. Such a star will expend its fuel in a few million years, even if it started entirely of hydrogen. Hence such stars cannot have been shining as long as the sun; either they have existed in some non-

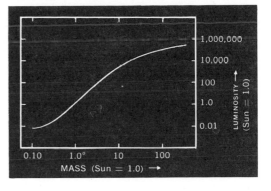

FIG. 11. Stars of the greatest intrinsic brightness are in general the most massive, as this mass-luminosity diagram shows. The scale is logarithmic in both coordinates. (From *Atoms, Stars and Nebulae* by Leo Goldberg and Lawrence H. Aller, McGraw-Hill, Blakiston Division, 1943. Permission, Harvard University Press)

luminous state for a long period and have burst into incandescence just recently, or they derive their energy from some process wherein all the mass is converted into energy. Nuclear physics provides no basis for the latter alternative, and we are forced to the conclusion that the brightest jewels of the firmament are newcomers. Recent investigations suggest that the highly massive and luminous stars are formed from condensations of dust and gas in interstellar space. . . .

....

The Spendthrift
Bright Stars

LEO GOLDBERG

(*The Telescope*, November–December 1940)

The extravagant rate at which the stars are expending their energy poses two questions that must be answered satisfactorily by any theory of stellar energy generation: (1) What is the source of the energy? (2) Is the supply sufficient to have kept the stars shining for two billion years, the currently accepted age of the universe? It is true that this time scale has been criticized in some quarters, but only on the grounds that it is, if anything, too short. [The presently accepted value is over ten billion years.]

The mechanism that seems to offer the best hope of explaining the source of stellar energy is that of transmutation of hydrogen into helium. A helium atom may be formed by the combination of four hydrogen atoms. During the course of the union, energy is released in a manner analogous to the release of heat that occurs during a chemical combination, when atoms join to form molecules. In the process of transmutation, a minute fraction, about one hundredth, of the mass of each hydrogen atom is converted into energy. The fuel supply for the great stellar radiators is thus supplied as the end product of a continuous process of atomic or nuclear synthesis, which is carried on in stellar interiors. The ability of stars to continue shining over cosmic time intervals thus depends both upon the adequacy of their supplies of hydrogen and upon the rate at which the supplies are being used up, *i.e.*, upon the amount of energy per gram of stellar mass that is being lavished upon interstellar space.

Stars of moderate luminosity, like the sun, appear to be in no danger of "going out" in the near future. Although the sun is squandering energy at the rate of five hundred thousand billion billions of horsepower, its supply of hydrogen is ample for about one hundred billion years. The questions posed above may therefore be considered satisfactorily answered for stars of average luminosity.

The situation is by no means so favorable when we consider the highly luminous stars. Although such stars may be ten times as massive as the sun, their luminosities are greater by a factor of several thousand [as shown in Fig. 11]. Their dissipation of energy, measured in terms of liberated energy per unit mass, makes the sun's seem niggardly by comparison. At this rate the bright stars would last but a mere half billion years.

If we assume that the stars have always been radiating at their present rate, three possible alternatives present themselves: (1) the luminous stars are relatively newly formed and are therefore considerably younger than their fainter contemporaries; (2) some hitherto unknown atomic process, other than the transmutation of hydrogen into helium, is a potent source of energy; (3) the stars replenish their stocks of hydrogen by sweeping up diffuse matter in space. The last alternative has recently been receiving considerable attention. The space between the stars is filled with a tenuous cloud of gas, a majority of it probably hydrogen. In traversing the interstellar cloud, a star will probably exert sufficient gravitational attraction to capture large quantities of the gas. The important question is whether the accretion of interstellar matter by a star will progress at a sufficiently rapid rate to sensibly prolong the star's life. A recent investigation by R. d'E. Atkinson (*Monthly Notices* of the Royal Astronomical Society, 100,

p. 500, 1940), however, makes a negative answer seem fairly conclusive. An exact formula for the rate of accretion is not known, but Atkinson demonstrates that there is no reasonable accretion process that will provide a star with sufficient hydrogen to make up for the loss by transmutation. One of the difficulties seems to be that the rate at which a bright star radiates (and uses up its hydrogen) is approximately proportional to the square of its mass. Hence if a star doubles its mass by accretion, it will radiate four times more rapidly. In fact, any increase of hydrogen by accretion is almost exactly balanced by the increased rate of radiation. . . .

The problem of the spendthrift bright stars thus remains unsolved. Further study may perhaps reveal some hidden reserve of energy that these stars can tap in order to continue shining as long as dwarf stars.

No other solution to this problem of the highly luminous stars has been found. It must be that they are evolving rapidly, and that they were formed relatively recently—two facts of importance in the overall study of stellar evolution.—TLP

The Source of Energy in the Fainter Stars

LAWRENCE H. ALLER

(*Sky and Telescope*, April 1951)

The best-known process by which hydrogen is converted into helium is the celebrated carbon cycle, wherein carbon acts as a catalyst. This process was independently suggested in 1938 by Hans Bethe and C. F. von Weizsaecker. Another process, suggested by Bethe and his co-worker at Cornell, Critchfield, may be more important in the fainter stars of the main sequence [at the lower right in Fig. 12] and even in the sun. This is the proton-proton reaction, which proceeds without the aid of a catalyst such as carbon.

The first (and at higher temperatures the most difficult) step in the process is the jamming together of two protons to form a deuteron—the nucleus of a heavy hydrogen atom. A deuteron consists of

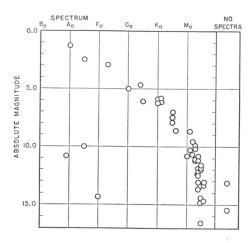

FIG. 12. The spectrum-luminosity chart for stars nearer than five parsecs, indicating the abundance in space of stars fainter and redder than the sun, which is at absolute magnitude 5, spectrum Go. A few white dwarfs are at the left. (Sproul Observatory diagram)

a proton and a neutron bound tightly together. The neutron has very nearly the same mass as the proton (1.66×10^{-24} gram), but it carries no charge. Hence, in the formation of a deuteron by the combination of two protons, each of which carries unit positive charge, one excess positive charge must be carried away. At the same time as the deuteron is formed, a positive electron, or positron, is created, which carries a unit positive charge. Thus we write the fundamental step in the proton-proton reaction as formula A in Figure 13.

Now the probability of the formation of a deuteron in this fashion is very low indeed. Each proton carries a positive charge, so protons repel one another. Only when the collision is head on is there a chance for a deuteron to be formed, and then only if a positron is created simultaneously. In the interior of a star like the sun a given proton is likely to last billions of years before it forms a deuteron,

A $\quad _1H^1 + {_1}H^1 \rightarrow {_1}H^2 + {_1}\epsilon^0$

B $\quad _1H^2 + {_1}H^1 \rightarrow {_2}He^3$

C $\quad _2He^3 + {_2}He^4 \rightarrow {_4}Be^7$

D $\quad _4Be^7 + {_{-1}}\epsilon^0 \rightarrow {_3}Li^7$

E $\quad _3Li^7 + {_1}H^1 \rightarrow {_2}He^4 + {_2}He^4$

F $\quad _1H^1 + {_1}H^1 \rightarrow {_1}H^2 + {_1}\epsilon^0$

G $\quad _1H^2 + {_1}H^1 \rightarrow {_2}He^3$

H $\quad _2He^3 + {_2}He^3 \rightarrow {_2}He^4 + {_1}H^1 + {_1}H^1$

FIG. 13. The series of nuclear reactions of the hydrogen-beryllium-lithium process of energy generation (A to E), and those of the hydrogen-helium-light-isotope process (F to H), now considered more important, by which dwarf stars may produce energy. The subscript represents the electric charge of the particle, which is also the atomic number of the element. The superscript gives the mass, or the atomic weight, to the nearest whole number.

even though it suffers encounters with other protons millions of times a second!

The deuteron, once formed, enjoys but a short life. It readily captures another proton to form the light isotope of helium, as in formula B in Figure 13. What happens next? It was originally thought that the light isotope of helium would collide with a nucleus of ordinary helium, an alpha particle, to form beryllium of atomic weight 7. The beryllium nucleus would then capture a negative (ordinary) electron to form lithium of atomic weight 7. The lithium nucleus finally would capture a proton and break down into two alpha particles, or helium nuclei. This process is shown by formulas C, D, and E in Figure 13.

Very recently, W. A. Fowler and C. C. Lauritsen have demonstrated that the reaction of the light isotopes of helium with each other is more important than the lithium-building reactions, even though He^3 is much less abundant than He^4. This "simplifies" the proton-proton "cycle" to the three steps shown in formulas F, G, and H in Figure 13. As a consequence, however, two deuterons must be formed for every helium nucleus created, and the rate of energy generation is half of what would be given by the process involving lithium of atomic weight 7.

The time required for a helium nucleus to be formed is very long. At a temperature (T) of 15,000,000° absolute, a density of 80 grams per cubic centimeter, and with a hydrogen content of stellar material 30 per cent by weight, it requires 500 million years. The dependence on the temperature is not nearly so steep as for the carbon cycle. The rate of energy generation by the carbon cycle varies as about T^{20} at 17 to 20 million degrees, whereas it varies only at T^4 for the proton-proton reaction. . . .

The investigation of stellar interiors depends on observations of the luminosity, mass, and radius of a star. These are what the mathematician calls the boundary conditions of the problem. Given the condition that the star is in equilibrium (neither swelling up nor shrinking down), and a knowledge of its chemical composition, we can calculate the structure, or *model*, of the star. It is found that it is not possible to fit the observed boundary conditions with just any chemical composition. In fact, the hydrogen content and the helium content may be determined from the observed mass, luminosity, and radius, if we know the relative abundances of the heavier elements, carbon, nitrogen, oxygen, metals, and so forth.

All of this presupposes that we know the law of energy generation, its dependence on temperature, density, and chemical composition; and also the law of opacity, which limits the rate at which energy flows through nonturbulent stellar material. The quantities are now sufficiently well known to permit a reasonable estimate of conditions in stellar interiors.

The analysis gives two simultaneous equations which involve the hydrogen and helium contents and the luminosity, mass, and radius of the star. The first equation amounts to the mass-luminosity law, whereas the second equation involves the rate of energy generation. We can lay no claim to accuracy for other results, as we have assumed that the same opacity law holds as for the sun. Since a red dwarf is a much denser star than the sun, the dependence of the opacity on density and temperature necessarily will be a little different.

Now, the solution will depend on the assumed law of energy gen-

FIG. 14. The sun and some typical dwarf stars drawn to scale. Their masses in terms of the sun's are shown. Their densities average about twice the sun's, except for the white dwarf Sirius B (for which the energy generation must also differ). Their spectral types are G for the sun, K1 and K5 for 70 Ophiuchi A and B, M1e for Castor C, M4 for Krueger 60 A, M4e for O_2 Eridani C, and A7 for the companion of Sirius.

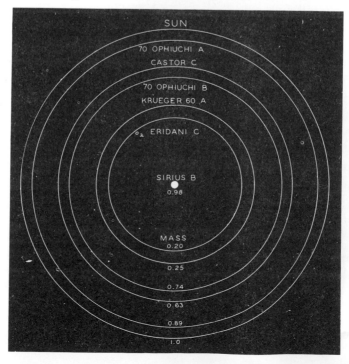

eration. We may suppose that only proton-proton reactions take place. Then we obtain for o_2 Eridani C a central temperature of 13,000,000°K. The other assumption is that both the carbon cycle and proton-proton reactions hold. Then the central temperature is 15,000,000°. Both of these solutions "represent" the star within the framework of the theory, but the mechanism actually followed will depend on the hydrogen and helium contents. At 13,000,000° the carbon cycle is unimportant. In the same way, we find the red dwarf Krueger 60 A could have a central temperature of 15,400,000° if it operates on both the carbon and proton-proton cycles, or a central temperature of about 10,700,000° if it operates purely on the proton-proton cycle.

The Two Fundamental Relations of Stellar Astronomy

OTTO STRUVE

(*Sky and Telescope*, August 1949)

When we examine the apparent brightnesses of the stars in a cluster like the Pleiades we immediately recognize that the *intrinsic luminosities* of the individual members are not the same. As a rule, the brightest stars in each cluster are either blue stars or very red. The faintest members of each cluster are always red. The true luminosity of the brightest objects may be as much as 100 million times that of the faintest. This enormous disparity makes it immediately apparent that the luminosity of a star must be a particularly important quantity and one that is likely to give us considerable information concerning the physical properties of the stars.

In a cluster we can arbitrarily assume as our unit of measurement the luminosity of the brightest star and refer to it the luminosities of all other stars. In order to determine stellar luminosities with respect to the luminosity of the sun, we must make allowance for the distances of the stars, which are now known for a few thousand. For them, at least, we can compute intrinsic luminosities in terms of the sun; the most luminous stars are approximately one million times more luminous than the sun, and the faintest stars about one million times less luminous than the sun.

The next significant parameter describing the properties of a star is its *mass*. This can be determined only for double stars, either of the visual type or of the spectroscopic type. In the case of a spectroscopic binary we can measure the orbital velocity and the period. From these two quantities we obtain the size of the orbit, in linear measure, and the masses of the stars in terms of the mass of the sun. . . . These range from about fifty times the mass of the sun to about one tenth the mass of the sun. It is possible that even less massive stars exist as planetlike companions to such well-known objects as 61 Cygni and two or three other systems. There is no reason to think that small masses of the order of one hundreth of that of the sun may not be frequent in our galaxy.

The third principal parameter in stellar astronomy is the *radius* of a star. In a few exceptional cases this quantity can be measured in angular units with the help of a large interferometer. But even the largest stars are not big enough to give us an accurate determination of their radii. For example, Antares has an apparent radius of only 0.02 second of arc. Since its distance is of the order of 300 light years, we find that the true radius is approximately 150 times that of the sun.

Much more reliable values of the radii can be obtained from photometric and spectroscopic observations of eclipsing binaries. In principle, it is always possible from the duration of the partial and total phases of each eclipse, and from the orbital period, to determine the radii of the two stars in terms of the distance between their centers. The spectroscopic observations permit us to express this latter quantity in kilometers.

Finally, there is a simple relation between the temperature and the radius of the star on the one hand, and its luminosity on the other. The total amount of energy emitted by a square centimeter of the surface of an object is a known numerical constant times the fourth power of the temperature. Hence if we know the temperature from the spectrum of a star, we find immediately how much radiation is emitted by every square centimeter of its surface. But the total surface is $4\pi R^2$. If we multiply this by the radiation of each square centimeter, we obtain the total luminosity. Therefore if the total

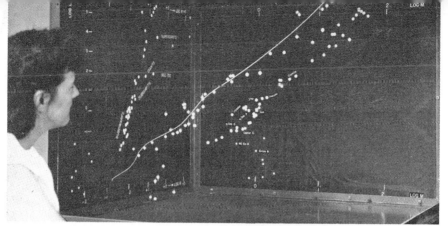

FIG. 15. Photograph of a model constructed by G. P. Kuiper to illustrate the two principal relations of stellar astronomy, the Hertzsprung-Russell diagram on the left, and the mass-luminosity relation on the right. The stars are shown by means of beads suspended on thin wires. A white string runs approximately through the main sequence. The white dwarfs form a separate group. The principal coordinates are the luminosity, plotted vertically, the mass, plotted to the right, and the radius, plotted at the left. (Yerkes Observatory photograph)

luminosity of the star, as known from its distance and brightness measurements, is divided by the radiation per square centimeter, the area of the total surface and the radius of the star are obtained.

As information concerning the radii, masses, and luminosities of stars began to accumulate, astronomers noticed that not all combinations of the three parameters were actually realized in our galaxy. It is often convenient to represent each star as a point in a three-dimensional model in which the three coordinates are respectively the luminosity, the radius, and the mass. Such a model was constructed several years ago at the Yerkes Observatory by G. P. Kuiper (see Fig. 15).

In a square-cornered box the vertical dimension is taken to be the logarithm of the luminosity in terms of that of the sun. At the reading $\log L = +1$, the corresponding star has luminosity 10. The mass is represented as the horizontal coordinate running toward the right and is also given in logarithmic measure ($\log M$ is 0 for a star having the mass of the sun, and 2 for a star having a mass 100 times that of the sun). The radius is plotted as $\log R$ along the other horizontal scale, running from left to right (-2 for a star whose radius is 100 times less than that of the sun, and $+3$ for a star whose radius is 1000 times that of the sun). The stars are shown by means of beads suspended on thin wires in such a way that each bead has the correct values of log L, log M, and log R for one star. The beads are found to be arranged in a fairly narrow band from the lower left side of the model to its upper right side. A white piece of string was used to show the region where the beads are most concentrated, in a grouping known as the main sequence.

Another group of beads corresponds to very small values of L, M, and R—the white dwarfs. Finally, there are a number of smaller groups—the giants, the supergiants, the subgiants, and the subdwarfs, which are not very frequent in galactic space and are therefore represented by only a few beads in the plot.

It is instructive to examine the actual model (plot) from different sides. If we look at it from the right, we see the beads projected against the narrow left-hand surface of the model, whose coordinates are log L and log R. The actual projections of the beads are shown by white dots pasted on the black surface. We see that in this projection the main sequence forms a fairly conspicuous straight line with a few stars departing from it on the right, and a group, distinctly removed, in the left-hand corner. The stars on the right side of the main sequence have larger radii and are giants. The stars on the left are white dwarfs and subdwarfs.

If we examine the model from the left, as the young lady in the picture was doing, we observe the stars projected upon the right-hand side of the model, whose coordinates are log L and log M. Here again the great majority project themselves as a narrow band running from the lower left to the upper right; this shows the *mass-luminosity relation*, first extensively treated by A. S. Eddington. In this projection the white dwarfs form a detached group (below the mass-luminosity curve). In other words, they have luminosities smaller than expected for their masses.

The view from the right, which shows the main sequence, is almost identical with a famous diagram now known as the Hertzsprung-Russell or H-R diagram [see Fig. 4]. It was first described by Henry Norris Russell in a famous lecture on December 30, 1913 [see p. 77]. Because of the relation between luminosity L, temperature T, and radius R, which is written $L = 4\pi R^2 \sigma T^4$, it is always possible to transform the original H-R diagram into another diagram in which the horizontal scale is not the temperature, but the radius. In this representation, of the *radius-luminosity relation*, the main characteristics of the H-R diagram are retained, but the sequences are tilted in a slightly different manner. It is remarkable that the sequences are so clearly marked both in the *L-R* projection and in the *L-M* projection.

During the years since Russell's lecture a large amount of information has been accumulated on the stars. We now know that the *L-M* and *L-R* relations are statistical in nature; actually there are few, if any, parts of the space on our three-dimensional plot which are "prohibited." For example, it was thought in 1913 that all blue and white stars had large luminosities and fell in the upper part of the H-R diagram. Soon afterwards it became apparent that the companion of Sirius, though white in color, has a very small mass. It was the first clearly recognized member of the white-dwarf group. Later we began to notice that the so-called Wolf-Rayet stars, though very blue and hot, are not as luminous as are the normal O-type stars with which they are often combined in binary systems. Still more recently it was recognized, especially by the Russian astronomer Vorontsov-Velyaminov, that the ordinary novae many years after their outbursts are often blue stars of relatively small intrinsic luminosity. . . . Points (representing stars) may be found in many parts of the plot which were previously believed to be completely empty.

We must not confuse this result with the well-established statistical tendency of stars to occur in preferential bands within the plot. It has been estimated that approximately 100 billion stars of the Milky Way system belong to the main sequence and obey the mass-luminosity relation. The total number of white dwarfs may be a hundred times less and the number of subdwarfs about the same. The giants are probably 10,000 times less frequent than the main-sequence stars, and the supergiants are so rare that there may not be more than 1000 or 10,000 of them throughout our entire galaxy.

An important quantity is the true spread of the main sequence at right angles to its extent. If we make a plot for the stars in just one galactic cluster, we obtain an arrangement that runs almost exactly along a straight line (departures almost wholly accounted for by the errors of measurement). . . . This is accounted for by the fact that the stars in a cluster have similar physical properties and were probably formed at the same time. We cannot expect this kind of uniformity when stars are selected more or less at random.

For stars in general (in our galaxy), the spread of the main sequence at temperature 8000°K is about two magnitudes, caused by the different chemical compositions of the stars. A large amount of hydrogen, compared to other elements, results in a smaller luminosity than would be observed for a star consisting mostly of heavy elements.

This relation between the chemical composition and the location of a star on the H-R diagram near the main sequence led some years ago to the hope that we could use it to determine accurately the abundance of hydrogen in stars (and consequently their ages). However, more recent work has shown that the problem is not so simple. There are many objects which depart from the main sequence and from the mass-luminosity relation for causes other than abnormal chemical composition. For example, the companions of certain close double stars, like XZ Sagitarii, R Canis Majoris, and DN Orionis, are fairly luminous objects with masses only a fraction of the mass of the sun. These unusual stars depart in a most conspicuous manner from the mass-luminosity relation.

It has recently been emphasized by A. J. Deutsch of the Mount Wilson and Palomar Observatories that we should somehow plot the *density* of points representing stars on *L-M* and *L-R* plots. In this manner we would not only obtain the geometrical properties of the different sequences in each of the two projections, but we could read off directly the probability of finding a star at a given point. Without a clear recognition of the stellar densities in space, we shall not have

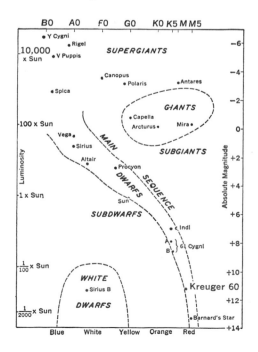

FIG. 16. This H-R diagram shows the positions of many important stars in relation to the main sequence and other statistical groupings. (Adapted from *Astronomy*, Revised Edition, by William T. Skilling and Robert S. Richardson. Copyright 1939 by Holt, Rinehart and Winston, Inc. Copyright © 1967 by William T. Skilling and Robert S. Richardson. Adapted and reproduced by permission of Holt, Rinehart and Winston, Inc.)

an adequate basis for studying the origin and the evolution of the stars. For example, it must be cosmogonically important that along the main sequence the density increases from top to bottom, so that the red dwarfs are 100 or 1000 times more frequent, per unit volume, than are the blue stars.

The model of Figure 15 applies only to the region of space immediately surrounding the solar system. In the central regions of our galaxy, and in outside galaxies, the distribution of the points representing stars in our model would be entirely different. This has led to the recognition of different types of populations in the universe. Long ago H. Shapley noticed that in globular clusters the giant sequence is quite different from that of our galaxy, and Baade has introduced the term *Population II* [see p. 250] to describe the arrangement of the stars with respect to *L*, *M*, and *R*, in globular clusters and in the central nucleus of our galaxy.

Mass Distribution
in Stars

(*Sky and Telescope*, February 1952)

In the study of stellar structure it is desirable to have an estimate of the precise manner in which the mass is distributed within the star. There is no direct way to obtain this information. However, in a few binary systems the stars are moving in close orbits, and are distorted as a result of gravitational forces in the same way as tides are produced on the earth by the moon and sun. The tides produced in close binaries cause a small departure of the orbital motion of the stars from what would otherwise be motion in a fixed ellipse. Instead, the orbit is an ellipse whose major axis (line of apsides) revolves very slowly. If the system is an eclipsing binary whose elements are known, it is possible to compute, from measures of the rate of the

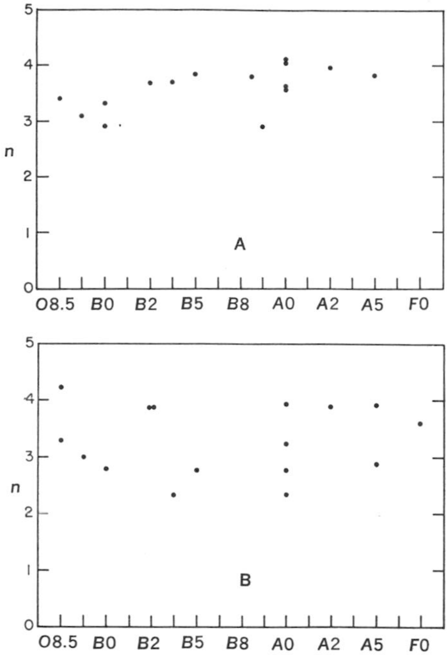

5

4

3

n

2

1

0

A

O8.5 B0 B2 B5 B8 A0 A2 A5 F0

FIG. 17. Effective polytropic index versus spectral type. A. By Zechiel and Keller, 1951. B. By H. N. Russell, 1939. (Perkins Observatory charts)

5

4

3

n

2

1

0

B

O8.5 B0 B2 B5 B8 A0 A2 A5 F0

revolution of the line of apsides, the coefficients describing the manner in which the mass is distributed.*

Leon N. Zechiel and Geoffrey Keller at Perkins Observatory studied a group of eclipsing binary systems of known or suspected apsidal motion. The most recent available data were used, and Figure 17A shows the result of the computations. The ordinate is the effective polytropic index, n, and the abscissa is the spectral type. The value of n is an indication of the degree of central condensation of the mass; a value of $n = 0$ corresponds to a star with homogeneous mass distribution (uniform density throughout), and $n = 5$ corresponds to a star in which the entire mass is concentrated at the center.

Figure 17B is constructed from an earlier analysis by H. N. Russell. A comparison shows considerable change in the plot since 1939, due to improved observational data obtained since then. There is an apparent limitation of n to values between 2.9 and 4.1, and a tendency for the lower values to be associated with the earlier spectral types. In a star for which $n = 3.5$, the central density is about 100 times the mean density.

* Gas can be compressed in various ways to form a spherical star, hotter and denser at the core than at the surface. Theoretical formulas for the density at various depths inside such gas spheres ("polytropes") include a constant, n (the "polytropic index"), which may have any value from 0 to 5.—TLP

···

The Internal Constitution
of Some Stars

OTTO STRUVE

(*Sky and Telescope*, November 1953)

One of the most interesting results of recent astronomical exploration was announced by Harold L. Johnson in the May 1953 issue of *The Astrophysical Journal*. With the help of a photoelectric photometer [see p. 323] he measured the visual magnitudes and the color indices of forty visual double stars selected from R. G. Aitken's catalogue of double stars. The two components of each pair were measured separately. Since the distances of these stars from us are not accurately known, the absolute visual magnitudes cannot be directly inferred from the measured apparent magnitudes. Nevertheless, the difference between the absolute magnitudes of the two components of each pair is, of course, identical with the difference in apparent magnitude.

In previous work Johnson had determined the exact location of the main sequence in the Hertzsprung-Russell (H-R) diagram. His final curve, based upon several galactic clusters and selected nearby single stars with accurately known parallaxes, is shown in Figure 18. The ordinate is visual absolute magnitude, M_v, and the abscissa is color index, the difference in apparent magnitude for blue (**B**) and visual

FIG. 18. The Hertzsprung-Russell diagram constructed by H. L. Johnson and W. W. Morgan for stars at very accurately known distances. Ordinates are visual absolute magnitudes, abscissae are color indices. Nearly all the stars plotted belong to the main sequence, but a few giants and white dwarfs are included. The open circles represent Praesepe stars that may be unresolved binaries. Note the narrowness of the main sequence, in contrast to its appearance in earlier H-R diagrams from less accurate data. (From *The Astrophysical Journal*, The University of Chicago Press)

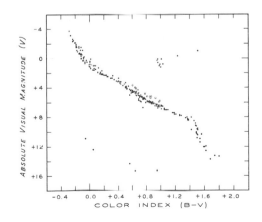

(V) light. Nearly all the dots fall in a narrow band, the best representation of the main sequence known to us at the present time. The only exceptions are a few giants above the main sequence, and five white dwarfs below it.

If it is now assumed that the fainter component of each of the forty double stars is a member of the main sequence, then its position in Figure 19 can be exactly defined by the main sequence of Figure 18 and the fainter star's color index, B—V. These points are not actually marked in Figure 19; the black dots are the corresponding locations of the brighter stars in the forty pairs, which were located by means of the color index, B—V, measured for each brighter star, and by the observed difference in visual magnitude.

The resulting arrangement of dots in Figure 19 indicates a surprisingly large scatter. We are not concerned here with those stars in the upper right corner, which are obviously giants. We are interested in finding that nearly half of the dots fall considerably above the main sequence, sometimes by as much as one magnitude or more. . . . This dispersion of the components of visual double stars is very much greater than the small scatter found in galactic clusters and single nearby stars.

Johnson's conclusions, if accepted, must have an evolutionary significance. It is certainly surprising that we cannot, apparently, regard the visual double stars as being closely related to the galactic clusters with respect to their origin and evolution.

In order to explain the high dispersion of the double stars, we are tempted to think first of a nonnuclear process of evolution that will proceed at different rates in the two components. . . .

It is also possible that when a double star is formed, the processes of condensation in the original cloudlike medium may favor different atomic abundances in the two stars. Such a difference would probably depend upon the distance between the two components and might be of importance in very close pairs such as those we observe as spectroscopic and eclipsing binaries. Among these very close pairs, similar large departures from the main sequence have been recorded. For example, the spectrographic observations at the McDonald Observatory of Algol-type binaries have shown conclusively that the faint companions in these systems are stars of relatively small mass but of excessive luminosity. They often violate the mass-luminosity relation by factors of the order of 100, or even more, in intrinsic brightness.

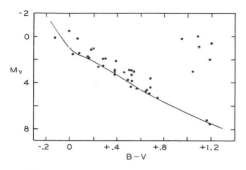

FIG. 19. The Hertzsprung-Russell diagram of the brighter members of forty double stars, from H. L. Johnson's observations. The ordinates are visual absolute magnitudes, the abscissae, color indices. The curve represents the main sequence, transferred from Figure 18, and the scale is the same. (From *The Astrophysical Journal,* The University of Chicago Press)

There is also a strong indication that the spectral types of these stars may be earlier than would be consistent with their masses. For example, an ordinary main-sequence star of one third the mass of the sun has a spectral type of about M5, yet the subgiant companion of the binary XZ Sagittarii has a G spectrum.

We are therefore justified in concluding that these subgiants are not only very much too luminous for their masses, but they also possess spectral types which indicate effective temperatures higher than would be consistent with their small masses. The resulting departures from the mass-luminosity relation and from the main sequence in the H-R diagram are not the same as those in Figure 19, but they constitute another interesting evolutionary problem.

In order to solve this problem we must explore the interior constitution of stars other than the sun, and we shall use three fundamental laws of physics.[1]

1. The general law of perfect gases states that the pressure is proportional to the temperature and inversely proportional to the volume of the gas. But for our purpose it is useful to remember that the volume is equal to the mass of the gas divided by the density. Hence we shall assume that the pressure (p) at any point inside a gaseous star is proportional to the density (ρ) and the temperature (T), and inversely proportional to the mean atomic (or molecular) mass (μ) of the gas particles:

$$p \sim \rho T / \mu.$$

2. The very intense light and heat inside a star is all produced by nuclear reactions near its center. This radiation is trying to escape

___

[1] We shall follow here H. N. Russell's very simple line of reasoning, first employed in Russell, Dugan, and Stewart, *Astronomy* (Ginn; Boston, 1945), Volume 2. A more modern and exceedingly fascinating account of this problem is contained in W. H. McCrea's book *Physics of the Sun and Stars,* Hutchinson's University Library, London, 1950.

to the outside, but is restrained by the opacity of the gases, which act just as a sieve acts upon a stream of water. The radiation exerts pressure upon the semiopaque gases proportional to the fourth power of the temperature of the radiating material. The resistance of the gases to this outward pressure causes them to expand a little, thus adjusting the star's radius until the pressure is just balanced by the resistance of the gases. It is as though our sieve were made of a rubber membrane. As the water presses upon the membrane it expands; the holes also expand and more water can flow through. Finally, the resistance of the membrane prevents further expansion, and from then on a uniform flow of water passes through the sieve.

The resistance of the gases to the pressure of radiation is called the absorption coefficient (K). It turns out to be, for a one-centimeter thickness of gas, proportional to the square of the density of the gas and inversely proportional to the 7/2 power of the temperature:

$$K \backsim \rho^2 / T^{7/2}.$$

3. We require some knowledge of the process that creates the radiation inside a star. This information comes from the theory of nuclear fusion of hydrogen into helium. It follows from this theory that the amount of energy produced by one gram of gas (ϵ) in the form of heat and light is proportional to the product of the density and the eighteenth power of the temperature:

$$\epsilon \backsim \rho T^{18}.$$

Let us now consider two stars: the sun (for which we know the internal distribution of density and temperature, and also, from observation, the total output of heat and light; this total output is the luminosity, 4×10^{33} ergs per second); and a star of spectral type B having a mass 10 times that of the sun.

Let us see what we can infer about the luminosity and surface temperature of this B star. Our method will be to apply the three physical laws to the sun, and then see what changes result when the sun is converted to a star of 10 times its present mass. Then we shall compare our theoretical results with observations.

If we had enough patience, we could start with any assumed value of the radius for the B star. For example, we could make it equal to that of the sun. However we would soon find that this assumption would lead to contradictions with one or the other of the three physical laws. By trial and error we would conclude that the only possible radius of the B star is 5.1 times the radius of the sun. The reader who wishes to convince himself that any other value is impossible may assume any radius he wishes and carry out the rest of our calculations. At the end he will see why only 5.1 gives a satisfactory result. We shall here take on faith the results of similar calculations by others and proceed with a mass of 10 and a radius of 5.1.

The mean density of the larger star is obtained by dividing its mass by its volume, which gives 0.075 times the density of the sun. Since the mean density of the sun is 1.4 grams per cubic centimeter, that of the B star is 0.1 gram per cubic centimeter. Does this ratio apply only to the mean densities? Or does it apply to the densities at any corresponding points inside the two stars? If the latter, then we say that the sun and the B star are "built on the same model," or that they are *homologous*. Eddington and others have justified this assumption, and we adopt it here because it seems plausible for stars of the main sequence.

If, then, the densities in the B star are 0.075 times the corresponding densities in the sun, we can next compute the corresponding pressures. The pressure is equal to the weight of material located above any given point, and is given by the force of attraction of the star on this overlying matter. Consider any region of the B star; its mass is 10 times greater than that of the corresponding region in the sun. But the mass of the whole B star is also 10 times greater than the sun's, while the distances in the B star are all enlarged 5.1 times. Therefore the force of gravity is

$$10 \times 10 / 5.1 \times 5.1$$

times that in the sun. But in the B star the weight presses upon an area which is itself 5.1 × 5.1 larger than it would be in the sun. Accordingly, the pressure at any point in the B star is

$$10 \times 10 / 5.1 \times 5.1 \times 5.1 \times 5.1$$

= 0.15 times the pressure at the corresponding point in the sun.

We are now ready to apply the first physical law and compute the relative temperatures. We assume that both sun and star have the same chemical composition; if they are made of pure hydrogen, the mean atomic mass will be $\mu = \frac{1}{2}$. (Because the hydrogen atoms are all ionized, the average weight of a particle is equal to the mass of a proton plus the much smaller mass of an electron, divided by two.)

Then the temperatures within the B star are proportional to the pressures and inversely proportional to the densities, $0.15/0.075 = 2.0$ times greater than in the sun. For example, if the central temperature of the sun is 20 million degrees, a B star with the same chemical composition but with 10 times the mass of the sun would have a central temperature of 40 million degrees.

Next we compute the flow of energy through the star. Take again the analogy of a sieve. If there is water pressing on both sides of the membrane, the flow will be proportional to the difference of the pressures on the two sides. The flow will also be inversely proportional to the resistance of the membrane, or in the case of the star to its absorption coefficient (K).

A layer one centimeter thick in the sun is expanded in the B star to a thickness of 5.1 centimeters. Since radiation pressure varies as the fourth power of the temperature, in the star this will be $T^4 = 2^4 = 16$ times greater than in the sun. Then the *difference* of the pressures at the inside and outside of the one-centimeter layer is $16/5.1$, about three times greater in the B star than in the sun. Furthermore, according to our second physical law, the absorption coefficient per centimeter is $(0.075)^2/2^{7/2} = 0.0005$ times the sun's.

Now we are ready to compute the flow of energy through our one-centimeter layer. It is proportional to the difference of pressures and inversely proportional to the coefficient of absorption. This is easily calculated: $3/0.0005 = 6000$ times that for the sun.

It is rather interesting to realize that without as yet knowing anything about the generation of the B star's energy, we can find that the outward flow of energy, per centimeter, must be 6000 times greater than in the sun.

The flow measures the amount of radiation escaping per square centimeter. But the B star's surface area is $5.1 \times 5.1 = 26$ times the sun's. Hence, the total energy of the B star, or its luminosity, is 26×6000, or about 150,000 times that of the sun. This is about 13 magnitudes more luminous than the sun. Since the latter has a bolometric absolute magnitude [a measure of its radiation over the entire spectrum] of about $+5$, the B star's bolometric absolute magnitude would be about -8, and the corresponding visual absolute magnitude -7. From observations of such B stars as Eta Orionis and

FIG. 20. A. S. Eddington, on whose investigations present-day knowledge of stellar interiors is largely based.

Spica we actually obtain −5. Our calculation has made the B star about two magnitudes too bright.

The discrepancy is not large when we consider the enormous ratio in luminosity of 150,000 to 1. It must be due to incxactness of one of our basic assumptions, perhaps that of uniformity in chemical composition.

But we must still justify our other assumption, that the radius of the B star is 5.1 times that of the sun. To do so we make use of our third physical law, that of the energy generation, which, per unit mass, is proportional to the density and the eighteenth power of the temperature. For the entire mass it will be 10 times greater. Hence the total energy generation of the B star exceeds that of the sun by a factor of $10 \times 0.075 \times 2^{18}$, or about 200,000. But the total energy generation is the same as the luminosity. Thus, we obtain nearly the same luminosity in this manner as the 150,000 suns we derived from the flow of heat and light through a one-centimeter layer. No such agreement would have been reached had we used a different radius for the B star.

The fact that the luminosity is approximately 10^5 times the sun's gives us the famous mass-luminosity relation developed by A. S. Eddington. Had we taken a star of spectral type F, with a mass twice that of the sun, the luminosity would have been 2^5 times that of the sun. We say that the exponent of the theoretical mass-luminosity relation is 5. The exponent that fits actual observations is slightly smaller—about 4.

There is also a mass-radius relation. We used it implicitly when we adopted a radius of 5.1 for our B-type star. This relation is the theoretical counterpart of the observational H-R diagram.

We are especially interested in how our results would be modified by assuming a different chemical composition. Consider an old star (or one of unusual initial composition) consisting mostly of helium, and of mass equal to the sun's mass. For hydrogen, as we have seen, the average particle mass is ½. For helium, also completely ionized, there will be an alpha particle (helium nucleus) of mass 4 and two very light electrons. The average mass per particle is thus 4/3. If the sun is mostly hydrogen, and the star mostly helium, their particle weights are roughly in the ratio 1:2.

In this new problem it again appears that the radius cannot be arbitrarily chosen. By reasoning similar to that used previously, we find the radius of the helium star to be 1.4 that of the sun.

We can again compute density, temperature, flow of energy, and finally luminosity—always allowing for the difference in particle weight, which enters only into the first physical law. While these computations are recommended as a useful exercise, only the final result is stated here. The helium star turns out to have a luminosity 128 times the sun's. It is approximately five magnitudes brighter than the sun, and has a bolometric absolute magnitude of 0, even though its mass is the same as that of the sun.

We could show that the helium star will have a much higher surface temperature than the sun, about 18,000°. The star will thus appear slightly below the upper part of the main sequence; its spectrum will appear to be that of an underluminous B star. But its mass will be equal to the sun's. Accordingly the very old stars of solar mass, which have converted their hydrogen into helium, should now appear as hot stars of abnormally small mass. Perhaps VV Orionis, or even better, the B-type companion of Antares, is such an object.

The final theoretical result is that we expect a large dispersion in the mass-luminosity relation and a small one in the H-R diagram. However, observations show that the subgiants have rather large dispersions in both. Hence, the simple Eddington model we have used does not answer our purpose.

We have just seen that a star formed with a subnormal amount of hydrogen, but which otherwise obeys the physical laws for main-sequence stars, would be much too luminous for its mass, and also would be shifted in the H-R diagram into a position slightly *below* the main sequence and far to the left of its normal location. We have already noted that the very small subgiant companion of XZ Sagittarii, with a mass about 0.2 that of the sun, would normally be expected to have a dwarf M-type spectrum, while its observed spectral type is G. But it is reasonably certain that this companion falls *above* the main sequence and not below it; thus the simple theory which we have used will not fully account for the observations.

Of course, it is possible that relatively small changes in the physical laws might move the subgiant companions from their predicted locations below the main sequence to positions slightly above it. It is not, however, at all clear which assumption would have to be modified. One possibility would be a change in the law of energy generation for stars of very small mass. The formula we have used, in which energy generation is excessively sensitive to temperature, was derived by H. Bethe on the assumption that hydrogen is converted into helium by the carbon cycle [see p. 36]. There are reasons to believe that the cooler stars obtain their energy from another process known as the proton-proton reaction [see p. 45]. . . . This process is less sensitive to the temperature; the amount of energy produced by a gram of gas is proportional to the density (as in the carbon cycle) and to the *fourth* power of the temperature. In the carbon cycle the temperature appears to the eighteenth power.

We can now go back and repeat all of our calculations with this new law of energy generation, leaving the other two laws unchanged. The result is no change whatever with respect to the location of a hydrogen-deficient star below the main sequence. Altogether, we can probably conclude that this otherwise tempting hypothesis does not account for the observed properties of the subgiant stars.

Another important modification might result if we had used a different form of the absorption coefficient. In our second physical law, we had assumed that throughout the star the absorption per centimeter was proportional to the square of the density and inversely to the $7/2$ power of the temperature. In reality the absorption processes are quite complicated and are almost certainly not the same in different stars or in different regions of the same star. However, as yet very little is known about the actual form of the absorption coefficient, and thus it would be premature to make any substantial changes in the formula we used. The extensive calculations made by astrophysicists with various absorption coefficients do not seriously modify our results. But it is probable that when we know more about the absorption of gases at many millions of degrees we shall be able to explain why the exponent in the mass-luminosity relation is actually about 4, instead of 5. We may then be able to say why the subgiants tend to fall above the main sequence, instead of below it as predicted by our simplified theory.

Returning now to the stars observed by Johnson, it would appear quite unreasonable to believe that the brighter components were hydrogen deficient from their beginning. Hence we cannot suppose that the same physical process operates in them as in the subgiant secondaries of the eclipsing systems.

If we arbitrarily modify Johnson's diagram to place all the brighter components on the main sequence, many of the fainter components will be below the main sequence. This would be in the required sense, and could be explained formally on the hypothesis that the less massive components of visual binaries are deficient in hydrogen. However, on physical grounds it seems quite improbable that such a deficiency could occur in double stars with separations of several astronomical units without having also occurred in the much closer eclipsing and spectroscopic binaries. Hence the physical processes that have produced the dispersion in the components of double stars are quite unknown. Physical theory is now capable of explaining the major features of the mass-luminosity relation and of the H-R diagram, but it is *not* adequate to account fully for the details illustrated by the observations of double stars in Figure 19.

Struve's calculation serves to show the complexities (and frustrations!) of computing stellar models. The assumptions, though they may seem arbitrary, are based on years of research by theoretical astrophysicists such as Eddington, Chandrasekhar, Schwarzschild, and others. Note that the assumption of homologous models (similar increase of density from surface to center of different stars, or models all with the same polytropic index) is roughly confirmed by observations plotted in Figure 17A showing that B and A stars have about the same polytropic index. (If the indices, n, were exactly the same, all those stars would be homologous.) Of course, the trick of comparing homologous stars to the sun avoids the more complex calculations based on the same physical laws to get the run of density and temperature from the surface down to the center of the sun.

The details of this "mathematical boring," as Eddington called it, are beyond the scope of this book, although they are involved in interpreting the different H-R diagrams for different star clusters as an effect of age. That effect is most readily understood in theoretical terms as a result of nuclear reactions changing the composition of each star's core. As hydrogen is converted to helium the mean molecular weight (μ) changes, and the opacity (κ) changes. These in turn cause changes in the temperature and density, so the whole model changes. In some cases the temperature gradient (increase with depth) becomes so steep that turbulence sets in, and carries stellar material from the core to outer layers, changing the composition, μ, and κ there.

These, and many other deviations from the stable, "balanced" conditions assumed in Struve's calculations, are discussed in later chapters.—TLP

H-R and
Color-Magnitude
Diagrams

....

At this point it should be clear that the Hertzsprung-Russell diagram provides a powerful tool in the statistical study of stars. Among
other things, it enables astronomers to recognize various "species" of
stars and their relative frequencies. Like many statistical studies, those
made with the help of H-R diagrams are complicated by the effects
of selection; errors of measuring or estimating luminosity and spectral
type provide other complications. The simplest selection effect is
the limit of brightness (or apparent magnitude) of the stars observed.
With the naked eye one can see many high-luminosity giants in the
sky, but no white dwarfs. This does not mean that there are more
giants than white dwarfs, but only that one can see giants at a
greater distance (therefore in a larger volume) than the low-luminos-
ity dwarfs.

Errors introduce a false scatter on the H-R diagram, and one of the
important astronomical advances during the past thirty years has been
the increased use of photoelectric photometers to measure brightnesses
and colors of stars more accurately (and for fainter stars). As this chapter will show, this use of sensitive and accurate photoelectric equip-

ment has tended to substitute color-magnitude arrays for H-R diagrams based on spectral types.

Of course, there is more information in a complete spectrum than in a color measurement. Recognition of giants and dwarfs on the H-R diagram led to refinements in spectral classification and thus allowed estimates of the luminosity as well as the surface temperature of a star.—TLP

....

Some Uses of
Spectral Classification

W. W. MORGAN

(*The Telescope*, July–August 1941)

In the course of the past fifty years astronomers have examined the spectra of hundreds of thousands of stars. From this examination— due principally to Miss Annie J. Cannon at Harvard—one important and fundamental conclusion can be drawn: the very great majority of all stellar spectra fall into a few definite groups, which may be represented by several typical stars. If we select a "helium star" (γ Pegasi), a "hydrogen star" (γ Geminorum), a star having a strong metallic spectrum (the sun), and a star whose spectrum shows the bands of titanium oxide (o Ceti), we have a set of four comparison stars which are sufficient to classify roughly more than 99 per cent of all stellar spectra. By adding three other typical stars, making a total of seven in all, we can illustrate closely the appearance of all but an insignificant number of the hundreds of thousands of spectra examined. In this marked similarity of thousands of stellar spectra lies much of the contribution spectral classification has made to modern astronomy.

There is a second important conclusion resulting from the classification of stellar spectra. Each type group bears a definite relation to the other groups, enabling us to arrange them in a unique sequence. In this sequence, each group has certain similarities to the groups adjacent, with the spectra changing smoothly from one end to the other. We have in fact a continuous sequence. Astronomers have shown that this sequence is controlled principally by the stellar temperatures, from the hot white helium stars to the relatively cool red titanium-oxide stars.

In the most general sense, there are two major uses for the material provided by spectral classification. First, we segregate the "ordinary" stars into groups. The nearer and more favorably located groups we can study in detail, determining their average characteristics, such as true brightnesses, colors, space velocities, and the like. We may study, for example, the nearby A stars in great detail. Then, if we have a group of faint stars whose spectra have also been classified as of type A, we may, having taken certain precautions, transfer the average characteristics found for the bright nearby objects over to the group of faint stars. From the difference in the apparent magnitudes we are able to compute how much more distant the fainter stars are than the brighter ones. Such studies enable us to picture how these objects are distributed in our region of the galactic system. Again, investigation shows that the colors of the distant A stars are, in general, redder than those of our standard group close to the sun. This reddening is attributed to the presence of fine dust in cosmic space, which absorbs the blue light more than it does the red. The amount of reddening is an indirect measure of the distance of a star.

With increasing accuracy in spectral classification, the details in the picture we are attempting to construct of the visible universe become more finely delineated. The more closely we can subdivide the various groups of stars, the more accurately do we define the average group characteristics, and we are able to use groups made up of relatively few members.

As we carry out such a subdivision among stars that have a similar spectral type, i.e., similar surface temperature, we discover that the spectral features are not all alike. The spectrum of a large (bright) star may show marked differences from that of a small (faint) one even though the provisional temperature classifications are identical. Many of these differences appear to be continuous, so that stars of intermediate size (luminosity) have spectral features intermediate between the most extreme giants and dwarfs. . . . Among "ordinary" stars . . . the hydrogen lines in the spectrum of the supergiant *B* star 55 Cygni are much weaker than they appear in the spectrum of the relatively small star 2 Cygni.

Now if we have the spectrum of any *B2* or *B3* star of unknown luminosity in which the hydrogen lines are intermediate in intensity between the dwarf and the supergiant, we can conclude that the luminosity of the unknown star is also intermediate. By such a process, refined by the use of a number of standard stars, we can locate any ordinary spectrum with regard to its *spectral type* (a measure of temperature or color) and *luminosity class* (a measure of true brightness or diameter). This process can be described as spectral classification in a general sense. It should be noted that we do not assign definite values of temperature and absolute magnitude during the classification process. We simply give each star a label that assigns it to a place with relation to our standard stars. The calibration of our system in terms of temperature and absolute magnitude is a separate process which can be done immediately or deferred until a later time. . . .

For the purpose of the present discussion we shall call a star "ordinary" if it can be fitted into the classification we have outlined, so that its spectral features will be intermediate in appearance between the extreme examples of spectral type and luminosity of our standard stars. . . .

And now we come to the second great use of spectral classification. After fitting as many spectra as possible to our "ordinary" system, we still find a number left over that do not seem to fit in the temperature-luminosity scheme. These are the "peculiar" spectra, and an important result of the classification is the segregation of these objects for further study. Investigations of the stars having peculiar spectra have resulted in many important discoveries in stellar astronomy and astrophysics, and the importance of the discovery of "nonconformist" members of the stellar system should not be minimized.

In future years many of the spectra that now have no definite place in our classification scheme will be found to possess a certain close relationship to our "normal" stars. The classification system itself will inevitably grow more complex, but that is the price we must pay for advances in our knowledge.

....

Spectral Classification

J. HUGH PRUETT

(*Sky and Telescope*, April 1952)

As early as 1824 the German scientist Fraunhofer employed the spectroscope for the study of the stars. About forty years later, stellar spectra were studied extensively by Sir William Huggins in England and Father Angelo Secchi in Italy. The latter finally decided, after examining about 4000 stars, to classify their spectra into four distinct groups. A great advance was made around 1880, when photography of stellar spectra began to supersede visual observations. Under E. C. Pickering of Harvard the photographic spectra of over 10,000 stars were studied, and the classification scheme was developed which, with a few modifications, is the one generally used at present.

Pickering used many more classes than had Secchi, and lettered them consecutively from class A to class Q. Later work brought about a revision in the list. Some of the classes were found to be unnecessary or spurious and so were dropped. When complete revisions and logical rearrangements were finally made, there remained the following general classes in this order: O, B, A, F, G, K, M. It is found that over 99 per cent of all stars belong in these seven groups, and that their spectral characteristics change progressively from O to M. There are also the minor classes R, N, and S, which appear to be offshoots from classes K and M.

As studies progressed, it became clear that many subdivisions were possible within any one spectral class. The present Henry Draper classification makes provision for ten such finer designations. Thus, in class A we have progressively up to class F the following: A0, A1, A2, A3, A4, . . . A9. Class O is for the hottest stars, which range from O0 to O5. Stars with bright (emission) lines in their spectra are designated by a letter *e*, such as M8e.

TABLE 2.   SPECTRA, COLOR INDICES, AND TEMPERATURES OF EARLY-TYPE, MAIN-SEQUENCE, AND GIANT STARS*

| EARLY-TYPE STARS | | | | MAIN SEQUENCE | | GIANT | |
Spectrum	Color Index	Temperature (absolute)	Spectrum	Color Index	Temp. (abs.)	Color Index	Temp. (abs.)
O5	....	50,000°	Go	0.57	5760°	0.67	5300°
Bo	−0.33	21,000°	G5	0.65	5400°	0.92	4500°
B5	−0.18	14,000°	Ko	0.78	4900°	1.12	4000°
Ao	0.00	10,600°	K5	0.98	4300°	1.57	3200°
A5	0.20	8200°	Mo	1.45	3400°	1.73	3000°
Fo	0.33	7100°	M2	....	2870°	....	2800°
F5	0.47	6300°	M8	....	....	....	2000°

* After *Astronomy*, by R. H. Baker (Van Nostrand: Princeton, New Jersey, 5th ed., 1950).

There is a continuous change in color from class O to M. O stars are blue-white, although perhaps not as intensely so as the B stars. Type A is white; F, yellowish; G, yellow; K, orange; and M, red. Therefore the spectral class of a star is related to its color index, and these are both related to the temperature of its light-emitting surface.

The O and B stars have the highest temperatures, and the M stars are coolest, as shown by Table 2.

FIG. 21. Standard spectra of types O, B, A, F, G, K, and M. (Mount Wilson and Palomar Observatories photograph)

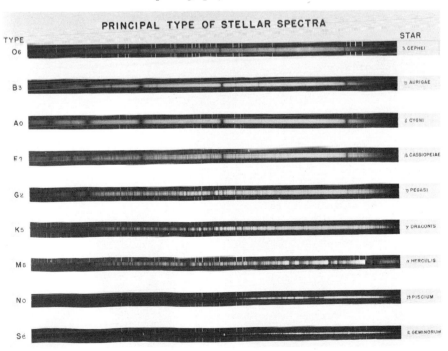

PRINCIPAL TYPE OF STELLAR SPECTRA

The spectra in Figure 21 were photographed one at a time with a spectrograph attached at the focus of a telescope. With some loss in precision, it is possible to photograph hundreds of spectra all at once with an "objective prism" in front of a telescope. (This forms a little spectrum in place of every star image on a photograph.) Such techniques, and a great deal more about spectral classification, are described in Volume 5 of this series, Starlight.—TLP

■■i

Quantitative
Spectral Classifications

OTTO STRUVE

(*Sky and Telescope*, March 1954)

Spectral classifications of the stars based upon their absorption lines and bands depend upon eye estimates of the relative intensities of certain features in the spectra—features which are sensitive to differences in stellar surface temperatures, or to differences in stellar atmospheric pressures.

The most elaborate classification of this kind is the one developed by W. W. Morgan and his associates at the Yerkes Observatory. The purpose of Morgan's work was to discover observationally those criteria that are best suited to arrange the stars in pigeonholes, each characterized by a small range of temperature and pressure. Many of the spectrum features used by Morgan are blends of absorption lines, and cannot be readily interpreted in terms of the physical parameters of the star under observation, namely, radius, mass, and luminosity.

In order to improve the classification and render it suitable for a physical interpretation, two new methods have been proposed during the past few years. The first is the work of D. Chalonge at the Astrophysical Institute in Paris, while the second is due to B. Strömgren at the Yerkes and McDonald Observatories.

The method of Chalonge and his collaborators depends upon photographic observations of the spectra of stars, principally in the ultraviolet region. . . .

Three fundamental quantities are measured in each spectrum. Two

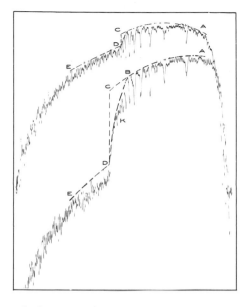

FIG. 22. These tracings of the spectra of two early-type stars, Gamma Pegasi (above) and BD +44°4014, with brightness plotted against wavelength (the latter increasing toward the right), are lettered to illustrate the three quantities measured in the Chalonge method. The spectrophotometric gradient can be evaluated from the form of the curve *AB*.

of these are illustrated in Figure 22, which has been adapted from similar diagrams by Chalonge. They show for Gamma Pegasi, a B-type star, and for BD +44°4014, a star of class A, the amount of the *Balmer jump*, marked by the line CD; this is the first quantity. The second is the *wavelength of the point K*, which is located halfway between D, where the continuous Balmer absorption is complete, and the point B, where it has not yet started.

The third quantity is the *spectrophotometric gradient*, ϕ, which in effect measures the slope of the energy curve of the star on the red side of the point B. The quantity ϕ is therefore closely related to the color index, and to the spectrophotometric temperature of the star derived by fitting a theoretical Planck curve to the observed energy curve of the star.

The Balmer jump (CD in Figure 22, usually designated by the letter D) is a measure of the number of those hydrogen atoms which are being ionized per unit of time by the ultraviolet radiation of the star's photosphere. This quantity does not give the abundance of *all* hydrogen atoms in the star's atmosphere, but only of those being ionized.

The wavelength of the point K, designated by λ_1, is an indication of the broadening of the individual Balmer lines of hydrogen and is therefore a measure of the intensity of these Balmer lines as well as of their widths. In a supergiant, where the broadening of the hydrogen lines is small, the wavelength λ_1 is very close to the Balmer limit at 3647 angstroms. In an ordinary main-sequence A-type star like Vega, the hydrogen lines are broadened by the Stark effect caused by ionized particles in the reversing layer of the star. This effect produces very broad wings which flow together even between the hydrogen-delta (Hδ) and hydrogen-gamma (Hγ) lines. In such a star, λ_1 has a value of the order of 3800 angstroms. . . .

Both quantities, D and λ_1, can be accurately measured from microphotometer tracings[1] of the spectra. They are independent of reddening by interstellar dust, which is a source of uncertainty in those spectral classifications that rest upon measures of the color index. Both quantities can be obtained from spectrograms of very small dispersion (of the order of 250 angstroms per millimeter), which are easier to obtain than those of the dispersion required in the Morgan classification.

The principal disadvantage of the Chalonge method is its limitation to stars in which the hydrogen lines and the Balmer jump are sufficiently marked to show on photographs of the spectra. In other words, the method is good only for spectral types earlier than about G0.

The precision the French astronomers have reached is as good as, or possibly better than, that obtained in the Morgan classification . . . and it is possible to convert the French measures into the spectral types and luminosity classes of Morgan. . . .

The principal advantage of the Chalonge method is its dependence solely on the properties of the hydrogen atom. It should therefore be possible to use Chalonge's scheme in future investigations of many problems involving spectral types, such as the interpretation of the H-R diagram, the relation between the ages of the stars and their hydrogen abundances, and so on.

The second of the new methods for quantitative spectral classification is Strömgren's. In principle, the investigations by Strömgren are quite similar to those of Chalonge, but while the latter uses spectrograms, the former examines directly the light of each star with a photoelectric photometer. Various wavelengths of the star's light are isolated by interference filters and compared. A two-dimensional classification (luminosity and temperature classes) is established for

---

[1] A microphotometer is used to scan photographic negatives with a small beam of light to measure how dark a negative is—a measure of how much light fell on the plate before it was developed. Each scan gives a "tracing" like those in Figure 22.—TLP

B, A, and F stars based on measures of the strength of the hydrogen-beta (Hβ) absorption line and of the Balmer discontinuity.

For Hβ, three filters are used with maximum transmission at 5000, 4861, and 4700 angstroms respectively. The middle one of these is for the absorption line itself; the other two filters furnish comparison intensities from regions where the spectrum is essentially continuous. For the Balmer discontinuity index, filters passing 4500, 4030, and 3550 angstroms are used. The last of these is situated where the continuous Balmer absorption is strong. Both indices are practically uninfluenced by interstellar reddening. The half-width of the Hβ filter is 35 angstroms; the other filters have half-widths around 100 angstroms.

Strömgren calibrated his method by measuring about a hundred stars for which Morgan classes and luminosity types were known. He found that he can classify spectral types to about 0.02 of a spectral (temperature) class see p. 76. This so far exceeds all previous methods of classification that it constitutes a new epoch in astrophysics. Similarly, the absolute magnitudes of the stars to which this method applies are obtained with a probable error of only about 0.2 magnitude from a single observation. . . .

It is clear that these new methods open up fresh vistas for the astrophysicist. We can now investigate whether there are really cosmic differences between the spectral types of stars known to have identical values of mass, radius, and luminosity. Two of the most interesting problems suggested by the new methods are the following:

Can two stars, identical in mass, luminosity, and radius, differ in atmospheric composition? Such differences might perhaps be expected if some stars happen to travel through dense clouds of interstellar dust and gather up by the process of accretion appreciable quantities of this dust. Other stars, traveling through empty regions of the Milky Way, would possess "uncontaminated" atmospheres whose composition would be similar to that of the original medium out of which each star was condensed.

Does the axial rotation of a star produce an effect upon its absorption features? We have usually assumed that it does not, and that rotation (unless it is very large) can be disregarded in spectral classification work. However, O. J. Eggen has shown that this assumption is probably incorrect. When we think of the sun, with its pronounced latitude effects in the distribution of spots and prominences, it would

FIG. 23. The Double Cluster in Perseus. (Harvard College Observatory photograph)

be reasonable to expect that moderately large rotational velocities in stars might trigger off violent prominences which could easily modify the absorption features of their spectra without in any way affecting the other characteristics, such as mass, luminosity, and radius.

An accuracy of "0.02 of a spectral class" means that Strömgren can distinguish between an A5 star and an A5.2 star, which has a surface temperature about 300° lower. Such photoelectric photometry, without the precise narrow-band filters introduced by Strömgren in 1954, had been going on for twenty or thirty years, instigated primarily by Joel Stebbins at Lick Observatory and the University of Wisconsin. It was soon found that interstellar dust often reddened the color of a distant star, and this effect was used to study the nature of interstellar dust and the locations of interstellar clouds around us (a topic to be discussed in Volume 7 of this series).

In some cases the interstellar reddening can be assumed to be the same for a whole group of stars, such as the cluster illustrated in Figure 23.—TLP

''

Color-Luminosity Arrays

OLIN J. EGGEN

(*Sky and Telescope*, November 1951)

One of the most important single contributions to astrophysics was made by Henry Norris Russell on December 30, 1913, at the sixteenth meeting of The American Astronomical Society, at Atlanta, Georgia, in a joint session with Section A of the American Association for the Advancement of Science. There Russell presented the diagram which has become associated with his name [see Fig. 4].

Nearly contemporary work by the European astronomer Ejnar Hertzsprung so closely paralleled Russell's that the diagram is now known as the Russell-Hertzsprung (R-H) diagram (or Hertzsprung-Russell diagram, according to one's preference). Russell's first chart [Fig. 4] is a plot of some 300 stars for which direct measures of parallax were available in the spring of 1913. . . .

Other, similar diagrams, such as for stars in moving clusters, were also presented by Russell to substantiate this spectrum-luminosity arrangement.

In working a jigsaw puzzle, it is helpful first to collect all pieces of the same color or those having a straight edge on one side—that is, to arrange the pieces according to some systematic scheme. Since, except for meteorites, direct physical contact with celestial objects is not possible, many astrophysical problems must be attacked with the hope that some regularity in form, or in progressive development, will be revealed by systematic classification of the observable quantities. The Russell-Hertzsprung diagram is an excellent example of a scheme in which the measurable properties of stars—the real brightnesses, or luminosities, and the temperatures as indicated by the spectral types—are correlated with one another.

The immediate effect of such a correlation was the discovery of two different kinds of stars, called *giants* and *dwarfs* by Hertzsprung. These make different patterns on the R-H diagram, the dwarfs forming a diagonal band running from the blue, hot, and bright stars to the red, cool, and faint stars, and the giants forming a nearly horizontal band which shows little change in brightness with changing temperature. The R-H diagram resembles an inverted 7 or perhaps an incomplete Y. The width of the band formed by the dwarfs is such that two stars of the same temperature, one at the top and the other at the bottom of the band, may differ in real brightness by as much as a factor of 2.5, although in Russell's early [1913] diagrams this difference was more than twice as great, owing to uncertainties in the observational data at that time.

Since the R-II diagram was first presented, most theories of stellar structure and stellar evolution either have been directly based upon it or have accepted it as a fundamental relationship between luminosity and temperature. Even the fact that the relationship is not precise (that is, the diagram consists of bands and not of lines) has been used in many of these theories.

What makes Russell's discovery doubly remarkable is the fact that two serious observational difficulties tend to mask the true relationship between temperature and luminosity. The first is in calculating the luminosity of a star. Since the stars are not all at the same distance from us, the distance effect has to be removed in order to compare their luminosities.

As the most obvious feature of a star is its light, it would be reasonable to expect that a measure of the amount of this light would be an accurately determined datum. In general this is true, but unfortunately it is not true enough; we do not know the brightnesses of many stars to an accuracy better than 10 to 20 per cent. The main reason for this uncertainty lies in the two devices most commonly used to measure the amount of starlight: the eye and the photographic plate. No two sets of eyes are quite the same, so that brightness estimates by different observers are not directly comparable. Also, the eye is not sensitive enough to small changes in light to yield results of the highest accuracy. The photographic plate is plagued by most of the defects of the eye and possesses many unique shortcomings of its own. Thus, although the brightness measures made photographically are more accurate than those made by eye, they still fall short of providing the highest accuracy. When the uncertainty in the apparent brightness of a star is added to the still greater uncertainty in the distance of the star, the resulting intrinsic luminosity may be quite inaccurate.

The second major source of error in the R-H diagram is that the temperature is not measured or plotted, but is inferred from the spectral type of the star. . . . Thus the hottest stars are termed type O, and then the sequence passes through types B, A, F, G, K, and M as the temperatures become lower. These letters, or spectral types, are used in the R-H diagram as expressions of the temperatures of the stars.

There are two difficulties with this procedure. First, the spectral types, although indispensable in astrophysics, are not sufficiently precise for the highest accuracy, since they do not represent a smooth, or even uniform, progression but rather a finite set of points arranged on an arbitrary scale. As a result, a certain amount of "lumpiness" is introduced into the diagram. Second, the spectra of the stars are often very complex, and it is not always possible to assign a unique letter for the spectral type.

In 1906 Joel Stebbins began the first experiments in this country with a new technique in stellar brightness measurements—photoelectric photometry—in which a photocell was substituted for the eye or the photographic plate as a light receiver. The photocell is a transducer, that is, it changes one form of energy to another. It works on the principle that if starlight falls on a certain type of coated surface, electricity is generated, and the more light, the more electricity, so that a measure of the generated electricity is also a measure of the brightness of a star. Fortunately most of the difficulties which in photometry plague the use of the eye and the photographic plate have not been encountered, as yet, in the use of the photocell. One initial drawback, however, in applying the new technique to astronomy was that only the brightest stars could be measured, since the sensitivity of the photocell to faint light was rather limited. This limitation has been largely overcome in recent years by the development by A. E. Whitford, of Washburn Observatory, of the thermionic amplifier, which permits the electricity generated by the photocell to be amplified before measurement, and by the application of a supersensitive photocell which has been adapted to astronomical photometry by Whitford and Gerald Kron, of Lick Observatory. This sensitive photocell, called a photomultiplier, was developed by the Radio Corporation of America and owes its success principally to the discovery of the unusually sensitive antimony-cesium photosurface by the German physicists Gorhlich and Meyer in 1938.

With the use of this sensitive light receiver we are not only able substantially to improve the accuracy of the brightness coordinate of the R-H diagram, but we also may circumvent the use of the spectral types as the temperature coordinate. Instead, we can measure the color of starlight by observing the difference in the amount of light passed by two different color filters. These filters are merely pieces of colored glass of optical quality, and of the two usually used with a photomultiplier, one lets through only blue light, the other only yellow. To be convinced that a color sequence is also a temperature sequence you have only to watch a metal rod being heated in a forge: it becomes first a dull red, then a bright cherry color, orange, and finally white hot.

With accurate photoelectric measurements of the apparent brightnesses of the stars and the smooth sequence of colors, we can reduce much of the uncertainty involved in the R-H diagram. Yet for many stars we have no precise distances, and these are necessary to convert apparent brightnesses to luminosities. This uncertainty can be largely overcome by observing only stars in clusters—groups of stars all moving together in the same direction and at the same rate. Familiar examples are the Pleiades and the Hyades. Since the stars of a cluster are all at nearly the same distance from the earth, the difference in apparent brightness of two cluster stars is also equal to the difference in their real brightness, without being confounded with the distance effect.

To summarize, then, with the photoelectrically determined colors, which are a measure of temperature, and apparent brightnesses of the stars in a cluster such as the Pleiades, we are able to redraw the R-H diagram with a large gain in accuracy. Since for these diagrams we use color instead of spectral types, they are referred to as color-luminosity arrays.

Figures 24, 25, and 26 show the color-luminosity arrays for some members of the Hyades, Pleiades, and Ursa Major clusters. The most obvious feature of these arrays is that the broad-band structure seen in the general R-H diagram is resolved into a fine structure of well-defined sequences, upon which the stars fall almost like beads on a

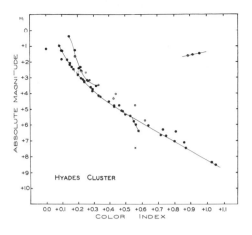

FIG. 24. The Hyades-cluster array, in which open circles indicate double stars. Note the giant sequence in the upper right of the chart.

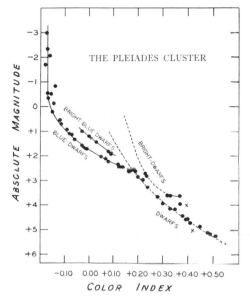

FIG. 25. The Pleiades color-luminosity array. One cross indicates a double star, the other a probable nonmember. The solid lines mark sequences added by the Pleiades to those of the Hyades (dashed lines).

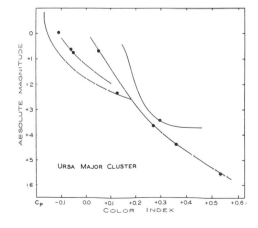

FIG. 26. The manner in which the stars of the nucleus of the Ursa Major cluster fall on several of the newly defined evolutionary sequences.

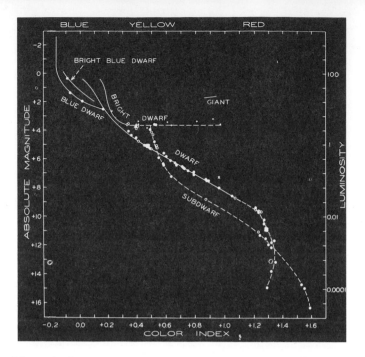

FIG. 27. The color-luminosity array for stars within forty-five light years of the sun. Solid dots are those nearer than 10 parsecs; open dots are stars between 10 and 14 parsecs. A double star is marked with a cross. (Lick Observatory diagram)

string. The names tentatively given the various sequences are admittedly cumbersome, but any attempt to systematize this nomenclature must wait until we are fairly certain that further sequences are not forthcoming. These names are shown in Figure 27, on the color-luminosity array for some of the stars within forty-five light years of the sun.

Only the nearest stars are included in Figure 27, in order to minimize the effect on luminosities of the uncertainties in their distances. A comparison among the charts shows that the sequences populated by cluster stars are also populated by stars near the sun. Also, two of the sequences found in the cluster arrays, bright dwarf and subdwarf, are greatly extended in the array for the nearest stars. Furthermore, certain types of stars appear to be mutually excluded in the cluster arrays; for example, the Pleiades stars heavily populate the blue-dwarf sequence but leave the upper portions of the dwarf and bright-dwarf sequences bare, while the Hyades stars populate these latter two sequences but contain no blue dwarfs. Other mutually exclusive groups of stars in clusters are the giants and the blue dwarfs, as can be seen by comparing the Pleiades with the Hyades and Ursa Major clusters.

From these color-luminosity arrays, and others like them, we get a strong indication that the stars in the sun's neighborhood, which includes the clusters, populate mainly the named sequences. There are several reasons that a few individual stars may depart from these sequences. A star may be behind, or imbedded in, a patch of interstellar material, making its apparent brightness too dim. A star may be double or multiple, so that the resulting measured brightness is the sum of the light of the stars involved, and the color represents the average temperature. Some distortion of the distribution of a star's light throughout the spectrum could affect the measured color. Finally, a few stars may be exceptions to the general rules by reason of peculiar chemical composition or unnatural evolution.

We are not able to extrapolate our knowledge of stars in the vicinity of the sun to the much larger number which are located throughout the more remote sections of our galaxy. In fact, we already have indications that a type of star greatly outnumbered in space near the sun predominates in other parts of the galaxy, particularly around the galactic center. The region of the sun has been referred to by Walter Baade of Mount Wilson and Palomar Observatories as the "local swimming hole," in contrast to the larger "ocean" of stars and galaxies beyond. We are, at the moment, learning to swim at home.

There was considerable disagreement about the reality of Eggen's "sequences," but the differences between color-magnitude arrays for different clusters of stars have led to our present understanding of stellar evolution.—TLP

....

Color-Magnitude Diagrams
and Stellar Evolution

OTTO STRUVE

(*Sky and Telescope*, January 1953)

The great precision attainable in the measurement of the brightnesses and colors of the stars with modern photoelectric photometers has given new impetus to the study of diagrams in which the intrinsic absolute magnitudes of the stars are plotted against their colors. In principle, such graphs are equivalent to the Hertzsprung-Russell diagrams in which the absolute magnitudes of the stars are plotted against their spectral types. They have been used extensively by many pioneering astronomers, for example, by Harlow Shapley in his famous studies of the globular clusters.

The recent increase in precision has been most convincingly demonstrated in a series of color-magnitude diagrams of stars in several open, or galactic, clusters by Harold L. Johnson at the McDonald Observatory, and in two diagrams for stars in the globular clusters M3 and M92 by H. C. Arp, W. A. Baum, and A. R. Sandage at the Mount Wilson and Palomar Observatories. The former were obtained with a photoelectric photometer; a yellow, a blue, and an ultraviolet filter were used to derive the colors. The measurements of the globular clusters were calibrated photoelectrically for selected stars, and the rest of the stars were then measured on photographs.

Figure 28 shows the diagram obtained by Johnson and W. W. Morgan for the Pleiades, while Figure 29 is for the open cluster of Praesepe (the Beehive). The diagonal array of dots is, of course, the main sequence, and (except for differences in the scales and zero points[1]) these arrays coincide in the two clusters, except at the upper ends. But the scatter is larger in the Pleiades than in Praesepe. This was already noticed by O. J. Eggen [see p. 80], but the Yerkes-McDonald astronomers do not confirm the individual sequences which Eggen's diagram [Fig. 25] had suggested.

The difference is largely one of interpretation. Both sets of observations indicated certain regions, along the main sequence, where the scatter is appreciably larger than in other regions, and in the case of medium blue stars having color index (photographic minus visual, $P - V$) between —0.1 and +0.1, it is debatable whether there are two narrow sequences or one sequence with a large dispersion. I am inclined to agree with Morgan and Johnson that large dispersion is the simpler of the two interpretations, and moreover, it is theoretically just as good as the other.

---

[1] In Figure 28 photographic magnitudes (P) are used; in Figure 29, visual magnitudes (V). The different distances to the two clusters means that zero absolute magnitude comes at different places on the vertical scales.—TLP

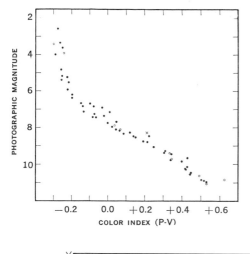

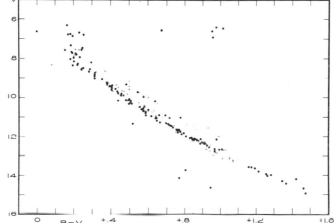

FIG. 28. A color-magnitude diagram of the Pleiades by H. L. Johnson and W. W. Morgan. The cross corresponds to a star that is heavily embedded in nebulosity. (From *The Astrophysical Journal*, The University of Chicago Press)

FIG. 29. A color-magnitude diagram of the Beehive by H. L. Johnson. Magnitude V is measured visual; B is measured blue magnitude.

Very recent observations of the Pleiades by W. A. Hiltner of Yerkes Observatory show the probable errors of his and Johnson's observations to be considerably less than 1/100 of a stellar magnitude, in color as well as in brightness. Hiltner states that his color-magnitude diagram is so nearly identical with the one by Johnson and Morgan [Fig. 28] that no star would have to be moved more than the diameter of the dot representing it.

The large scatter in the Pleiades might be caused by absorption of light in the nebulosity which envelops this cluster. But Harold Johnson has observed another galactic cluster, without any visible nebulosity, in which the scatter is even larger. Thus, in this respect, we accept the opinion of Eggen that there exist real physical differences among the cluster stars, even though their colors may be identical.

At the upper ends, the stars of the galactic clusters scatter widely, and the main sequence seems to curve steeply toward the top of the diagrams, departing from the usual prolongation of the main sequence. This is a well-known effect. It was discovered by R. J. Trumpler and was later interpreted by G. P. Kuiper as a consequence of evolutionary changes in the hotter stars of each cluster. The idea, amplified in my book *Stellar Evolution* (Princeton University Press, 1958), is that the different galactic clusters originally consisted of young stars, all rich in hydrogen. In the course of some tens of millions of years, the hottest stars of each cluster would have converted much of their hydrogen into helium, and this would have caused them to change their positions in the diagrams.

The observations suggested that there are now in existence very young clusters, like h and Chi Persei [Fig. 23], in which the normal main sequence is even now intact as far as the hottest B and O stars. But other clusters, such as the Hyades, are old—perhaps a few hundred million or even one or two billion years of age—and they have lost their blue stars.

In 1938 there was only a rudimentary theory of stellar energy production, and B. Strömgren had suggested that these hot blue stars might have evolved to the right sides of the color-magnitude diagrams, becoming in effect red giants. But it remained uncertain whether there would really be evolutionary changes of B stars along horizontal tracks on a color-magnitude diagram into the domain of the red giants.

It is of interest that the main sequence of Praesepe in Figure 29 looks as though it consisted of two parallel branches, about half a magnitude apart. This is due to the presence of binary stars in the cluster. A system of two unresolved stellar components of identical temperature and brightness would be observed three quarters of a magnitude too bright. Since not all binaries consist of identical components, the observations of these unresolved double stars scatter between the true main sequence and the three-quarter magnitude limit above it.

Figures 30 and 31 show the color-magnitude diagrams of the well-known globular clusters M3 and M92, while Figure 32 is a sketch of

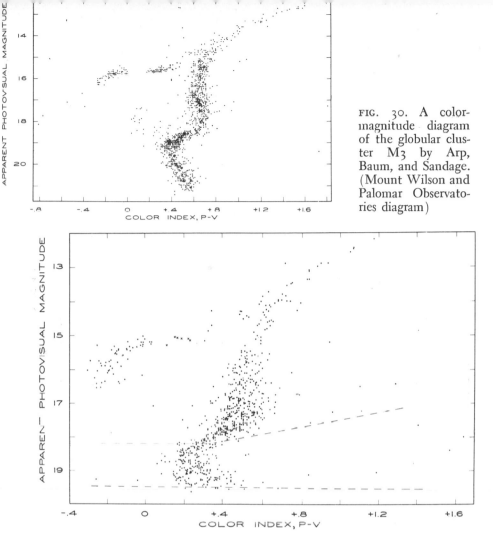

FIG. 30. A color-magnitude diagram of the globular cluster M3 by Arp, Baum, and Sandage. (Mount Wilson and Palomar Observatories diagram)

FIG. 31. A color-magnitude diagram of the globular cluster M92, by Arp, Baum, and Sandage, plotted on a slightly different scale than Figure 30. (Mount Wilson and Palomar Observatories diagram)

the main sequence of these diagrams (Population II) superposed over the conventional diagram of the stars in the neighborhood of the sun (Population I). The latter is shown by the shaded areas. At first sight there appears to be a tremendous difference between the two stellar populations. But the diagonal main sequence is present in both, although in the globular clusters only a short stub of it is apparent. Their main sequences are limited at the lower right because the stars are too faint to be observed; undoubtedly there are many faint red dwarfs in the unobserved lower region of the main sequence. But at the top the main sequences are fairly sharply bounded.

The horizontal branches which bridge the conventional Hertzsprung gap of Population I extend far to the left and include, in both clusters, a number of very blue stars, with color indices of the order of −0.65 magnitude, which resemble the blue galactic stars discovered by M. L. Humason and F. Zwicky of Mount Wilson and Palomar Observatories and also by Donald A. MacRae, then at Case Institute of Technology, Robert Fleischer, and Edwin B. Weston, then at the University of Michigan.

In M3 the short-period variable stars were omitted. In M92 they are shown as crosses. Arp, Baum, and Sandage conclude that these variables "are all isolated in a small segment of the horizontal branch of the array, in which region there are no nonvariable stars present." M. Schwarzschild suggested, many years ago, that all stars in a small region of a diagram like Figures 30 and 31 (possessing certain definite values of luminosity and color) tend to vibrate, or pulsate. This idea finds strong support in the new Mount Wilson data.

As we shall see, the most interesting information is obtained from a study of the strangely bent, nearly vertical, giant branches. Although they do not coincide in these two clusters, both join with the main sequence at about absolute magnitude +3.5.

There is no doubt that these color-luminosity diagrams (or their equivalents—the original Russell-Hertzsprung diagrams) contain a powerful key to the solution of the problem of stellar evolution. But we must actually get a hold on the key before we can unlock the secret. An important and perhaps decisive step in this direction has been made by Sandage and Schwarzschild in a theoretical paper being published in *The Astrophysical Journal* [Nov. 1952]. Their ideas will be discussed briefly here.

What happens to a star as it gradually converts its hydrogen into helium by means of the nuclear reactions known as the carbon cycle? The nuclear processes involved are very sensitive to the temperature of the medium. If the temperature is a little lower than 20 million degrees they are almost inoperative; at about 20 million degrees and above, on the other hand, they are very efficient.

We know that the temperature of a star increases from the surface, where it is of the order of a few thousand degrees, toward the center, where it exceeds the critical value required for the nuclear processes.

Hence the conversion of hydrogen into helium takes place only in the deep interiors of the stars. In earlier discussions of stellar interiors astronomers even spoke of a "point-source" model as representing the physical conditions inside the sun.

But it became gradually apparent, largely through the work of T. G. Cowling, that in the region surrounding the center of the star there must be violent convection of the gases, with a consequent mixing of the material inside this convective core. Hence all the hydrogen of the core passes many times through the hot center, and is there subjected to the carbon-cycle nuclear reactions.

Outside the convective core the mixing of the material is exceedingly slow (except perhaps in rapidly rotating stars). Hence this envelope remains rich in hydrogen—its temperature is too low for the nuclear processes, and its hydrogen atoms do not travel toward the center carried by convective currents.

Gradually the convective core would become exhausted of hydrogen, and would then consist only of helium and those heavier elements that were already present in the original cosmic material out of which the star was built. What would happen next was a difficult problem, and its solution required all the mathematical and physical skill that S. Chandrasekhar and Mario Schönberg could muster. They showed that with the dying out of the nuclear energy production near the star's center the driving force for maintaining the convective currents in the core would also disappear. The gas would come to rest and would no longer contain any sources of energy, but would, of course, be surrounded by the intensely hot envelope with its normal supply of hydrogen. This would tend to convert the convective core into an isothermal core—a mass of gas at a uniform temperature of the order of 20 million degrees, or slightly more.

Chandrasekhar and Schönberg have shown that the isothermal core will at first grow in mass and in radius. The core is surrounded by a thin spherical shell whose temperature is now of the order of 20 million degrees. This shell becomes the source of the stellar nuclear energy production, and as its hydrogen is converted into helium the resulting material is added to the isothermal core. At the same time, the temperature of the core rises, and the energy production passes on to the layer just outside of the "burned-out" shell.

However, this process of growth in the isothermal core cannot continue for long. It stops before all of the envelope is used up. As

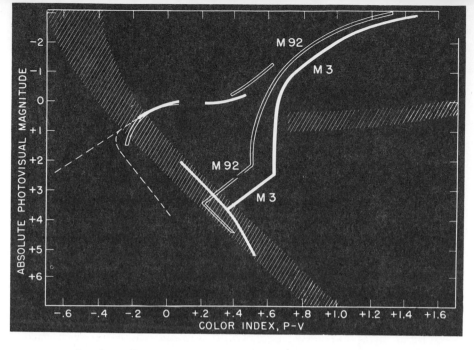

FIG. 32. A schematic representation of color-magnitude diagrams of Population I (shaded areas) and of Population II (globular clusters M92 and M3). The empty region near the middle of the upper giant branches of both clusters is occupied by the pulsating variable stars, which were not investigated. In Population I the horizontal giant branch does not join the main sequence; the space between is called the Hertzsprung gap.

FIG. 33. A schematic representation by Allan R. Sandage and Martin Schwarzschild of the evolutionary tracks in the color-magnitude diagram for stars of different masses. The heavy line represents the path of stars somewhat more massive than the sun, all starting 3.5 billion years ago, and strikingly displays the features of the lower portion of the observed diagram of Population II for the globular clusters M3 and M92 (Fig. 32). The vertical scale is absolute bolometric magnitude; the horizontal scale is the logarithm of the effective temperature. (Mount Wilson and Palomar Observatories diagram)

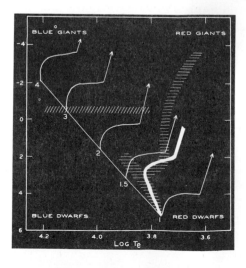

Chandrasekhar has stated, "It follows from quite general considerations that we cannot fit into a star an isothermal core beyond a certain maximum size. The reason for this is, physically, that in a star . . . we cannot build a steep enough temperature gradient in the outer parts to maintain more than a certain fraction of the mass at the highest temperature." This fraction turns out to be about 12 per cent of the total mass of the star. Chandrasekhar's conclusion was that "it would seem that when the isothermal core has expanded to its maximum size the secular evolution (by nuclear processes) will be definitely stalled." And in its final stages, he said, "The star has recourse to contracting in the manner imagined by Helmholtz and Kelvin, releasing gravitational energy."

It is with this late stage in the life of a star that the work of Schwarzschild and Sandage is concerned. Even before the outer envelope has consumed all the hydrogen it can, the isothermal core begins to contract, thereby releasing what appears to be a rather small amount of energy—so small in fact that for all practical purposes the light and heat we observe come entirely from the nuclear processes in the thin layer surrounding the isothermal core.

Yet it is this effect of contraction of the core that has unexpected and rather spectacular consequences: as the core condenses, the envelope becomes greatly blown out. The visible radius of the star increases, and its surface area increases as the square of the radius. The temperature of the photosphere decreases, so that the total luminosity of the star changes but little.

The results of the accurate computations of Sandage and Schwarzschild are illustrated in Figure 33. We start with five young stars, possessing their full normal supply of hydrogen and differing only in mass—4, 3, 2, 1.5, and 1 times the mass of the sun respectively. As the hydrogen begins to be converted into helium in the convective core, each star at first moves sharply upward from its original location on the diagonal line representing the main sequence. This part of the five curves was already known from the work of Chandrasekhar and Schönberg, and there have been many elaborations of it in recent years. The luminosity increases by about one stellar magnitude, and each star appears a little to the right of the main sequence.

As the 12-per-cent limit of the core is approached, the gravitational contraction of the core becomes effective, and each star moves rapidly to the right, on an approximately horizontal line. It becomes a typical giant.

The length of time required for the stars to pursue this course is not the same for all five of them. The more massive stars, with their large luminosities, rapidly exhaust their hydrogen, and for them the entire process may require only some millions of years. Stars having masses smaller than that of the sun have not yet turned 12 per cent of their hydrogen into helium, and are therefore still on the main sequence. Stars of slightly more than the mass of the sun require about three billion years to reach the horizontal branch of the evolutionary curves. These stars fall between the two curves in Figure 33 labeled 1.5 and 1 solar mass. Their absolute magnitudes are near 3.3, precisely the point in the globular cluster diagrams where the giant branch conspicuously branches off the main sequence. This agreement is truly amazing; it shows that the Sandage-Schwarzschild model must indeed be close to the truth.

The observations (Fig. 32) showed that in the globular clusters the (almost) horizontal giant branch on the right-hand side, is followed by an almost vertical branch that finally, at its upper end, trails off more nearly horizontally to the right. Sandage and Schwarzschild believe that this may be due to a new nuclear process of converting helium into heavier elements which was recently announced by E. E. Salpeter. If it were not for this process, which starts when the isothermal core has reached a temperature of the order of 100 million degrees, the evolutionary track described by Sandage and Schwarzschild would remain horizontal and extend indefinitely toward the cooler surface temperatures in the H-R diagram, or the redder colors in the color-magnitude diagrams.

The five vertical branches at the right of Figure 33 are based upon an estimate of the manner in which Salpeter's process will affect a star's luminosity and color. Presumably there would develop a new convective core, which in turn would give way to a new isothermal region—of very high temperature—which again would contract and release gravitational energy. There would then be another stage of expansion of the outer envelope with reduction of surface temperature, and so on.

Sandage and Schwarzschild have assumed that a typical globular cluster was formed 3.5 billion years ago, at that time consisting of a mixture of stars having masses between one and 2.5 times the mass of the sun. They then computed for each mass the present location of the star on its evolutionary track and drew a heavy line through the points thus obtained. The result gives a synthetic color-magnitude diagram (heavy line in Figure 33) which possesses the principal features of the observed diagrams in Figure 32.

Incidentally, in the observational diagrams the upper horizontal branch, with blue stars and short-period variables at absolute magnitude o, is not explained in Sandage and Schwarzschild's paper. Stars that originally had the high luminosities of this branch must have long ago moved out of the entire range of the Sandage-Schwarzschild curves. What has happened to them we do not know. Perhaps they were never there to begin with. Or, if they did exist 3.5 billion years ago, they may have undergone the explosion process of a nova in order to get rid of their excess masses and have settled down to quiet existence as "degenerate" white dwarfs.

We can now detect a certain amount of agreement in the diagrams of Populations I and II, whereas at first they seemed to be entirely different. In the first place, both contain the same lower branches of the main sequence, where the red dwarfs are located. This means that stars of very low temperature and luminosity remain practically the same for many billions of years. The more luminous stars have evolved differently in the two populations. In the globular clusters they were formed about 3.5 billion years ago by some process of condensation which left no gaseous or dustlike medium behind. Once these stars were formed they were on their own, and their evolution followed the Sandage-Schwarzschild tracks.

In Population I we observe stars of all ages. Some were probably formed three or four billion years ago. Others could not have been what they are now much longer than one million years. Since there is even now a large amount of gas and dust in the spiral arms of our galaxy, these Population I stars can grow by accretion (or become rejuvenated, to use von Weizsaecker's expression), or they can perhaps even now be formed out of globules of interstellar matter. The galactic, or open, clusters must be relatively recent formations. This agrees with the ideas of V. Ambartzumian on the expansion of stellar associations, and it finds support in A. Blaauw's investigations of the motions in clusters.

The Ages
of
Star Clusters

....

Our interest in clusters, discussed in Chapter 2, stems from the fact
that the stars in a cluster are all at about the same distance from us
(and obscured by the same amount of interstellar dust), and from the
assumption that the stars in any one cluster were all formed at the
same time—in some cases, billions of years ago. During billion-year
periods of time, loose, open galactic clusters are subject to many
disruptive forces, and the more tightly packed globular clusters would
be expected to settle down to a predictable set of internal motions.
Studies of the motions of stars in clusters thus have a bearing on the
time scale of stellar evolution.—TLP

....

Very Young Stars

(*Sky and Telescope*, February 1952)

The formation of stars within the astronomical "present" of only
1.3 million years ago is indicated from studies by A. Blaauw, Leiden

Observatory, Holland, of a loose clustering of B stars surrounding Zeta Persei. Unpublished results of far-reaching significance were included in the Henry Norris Russell lecture [at the December 1951 meeting of the American Astronomical Society] given by Jan H. Oort, Leiden's director. His title was "Problems of Galactic Structure." He said, concerning Blaauw's work:

"These loose groups, stellar associations, aggregates, or relationships, as they have alternatively been called, are of a quite particular interest. They have been known for a long time, ever since spectral classes have been determined, and several have been extensively studied. It had also been well realized that because of their looseness these clouds of early-type stars must be torn up by the effects of differential galactic rotation in a period of the order of one revolution of the galaxy, and that therefore they must be comparatively young. During the last few years considerable work on the problems presented by the B-star clouds has been done by Ambartzumian and his coworkers at the Erevan Observatory in Armenia, U.S.S.R., . . . The most important new concept, which, I believe, was first suggested by Ambartzumian, is that the associations are expanding. And this is not only because of galactic rotation but also as an essential property of their own. This has proved to be a fertile idea, which seems, in a somewhat unexpected manner, to give an insight into the origin and the meaning of these groups.

"In a still unpublished investigation on a group of B stars surrounding Zeta Persei, Blaauw has succeeded in proving such an expansion by direct observation [see p. 100]. This loose clustering, measuring about forty by twenty parsecs, is situated between 12 and 20 degrees southern galactic latitude, at a distance of roughly 300 parsecs. The reality of the relationship between the stars cannot be doubted. In 1944, when he first discovered the group, Blaauw was struck by the fact that the proper motions of the members showed rather unexpected divergences. Recently he has determined new proper motions, . . . which prove that the group is expanding at a rate of $0''.0028 \pm 0''.0004$ (mean error) per year and per degree distance from its center. This surprisingly rapid expansion, of about five kilometers per second for stars halfway out to the edge of the group, corresponds to an age of only 1.3 million years (with a mean error of about 14 per cent). Low though this age may seem, it is entirely compatible with the age that may be ascribed on theoretical grounds to the most luminous members of the group, like the O star, Xi Persei.

"The most straightforward interpretation of these observations is that the members of this group were formed about 1.3 million years ago as a consequence of a dense conglomeration of interstellar clouds with turbulent motions of the order of five kilometers per second. These turbulent velocities now show up roughly as an expansion of the group, which has already grown very considerably since its birth. Even today the whole region is full of dark as well as luminous interstellar matter. . . . I believe this is the first direct evidence of the birth of stars from interstellar material. A remarkable thing is the extremely short time in which these stars must have contracted from interstellar clouds into actual stars. The available time is only barely long enough for a cloud with a radius of the order of one parsec to contract under its own gravitation.

"It is likely that the Zeta Persei aggregate is rather exceptional in the rapidity of its expansion. At least it is certain that in the other B-star clouds for which data are available the expansions are considerably less rapid. By far the best known association of B stars is the large Scorpius-Centaurus cloud. The most complete investigation has again been made by Blaauw. It is the only B-star group for which the space distribution can be determined. It is considerably larger than the Zeta Persei group, and has a strikingly oblong shape, with a long axis of about 290 parsecs, the other axes being about 100 parsecs and 70 parsecs, respectively. It is tempting to suppose that this aggregate has also formed from a much smaller conglomeration of interstellar clouds, the stars having dispersed as a consequence of the turbulent motions in this agglomeration. The motions are not yet known with sufficient accuracy to determine the amount of expansion, but they suffice to show that it is much smaller than in the case of the Zeta Persei group, probably not much larger than one kilometer per second. The Scorpius-Centaurus cloud does not contain very bright supergiants; the ages of the brightest stars might be estimated to be of the order of 50 or 100 million years. Blaauw has remarked that both the strong elongation of the group and its orientation in space can be understood as the natural consequence of expansion combined with the differential rotation of the galactic system. In fact, if an expansional velocity of one kilometer per second is assumed, the cloud would in 60 million years have gotten the dimensions, the amount of elongation as well as the orientation in space, that are observed today."[1]

••

What Happens to Star Clusters?

OTTO STRUVE

(*Sky and Telescope*, October 1953)

The method used by theoretical astronomers to estimate the stability of a cluster is one we associate with the name of E. Roche. He used it originally to determine the effects of tidal stresses of a planet on its satellites, and found that a liquid satellite would be disrupted by such tidal action if its distance from the center of the planet were less than about 2.5 times the radius of the planet. For example, a compact satellite could not exist in the region in which we now observe the rings of Saturn; if there ever was such a satellite, it was disrupted into many small particles which have retained their identity because of forces of cohesion that exceed gravitational forces when the solid particles are small.

If the internal gravitation of the parts of a star cluster exceeds the tidal disrupting force due to the Milky Way Galaxy, the cluster is stable; if the stability factor is great, we may assume that the cluster can retain its identity without serious disturbance for many billions of years. If, however, the disrupting tidal force of the Milky Way is greater than the internal gravitation, the cluster is not stable and will be disrupted within a relatively short time. When the two quantities are identical, the cluster is on the verge of instability.

We find that for a cluster to be stable the density must be greater than a specific value. This quantity is obtained when we multiply the mass of the galaxy by 10 and divide it by the cube of the distance between the center of the galaxy and the center of the cluster.

---

[1] For further background material on stellar associations and their ages the reader is referred to "Stellar Associations" by Otto Struve, *Sky and Telescope*, 8, 215, July 1949 [reprinted in Volume 5, *Starlight*].

Let us consider the Pleiades cluster. Near the center of this cluster there are about three stars per cubic parsec. Since the Pleiades are inside the Milky Way, we estimate that the attraction from the inner portions of the galaxy is equivalent to that of about 10^{10} solar masses. The distance between the Pleiades and the galactic center is of the order of 10,000 parsecs, the cube of which is 10^{12}. The ratio of 10 times the attracting mass to this cube is therefore $10^{11}/10^{12}$, or 0.1 star per cubic parsec. Thus the central regions of the Pleiades would be reasonably stable, even though the stability factor is not particularly large and in time intervals of a few billion years perturbations by the Milky Way might be expected to modify greatly the shape of this cluster.

In the case of the Hyades, where the observed star density is only about 0.25 per cubic parsec, the situation is definitely more critical, and this cluster is on the verge of instability. All those clusters and associations that have star densities less than one star per 10 cubic parsecs are unstable and must be disrupted rapidly by the tidal forces of the galaxy.

How, then, does this disruption proceed? For a reasonably compact cluster, like the Pleiades or even the Hyades, the theory is complicated. The lifetime of such a group must be computed by a statistical method of estimating the cumulative effect of perturbations from neighboring stars. The most complete work of this nature has been done by S. Chandrasekhar at the Yerkes Observatory. He has computed the fraction of the stars that are lost, or we might say "evaporated," from a cluster during a time interval Δt, and has found it approximately equal to $0.0074 \, \Delta t$ divided by the time of relaxation of the cluster. For any given group of stars the relaxation time is the period required for a random distribution of motions to be reestablished after it has once been disrupted. This time for a typical open cluster is about 30 million years.

We can compute, for instance, the time in years (Δt) during which one half of the original members of the cluster will have been evaporated. The computation is $\frac{1}{2} \times 3 \times 10^7/0.0074$. This is approximately two billion or 2×10^9 years.

Although the more stable clusters will be disrupted in slightly longer periods and the less stable ones will disappear in less than a billion years, the average value derived by Chandrasekhar is consistent with the idea that such a cluster can retain its identity for only a

FIG. 34. The Beehive cluster (Praesepe), a typical open cluster. (Harvard College Observatory photograph)

fraction of the age of the galaxy as a whole. This is an excellent confirmation of our hypothesis that the open clusters which we now observe are all relatively young formations, and those clusters that may have originated three billion years ago have long since been dispersed among the broad features of our galaxy's spiral structure.

In the case of a loose stellar association, the tidal action of the Milky Way proceeds even more rapidly in its work of destruction. The Armenian astronomer Ambartzumian has shown that those regions of a stellar association that are nearest to the center of the galaxy revolve more rapidly in the galaxy's rotation than do those regions that are farthest away. This is a consequence of Kepler's and Newton's laws which predict that the speeds of stars in orbit around the galactic center are inversely proportional to the square root of their distances from the center. The result is a tendency of the cluster to spread out along a circle around the center of the Milky Way; it can be shown that by this effect a stellar association will double its length in approximately 30 million years.

However, the observational fact, first noticed by Ambartzumian, that nearly all known associations are roughly spherical in shape and do not show any tendency to be elongated in the plane of the Milky Way led him a few years ago to conclude that such associations are much younger than 30 million years. Evidently, there has not been enough time for them to be spread out in the plane of the Milky Way. Furthermore, the fact that the associations are observed as spherical suggested that each is rapidly expanding with a uniform velocity in all directions. This would mask the tendency toward elongation due to the shearing effect by the Milky Way. Ambartzumian suggested that this hypothetical expansion should be about five kilometers per second, an average star within a given association moving away from the center of the group with that velocity.

This conclusion was recently confirmed in a most dramatic way by A. Blaauw at Leiden in the Netherlands. From a study of the proper motions and radial velocities of the stars in an association centered around the famous B-type star Zeta Persei, he established that this group expands with an average speed of about twelve kilometers per second.

Roughly speaking, the area in the sky occupied by this association has a diameter of 6 degrees. Its distance, found by comparing brightnesses of its stars with their absolute magnitudes taken from the Hertzsprung-Russell diagram, is about 1000 light years. Hence, in kilometers, the radius of this association is about 5×10^{14}. If a star at the edge of this system is now moving outward by 12 kilometers in one second, it would have been near the center of the association $5 \times 10^{14}/12$ or about 4×10^{13} seconds ago. This is roughly one million years. Hence Blaauw concluded that the age of this group is of the order of one million years.

The observational data on which this conclusion is based seem to be unassailable. The best argument is Blaauw's final diagram of the motions in the Zeta Persei association, from which Figure 35 has been adapted. This shows the proper motions of all O to B5 stars of the group, the arrows representing the relative proper motions for individual stars or weighted means for subgroups of two or three

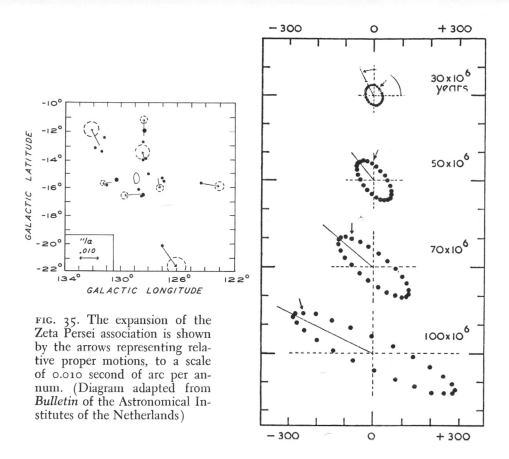

FIG. 35. The expansion of the Zeta Persei association is shown by the arrows representing relative proper motions, to a scale of 0.010 second of arc per annum. (Diagram adapted from *Bulletin* of the Astronomical Institutes of the Netherlands)

FIG. 36. Blaauw's diagram here shows how a stellar association elongates with age. The direction toward the galactic center is downward, and the distances are expressed in parsecs. For associations younger than 30 million years, a velocity of expansion of one kilometer per second will mask the elongation due to galactic rotation. Associations older than 100 million years are far advanced toward dissolution. The present shape of the Scorpius-Centaurus group closely matches the third figure from the top. (From *Bulletin* of the Astronomical Institutes of the Netherlands)

stars close together on the sky. The tails of the arrows are in the centers of these groups. The radii of the dashed circles represent the probable errors of the proper motions. Stars brighter than visual absolute magnitude −4 are represented by large dots. Blaauw says, "The directions of the arrows show clearly the expansion of the group, especially if we consider the stars at the greatest angular distance from its center." . . .

The manner in which the Milky Way proceeds with the destruction of an expanding association of greater age than the Zeta Persei association has also been demonstrated by Blaauw, in a paper in the *Bulletin* of the Astronomical Institutes of the Netherlands. In this he shows that the tidal, or shearing, effect of differential galactic rotation causes the association to become elongated as shown in Figure 36.

He finds for the specific case of the famous Scorpius-Centaurus group of *B*-type stars that the orientation of the elliptical configuration corresponds to an expansion age of about 72 million years, with original velocities of expansion for the outermost stars of one kilometer per second. This age seems to fit the observed brightnesses of these stars and the fact that there are no very young stars (earlier than type *B*o) in the group.

Since the publication of Blaauw's papers last year several other associations have been investigated, for example, one by Soviet astronomers and one more recently by Morgan and Blaauw at Yerkes Observatory. They all seem to confirm the existence of the expansions, and the resulting ages turn out to be in the vicinity of 10 million years.

We are still completely in the dark as to the origin of these expansions. At one time Ambartzumian had apparently been thinking of some catastrophic explosion in a prestellar body of hundreds or even thousands of solar masses and of a kind not previously recognized in astronomy. At the Rome meeting of the International Astronomical Union in 1952 he no longer stressed this hypothesis; it is perhaps best to retain an open mind as to the origin of the motions. It may be that expansion rather than contraction is a characteristic property of all formations of the universe, and we must not be surprised that such expansion occurs in associations of stars as it does in expanding stars or in the system of receding galaxies. . . .

We now turn to the problem of the globular clusters. These remarkable accumulations of virtually countless individual stars often contain a number of pulsating variables of the RR-Lyrae type. These stars have periods of less than one day and absolute magnitudes equal to zero. They are thus about a hundred times more luminous, intrinsically, than the sun. When we locate such a variable in a globular cluster and measure its apparent magnitude we can derive the distance in parsecs. With cameras of short focal length, we can next compare the total light of a globular cluster with the apparent magnitudes of neighboring stars and, knowing the distance, convert this integrated apparent magnitude into the corresponding integrated absolute magnitude, or total luminosity, of the cluster.

The integrated absolute magnitude of an average globular cluster is about −8. The absolute magnitude of the sun, as it would appear at the standard distance of 10 parsecs, is +5. Such a cluster is therefore intrinsically 13 magnitudes (a factor of 100,000 times) brighter than the sun. The average cluster, if it were made up of stars of the sun's luminosity, would contain about 10^5 stars. We thus find, without making any star counts, that a typical globular cluster consists of about 100,000 individual stars.

Complete star counts are not possible in globular clusters because near the centers of these objects the star images overlap to such an extent that we cannot count them. In the outer regions, however, where the star images do not interfere with each other, Harlow Shapley and F. G. Pease counted 5000 stars in the southern cluster Omega Centauri and 70,000 stars in M22 in Sagittarius.

The average star density of a globular cluster having a radius of 40 parsecs, found from the ratio of the total mass to the volume, is about 0.4 star per cubic parsec, but near the center the density could easily be 100 or even 1000 times greater. The criterion of stability, 10 times the mass of the galaxy divided by the cube of the distance between the cluster and the galactic center, is in this case, at most, about one star per cubic parsec. Clearly, the globular clusters are completely stable formations, and the degree of stability is so large near the centers of these objects that they can undoubtedly retain their identities indefinitely.

Unquestionably, this is the reason the color-magnitude diagrams of the globular clusters have been found to correspond to ages of the order of five billion years, differing fundamentally from the diagrams constructed for the open galactic clusters.

The formula for the critical density of a cluster with respect to its stability also appears to have great significance in the actual formation of individual stars. V. G. Fessenkov has stressed the idea that stars appear to form within a large system, such as a galaxy or a condensed cloud of dust and gas, when the density is at least as large as the ratio of 10 times the disturbing mass to the cube of the distance between the mass and the newly forming star.

For example, in the spiral arm of the Milky Way where the sun is located, the disturbing mass is approximately 10^{11} times the mass of the sun, or about 2×10^{44} grams. The distance to this mass, the galactic center, is 8000 parsecs or 2.4×10^{22} centimeters. The resulting critical density is approximately 10^{-22} grams per cubic centimeter. This is about 100 times greater than the average density of interstellar gas observed at the present time. But there are concentrations of gas, for example in the Orion nebula, where the density is 10^{-22} and even more. We must suppose that stars are now being formed in the region of the Orion nebula, and perhaps that the Orion association of O and B stars resulted from the very process of star formation going on at the present time.

No doubt we shall find that an important stage of star formation is indicated by the presence in the Orion nebula of hundreds of emission-line variable stars resembling T Tauri. As G. Haro in Mexico has shown, these stars are not only numerous but they are variable in light as well as in spectrum. His work and that of G. Herbig at the Lick Observatory, though not yet completed, strongly suggest that they are newly formed stars that are still growing as they pull interstellar dust and gas into themselves.

Fessenkov has pointed out that in a nebula of average density 10^{-22} grams per cubic centimeter the volume of space that contains one solar mass (2×10^{33} grams) corresponds to a radius of about 10^{18} centimeters or 100,000 astronomical units. The sun is 270,000 astronomical units from its nearest stellar neighbor, and other distances in our part of the Milky Way are similar. Here we have another argument in favor of the hypothesis that the stars have been condensed from a medium equal in density to the critical value: the average distances between neighboring stars are just about what would be required to produce the critical density of 10^{-22} grams per cubic centimeter if their masses were spread uniformly through the galaxy.

One of the difficulties in observing the individual members of clusters, such as the stars in Figure 34, is in eliminating foreground and background objects. This is least serious in tightly packed globular clusters, where the cluster members are many times more numerous than chance stars in the line of sight. Still, the edge of the cluster is difficult to define. With looser galactic clusters a nonmember can often be recognized because its brightness or motion doesn't fit in. The stellar associations are the loosest groupings, extending over wide areas in the sky where many other stars are to be seen, some nearer than the association members, some farther from us. Association members are picked out of the background stars by their common motion, on which Blaauw's expansion is superposed. That is, the twenty or thirty members arc all moving past us in the same direction at high speed, and are separating from each other at relatively low speed—something like buckshot from a shotgun.

In addition to outward velocities like these, caused by some sort of initial explosion, the stars of a cluster, or association, are all pulling on each other with gravitational forces. The complex calculations of how such forces and motions change the cluster have been carried out recently with high-speed electronic computers.—TLP

Evolution of a
Star Cluster

(*Sky and Telescope*, November 1954)

The Maniac at Los Alamos Scientific Laboratory is an electronic computer whose speed is some 10,000 times that of a desk machine operated by an exceptionally skilled calculator. Ralph E. Williamson reported on a number of astronomical and astrophysical calculations performed by Maniac that were too complex for attack by earlier means.

One such problem, run on the Maniac by S. Ulam and J. Pasta, dealt with a two-dimensional cluster of a hundred stars. Their motions have been studied with a time scale such that one minute of computation covers ten million years in the life of the cluster. At each time step, every star was moved by calculating the result of the gravitational attraction on it of all the other cluster stars.

In the course of the run, some stars were lost from the cluster, some double and multiple systems were formed, and certain fairly persistent clumping tendencies were noted.

Williamson remarked that, in a sense, modern electronic computers have brought the scope of the universe, in both time and space, within the realm of direct observation.

■■

Old and Young
Star Clusters

OTTO STRUVE

(*Sky and Telescope*, February 1956)

In the constellation of Cancer are located two conspicuous star clusters, one the well-known Beehive, or Praesepe, and the other an object of particular interest from the evolutionary point of view. This is Messier 67, or NGC2682, near Alpha Cancri.

M67 contains about five hundred stars between apparent visual magnitudes 10 and 16, and there may be many still fainter stars belonging to it. The bluest spectral type of any star in M67 is close to A0; the reddest thus far observed is about K4, representing reddish giant stars.

The distance of this cluster is, according to R. J. Trumpler's early value (1930), about 2400 light years, but a more recent determination by H. L. Johnson and A. R. Sandage gives 2600 light years (800 parsecs). The Beehive is much closer to us than M67, only 575 light years away. Although these clusters appear to lie near each other in the sky, one is actually 4.5 times farther from us than its apparent neighbor.

As Figure 37 shows, both clusters are a little more than 30 degrees from the central line of the Milky Way. Actually Praesepe is 97 parsecs above the central plane of our galaxy, while M67 is fully 440 parsecs, or about 1450 light years, above it. This differs from most galactic clusters, which are found in or near the Milky Way.

We might then expect M67 to be relatively immune to the tidal forces and other disturbances that tend to break up galactic clusters lying in the spiral arms of the Milky Way. M67 also contains an unusually large number of stars, and their mutual gravitational attraction should help preserve its identity over long periods. It appears on a photographic plate as a condensation of bright stars, about 16 minutes of arc in diameter, surrounded by many fainter stars (see Fig. 38). Some decades ago Harlow Shapley had concluded that the bright stars

formed merely a well-marked nucleus of brighter and redder stars in a
much larger system, which he estimated might be a degree in diameter.

In 1939 E. Ebbighausen measured the proper motions of the
brighter stars of M67 with reference to fainter background stars. He
compared four direct photographs, made with the 40-inch refractor at
the Yerkes Observatory, and corresponding pictures taken seventeen
to thirty-five years earlier to find which stars were cluster members
and which were not. He was able to determine the luminosities of

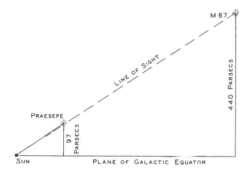

FIG. 37. In almost the same line
of sight, Praesepe and M67 are
at very unequal distances from
the galactic plane.

FIG. 38. One of the finest open star clusters in the northern sky, Messier 67
in Cancer. This area of one square degree is enlarged from a photograph made
by Bart J. Bok with the Jewett Schmidt telescope on December 10-11, 1948.
The exposure was 90 minutes, on a baked 103a-o (blue) plate. South is upward.
(Harvard College Observatory photograph)

the cluster stars and, with spectral types supplied to him by Trumpler, to construct an H-R diagram, which shows that the distribution of M67 stars resembles, to a considerable extent, that obtained for globular clusters. There is a prominent late-type giant sequence. This is confirmed by the color-luminosity plot published by Johnson and Sandage in the May 1955 issue of *The Astrophysical Journal*, where these authors discuss many problems relating to clusters.

In the upper left of Figure 39, notice a few bluish stars, some lying roughly on the main sequence. To the lower right are a great many dwarfs fainter than apparent magnitude 13 and with color indices of 0.5 and greater; these stars belong on the main sequence, in the same general region as that occupied by the sun (class G), and their spectral types are dwarf $F5$ and later.

Of great significance is the pronounced curved giant branch beginning at apparent magnitude 13 and extending to the right from the main sequence, thence upward to the top right corner of the diagram. This feature of M67 resembles (but does not exactly match) the giant branches of the globular clusters.

With the cluster's distance of 800 parsecs, the cutoff of the main sequence at apparent magnitude 13 corresponds to a visual absolute magnitude of $+3.3$. Using this value, Johnson and Sandage have shown schematically in Figure 40 how M67 compares with the globular clusters M3 and M92. Finally, in Figure 41, they have collected the H-R diagrams for a number of other galactic clusters to show how they differ from M67 and from the globular clusters.

We have seen previously [see p. 85] that the departure of the upper branches of the main sequences of the Perseus Double Cluster, the Pleiades, the Hyades, and Praesepe, may be interpreted in terms of unequal ages of these clusters. The farther into the region of hot blue stars the main sequence of a cluster extends, the younger it appears to be. Thus the Double Cluster is youngest of those shown here, while the Pleiades and Hyades are older in that order. On this evidence, the galactic cluster NGC 752 and especially M67 are even older. In fact, their main-sequence cutoffs occur at just about the same place as those in M3 and M92. Hence M67 may also be five billion years old, the present estimated age of the globular clusters.

If in its infancy M67 had a fully developed, normal main sequence extending well up into spectral classes A and B, then its A and B stars "have long since passed through their evolutionary development

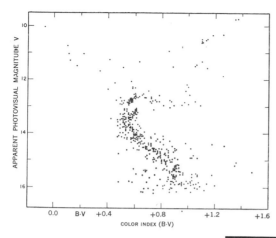

FIG. 39. Color-magnitude diagram for stars in M67, by H. L. Johnson and Allan Sandage. (From *The Astrophysical Journal*, The University of Chicago Press)

FIG. 40. H. L. Johnson and Allan Sandage's color-magnitude array for M67 is here compared with those for the globular clusters M3 and M92. The brightest giant stars in M67 are three magnitudes less luminous than those in the globular clusters. (From *The Astrophysical Journal*, The University of Chicago Press)

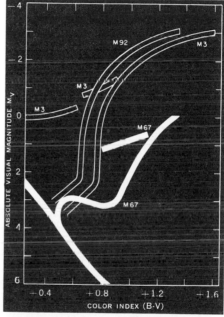

FIG. 41. In this comparison of M67 with six other open star clusters (solid bands), the failure of the main sequences of M67 and NGC752 to extend into the upper left part of the diagram is an indication of their great age. (From *The Astrophysical Journal*, The University of Chicago Press)

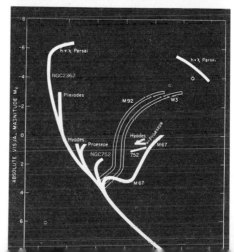

and may be present as white dwarfs in an unobservable portion of the diagram." Johnson and Sandage point out that although these hypothetical white dwarfs are too faint to observe readily in M67 and NGC752, we know that there are a few of them in the Hyades and Praesepe—clusters of intermediate age. But none has been discovered in the Pleiades, one of the younger clusters. A great many white dwarfs may therefore exist in M67 and NGC752.

As already mentioned, the giant branch of M67 differs noticeably from that of the globular clusters. The brightest red giant in M3 and M92 are near absolute magnitude -3.0, while those in M67 reach only 0.0. Johnson and Sandage argue that these stars are of approximately the same mass, because in all three systems they must have originally been on the main sequence just above the present cutoff at absolute magnitude $+3.5$.

Hence these stars evolved along different tracks to their present locations on the giant branches, probably because of an initial difference in chemical composition. The globular cluster stars originally contained relatively few metallic atoms, but the stars of M67 had a normal abundance of metals. This idea was confirmed by D. M. Popper, who found that the spectra of the red giants in M67 have normal metallic-line intensities; in M3 and M92 the metallic lines are exceptionally weak, especially in the latter cluster. Presumably the globular clusters were formed from clouds of gas and dust with low metal abundance. M67 and other open clusters originated in a medium which, five billion years ago, already had the same metal abundances as the gaseous nebulae we see at present.

This conclusion, if confirmed, would weigh heavily against the hypothesis that interstellar matter is gradually being enriched by stars that are forming heavy elements and dispersing them by means of corpuscular radiation, prominences, stellar explosions, and the like. For example, W. Baade has expressed the view that the interstellar medium in the galaxy's spiral arms may always have had its present chemical composition. If so, all stars of the "disk population," old and young, have the same metal abundances as the sun. But the original medium out of which the globular clusters were formed had fewer metal atoms.

Johnson and Sandage call attention to the fact that the giant branches of the Hyades and Praesepe appear almost to intersect those of NGC752 and M67. This they attribute to differences in the masses of the red giants in relatively young and old clusters, the former having giants about three times the mass of the sun which evolved along almost horizontal evolutionary tracks. In M67, stars three times as massive as the sun have long ago gone through their entire evolutionary development [see p. 92] and have become white dwarfs. Therefore the presently observed red giants in M67 are much less massive, about 1.2 times the sun, and are evolving slowly, following steeper evolutionary tracks at the present time. In the young clusters, such as the Hyades and the Praesepe, these stars are still very close to the original main sequence.

The red giant stars of the solar neighborhood, not associated with clusters, may be either relatively young, or they may be as old or older than the sun. Hence we might expect them to differ in mass, even though they might resemble each other in spectrum and absolute magnitude; but we lack reliable information regarding the masses of such red giants. Johnson and Sandage point out two cases, however, that may be of significance: the masses of the two components of Capella, according to K. O. Wright, are each about three times the sun's, while those of TW Cancri, from uncertain data by Popper, are 1.3 times the sun's. On the basis of this tentative suggestion, therefore, Capella would be a young system, while TW Cancri would be old.

Another interesting recent advance in our knowledge of stellar evolution comes from the study of a few very young clusters and star associations. Many of these objects contain hot, bright stars that cannot be much older than a few million years. The most luminous members are of class O and have masses of the order of 20 suns. They are now on the main sequence, because their contracting stage of evolution lasts only a few hundred thousand years. But stars of small mass, like the sun, require many millions of years to contract enough to reach the main sequence. Should we not then expect that the *lower* branches of the H-R diagrams of these very young clusters would lie on the right-hand side of the conventional main sequence?

The first indications of such anomalous H-R diagrams came from the work of P. P. Parenago on the cluster of stars associated with the Orion nebula. This is certainly a very young group, for it contains several O stars, and its large amount of nebulosity suggests that stars may even now be forming within it. Parenago found that the hotter and therefore more massive stars of this association lie on the conventional main sequence, but the less massive stars—those of approximately solar type—fall above it. Many of these stars are variables of the T Tauri type, and there is reason to believe, according to G. Herbig and G. Haro, that they are newly formed, contracting gas spheres which have not yet reached the main sequence.

Additional information concerning very young clusters comes from Merle Walker at Mount Wilson and Palomar Observatories. The open cluster NGC2264 is located almost in the galactic plane, at a distance of about 1200 parsecs. Walker finds that the hottest and therefore most massive stars in this cluster, from O7 to Ao, lie on the conventional main sequence. But the cooler stars, from Ao to about G or K, depart more and more, as seen in Figure 42. Some sixty of these overluminous (subgiant) stars have been discovered to be variable by Herbig and Walker, and many others may yet be found. Those whose spectra have been obtained show hydrogen emission. They are thus variables of the T Tauri type, a variety of star which Herbig had previously found to lie above the main sequence. Our theory thus seems to hold together pretty well: in the youngest clusters the lower branch of the main sequence is displaced upward, or to the right; in the oldest clusters the upper portion is completely distorted.

Walker points out that there are still many unexplained features among the youngest clusters. A few (for example, the one near Tau Canis Majoris) have only early-type stars. The lower branch of the main sequence is missing. Others seem to contain only late-type stars of the T Tauri variety. Walker suggests that the state of turbulence in the original medium may not always be the same, and that some nebulosities favor the formation of massive stars, while others produce stars of small mass.

It is also possible that the assumption of a uniform age for all members of a young cluster is an oversimplification. If stars can now be formed in the Orion nebula, we might conclude that its early-type stars are a million years or so older than the youngest members. Such a time interval allowed for the process of star formation would be negligible in the case of an old cluster. But in a young one we might expect that some stars of moderate mass have already run through most of their contracting stage of evolution, while other stars may still be a long way from the main sequence. The displaced main sequence of NGC2264, according to Walker, has considerable width. This may

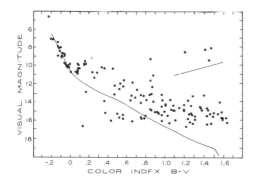

FIG. 42. A marked peculiarity of very young star clusters is illustrated by M. F. Walker's diagram of magnitudes and colors of stars in NGC2264. The diagonal curve corresponds to normal main-sequence stars. The cluster stars, except for the luminous blue ones plotted in the upper left, tend strongly to be too bright for the main sequence. (Lick Observatory diagram)

be due to the existence of stars in this cluster that were formed at somewhat different times.

The tremendous advances that have been made in the last few years in the study of different types of star clusters form one of the most interesting chapters of contemporary astronomical research. These advances were made possible by the earlier contributions of a great number of individual astronomers, among whom the names of Shapley and Trumpler stand at the very top. Much of their work was exploratory in character, and involved a large amount of routine. The fruits of their labor, which we are now gathering, far surpass their most optimistic expectations.

Ages of Star Clusters

(*Sky and Telescope*, January 1961)

Allan R. Sandage has made new determinations of the ages of the oldest galactic clusters. Using F. Hoyle's most recent stellar models, for M67 in Cancer he estimates an age of from nine to ten billion years, and for NGC188, 16 billion years.

Sandage points out that the difference between the old and new values for NGC188 is due to two factors: adoption of a new apparent brightness for the sun, determined by Stebbins and Kron, which leads to a solar absolute bolometric magnitude of 4.76, instead of 4.63; and a revision of the distance modulus of NGC188 by 0.15 magnitude to correct for the slight evolution of the faintest stars from the zero-age main sequence. The first factor increases the actual luminosities of stars of a given bolometric magnitude by 14 per cent, and therefore decreases the ages of all stars that were computed on the basis of a solar value of 4.63.

The ages of the oldest globular clusters are now believed to be 22×10^9 years for M13, and 26×10^9 years for M3 and M5. These ages are considerably greater than that of NGC188, even though the breakoff point on the main sequence is almost identical for NGC188, M3, and M5 [see Fig. 44]. The ages differ because the evolutionary rates depend on stellar metal abundances, which are different in globular and galactic clusters.

The new ages of both types of clusters greatly exceed the time interval since the beginning of the expansion of the universe of galaxies, which would be about 8×10^9 years, using a Hubble constant of 75 kilometers per second per megaparsec.* Sandage suggests that this difference from the cluster ages might be due to incorrect nuclear evolution times. It is also possible that cosmological theory is incorrect, or that the quantity called the deceleration parameter, obtained from the observed magnitude–red-shift relation, may not be correct.

··

The Oldest Star Clusters

OTTO STRUVE

(*Sky and Telescope*, November 1962)

Allan R. Sandage of Mount Wilson and Palomar Observatories reported extensive new data on the galactic cluster NGC188 at an international conference on stellar evolution held in November 1960 at La Plata, Argentina. He discussed the characteristics of a composite H-R diagram for eleven galactic clusters (Fig. 44) superimposed by fitting the lower part of the main sequence of each cluster on one line.

---

* The Hubble constant refers to the law of redshifts in spectra of galaxies, or the "expansion of the universe." On the average, galaxies 10 megaparsecs away are receding from us at 750 km/sec; those at 20 megaparsecs recede at 1500 km/sec, and so on. Therefore all the galaxies must have been close together 8 billion years ago, and this is assumed to be the age of the universe.—TLP

FIG. 43. Although NGC188 is about 5000 light years away, it occupies a good part of this field, which is about as wide as the moon. The faint cluster stars required a 1½-hour exposure with a 61-inch reflector. (Harvard College Observatory photograph)

FIG. 44. This is the H-R diagram for galactic clusters used by Allan R. Sandage to estimate their relative ages. The turnoff from the age-zero main sequence (on which the sun is located) is lowest for the oldest clusters, NGC188 and M67. The stars in the uppermost sequences, such as the red giants of the Perseus Double Cluster, are intrinsically some 10,000 or more times brighter than the sun.

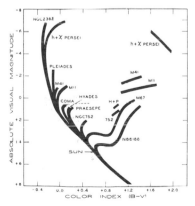

Earlier work by several investigators had brought out the fundamental significance of composite diagrams such as this. The departure of the upper ends of the main sequences of individual clusters from the "age-zero main sequence" (determined by the youngest clusters) can be explained by modern theories of the evolution of stellar interiors. The higher the turnoff point the younger the cluster. Thus in Sandage's diagram NGC2362 is the youngest cluster plotted, and NGC188 is the oldest.

A striking feature of several clusters in Figure 44 is that their domains are separated into two widely spaced parts. The Perseus Double Cluster has some blue stars of absolute magnitude −7 and color index near zero. It also has red giants around absolute magnitude −5 and colors of about +1.8, as was shown long ago at Yerkes Observatory by W. P. Bidelman. But there are no stars between these two groups. Similarly, the Hyades and Praesepe have some blue stars at absolute magnitude +1, and some red stars of similar luminosity, but intermediate ones are lacking. There are other clusters that show the same effect.

Looking at the chart as a whole, we see a vacant region that is triangular in shape, with its lower vertex at absolute magnitude +3, color index +0.7, and extending from a color of 0.0 to +1.6 at absolute magnitude −6. This area is often called the *Hertzsprung gap*, and has long been familiar in many H-R diagrams as a region stars tend to avoid. In Sandage's diagram, only M67 and NGC188 (the oldest galactic clusters) fail to show this gap.

The Palomar astronomer has remarked that most investigators regard the Hertzsprung gap as "a region through which a star moves rapidly in its evolutionary track away from the main sequence, and after traversing the gap, the stars slow down in their evolution to form the giant sequences so well known in galactic clusters."

If NGC188 is the oldest known galactic cluster, the question arises whether or not ordinary, noncluster field stars in the Milky Way show the Hertzsprung gap when their absolute magnitudes are plotted against their colors. Until a few years ago there were not enough data on the distances of individual stars. But a new method by Olin C. Wilson of Mount Wilson and Palomar has provided quite accurate absolute magnitudes of many dwarfs, subgiants, and giants of spectral types G, K, and M.

As applied by Wilson and M. K. V. Bappu, the method involves

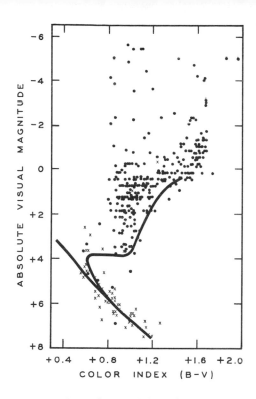

FIG. 45. The H-R diagram of nearby field stars plotted by Olin C. Wilson and modified to show the NGC188 sequence. The crosses represent stars for which trigonometric parallaxes have been determined. (Adapted from *The Astrophysical Journal*, The University of Chicago Press)

measuring the widths of emission cores of ionized-calcium lines on spectrograms of moderately high dispersion. The correlation between the emission-line width and absolute magnitude is clearly a powerful tool for studying the Hertzsprung gap.

Figure 45 is an H-R diagram of nearby field stars in the Milky Way, originally compiled by Wilson in 1959. Sandage has modified it, adding the black lines that mark the age-zero main sequence and the NGC188 main sequence.

Comparing Figures 44 and 45, we see two rather distinct differences. In Wilson's diagram many emission-line stars of color index +0.8 or redder fall inside the triangular vacancy in Sandage's diagram. The field stars, therefore, do not avoid the Hertzsprung gap. (The absence of stars on the left side of Figure 45 only means that blue and yellow stars do not, as a rule, show the emission cores in their calcium lines measured by O. C. Wilson.)

Sandage also noted that an H-R diagram for the Magellanic Clouds does not have the expected type of gap. This made him wonder whether the composite diagram of the clusters is really representative of Milky Way stars, and whether the Magellanic Cloud stars are essentially different from those in our galaxy.

At the same time, Sandage pointed out, the subgiant branch of

NGC188 on Figure 45 forms a lower envelope of the individual Milky Way stars, except for a few. That is, most field stars appear to be no older than NGC188.

Work on the problem of assigning specific ages to the galactic clusters M67 and NGC188, as well as to the "galactic-halo" globular clusters M3, M5, and M13, was resumed by Sandage and reported in the March 1962 issue of *The Astrophysical Journal*. There is also a detailed study of M5 and its probable age by another Mount Wilson and Palomar astronomer, Halton C. Arp. All of these studies are based in part on two evolutionary tracks of stars, computed theoretically by C. B. Haselgrove and F. Hoyle in 1959.

Hoyle calculated the tracks for several model stars, differing in assumed mass and initial chemical composition. One model was a fairly typical Population I star having 1.09 times the sun's mass and containing by weight 75 per cent hydrogen, 24 per cent helium, and 1 per cent heavier atoms. Figure 46 shows how the star brightens, then becomes redder, as it evolves. The last point at the right corresponds to an age of about 10 billion (10^{10}) years, counted from the age-zero main sequence.

As yet there are no extensive calculations of this sort for stars having somewhat different masses and compositions. Hence Sandage was compelled to use a crude but probably adequate substitute procedure. He assumed that the shape of the evolutionary track would remain the same, but that the paths for stars of different masses would be above or below the one in Figure 46. Furthermore, the time scale had to be changed by a factor equal to the star's mass divided by its luminosity, as is suggested by theory.

Assuming that all stars in one cluster have the same age, but that clusters may differ in age, Sandage drew a new set of curves, joining points of equal star age, shown in Figure 47, which also contains the H-R sequences of M67 and NGC188. Although these sequences differ somewhat in shape from the theoretical star age curves, there is a general resemblance, at least in the lower portions. From this chart, the Palomar astronomer concludes that M67 has an age of nine or ten billion years, while NGC188 is about 14 to 16 billion years old. These are based on distances of 825 parsecs for M67, and 1550 parsecs for NGC188, and on Sandage's assumption that as a star evolves it does not change appreciably in mass.

To obtain the ages of the three globular clusters, similar curves were

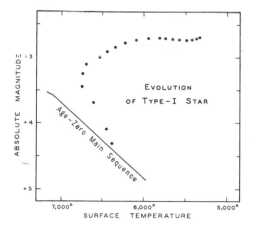

FIG. 46. The curve of dots shows Fred Hoyle's calculated evolution of a Population I star of mass 2.18×10^{33} grams from its turnoff point on the main sequence. At first the star becomes brighter and slightly bluer; then, as the surface temperature falls, it reddens. The star gradually expands, as its total luminosity changes very slowly. (Adapted from *Monthly Notices* of the Royal Astronomical Society)

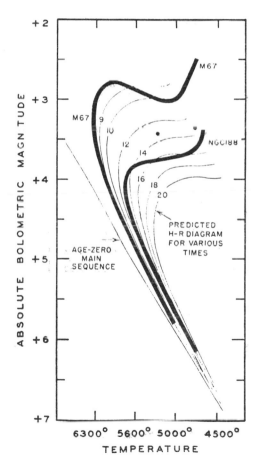

FIG. 47. The Sandage curves of equal age for stars of Population I. (Adapted from *The Astrophysical Journal*, The University of Chicago Press)

constructed for stars of Population II. Hoyle's calculation was made for a star of 1.35 solar masses, made up of 99 per cent hydrogen, 0.9 per cent helium, and only 0.1 per cent heavy elements. The observed H-R diagrams for M3, M5, and M13 agree very poorly with the theoretical curves, but an age of roughly 24 billion years might be inferred. We do not yet know how different assumptions regarding the initial chemical composition would change the fit. . . .

Both Arp and Sandage call attention to other work that indicates that the time scale of Hoyle's models needs revision. N. J. Woolf has considered the internal nuclear energy available for stars evolving in M3 and finds that if the age of M3 were 26 billion years, then stars at the blue end of the horizontal branch in the H-R diagram would have consumed more than twice their available energy store. This is clearly impossible and strongly suggests that Hoyle's time scale is too long by a factor of about 2.

From all these comparisons of measurements with calculation there emerges a pattern: globular clusters are of greatest age; loose associations and galactic clusters contain the most youthful stars; and the great mass of individual stars in the Milky Way has a spread of ages. This pattern shows up in other ways, as is indicated in Volume 5 of this series, Starlight. The "galactic halo" mentioned by Struve is a spherical array centered on the nucleus of our galaxy and containing the globular clusters (as well as odd types of blue stars and gas clouds). The disk of our galaxy contains many more stars, dust, and gas clouds, all rotating around the nucleus. Stars in the outer regions of this disk, where the sun is, were first recognized by Baade as Population-I young stars, different from the Population-II old stars in the globular clusters and near the galactic nucleus. It is now thought that this difference is due both to star age and to a different chemical content of the material from which the stars were formed.

The Magellanic Clouds are the nearest outside galaxies (visible only from places on earth south of 15° N. latitude), and are generally considered more youthful than our Milky Way Galaxy. These considerations of the structure and ages of galaxies are reserved for a later volume in this series.—TLP

Star Formation

The theory of stellar interiors and the nuclear reactions in them (Chapter 1) and the differences between H-R diagrams for different clusters (Chapters 2 and 3) lead us to believe that the stars are ageing, and that some are much older than others. Of course, the age of a star implies a beginning—the birth of the star. Until fifty years ago such an event was considered so remote in time as to be unobservable. In 1954 George Herbig obtained the right-hand photograph in Figure 48, purported to show the birth of a star from a glowing gas cloud.

In order to understand this idea of star formation, we must review the nature of interstellar material, its composition, clumpiness, and general physical condition.—TLP

FIG. 48. These pictures may be evidence of the birth of stars. They were taken with Lick Observatory's 36-inch reflector in 1947 and 1954, nearly eight years apart, of a region 1.5° from the center of the Orion nebula. North is at the top. The two brightest stars in the first picture are 8 seconds of arc apart. In the 1954 photograph each of these stars appears to have a seventeenth-magnitude companion, where no star of even one-tenth their brightness was detectable before. George Herbig suggests that they may be T Tauri variable stars in the earliest stage of their history, or possibly that this knot of seven starlike objects, embedded in a minute nebula, may eventually develop into a highly luminous multiple star like the Trapezium in the Orion nebula. (Lick Observatory photographs)

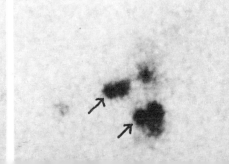

■■■

Interstellar Matter

OTTO STRUVE

(Sky and Telescope, January 1956)

The Milky Way contains a vast amount of finely divided interstellar dust and gas. Most of it is concentrated in clouds, ranging from round black compact globules of dust about a tenth or a hundredth of a light year in size to enormous chaotic complexes of gas and dust several hundred light years across, such as those in Orion, Taurus, Cygnus, and Scorpius.

These cosmic clouds are associated with the spiral arms of our galaxy. They are strongly concentrated toward the plane of the Milky Way in a layer about 1000 light years in thickness, but extending at least fifty times as far in the plane of symmetry.

In the vicinity of the solar system the hydrogen gas amounts, on the average, to about one atom per cubic centimeter, or 10^{54} atoms per cubic light year. Since the weight of a hydrogen atom is of the order of 10^{-24} gram, the gas contained in a cubic light year has a mass of 10^{30} grams. If we could spread out all the stars uniformly in space, we would find that the resulting density is about the same. Matter in our spiral arm of the galaxy (near the sun) is pretty evenly divided between the stars and the hydrogen gas.

Gases other than hydrogen are also present, in proportions similar to those found in the sun and in most other stars of the spiral arm population. These gases are so rare in space that we can regard them as impurities—they add very little to the total mass of the medium.

In the vicinity of hot stars the hydrogen gas is almost completely ionized; the ions and electrons move independently of each other through the cloud. When they accidentally collide they produce the familiar red-green glow of the gaseous nebulae. A single O-type star may ionize all hydrogen within a sphere 400 light years in radius. But a somewhat cooler star, of class Bo, ionizes the gas to a distance of only 80 light years. The ionizing action of G stars, which are like the sun, is so insignificant that they produce no luminous nebulosities visible on direct photographs. The temperature of the ionized hydrogen spheres around hot stars is about 10,000°.

Some faintly luminous hydrogen nebulosities, in Cygnus and Orion for example, are excited not by the radiation of a single very hot star, but rather by the integrated ultraviolet light of many stars embedded in the gas clouds or surrounding them.

There are also many clouds of *cold* hydrogen. These are located far away from any O or B stars, and their hydrogen is not ionized. The presence of these clouds of neutral hydrogen was first detected by means of the hydrogen emission line at wavelength 21 centimeters, which can be observed only with radiotelescopes. The temperature of these clouds is of the order of 100°, counted from the absolute zero of temperature at −273° centigrade.

Some cold hydrogen is also present between the spiral arms of the Milky Way, in the central nucleus of the galaxy, and perhaps even in the galaxy's outer spherical halo of old stars and globular clusters. But the density of the atoms in these regions is only one tenth or one hundredth of that in the spiral arms.

When a large hydrogen cloud contains one or more hot stars the interior volume of hot ionized gas is surrounded by un-ionized hydrogen, the temperature difference being that of 10,000° and 100°. The result is a tremendous outward pressure at the interface between the hot and cool gas. The hot core expands—essentially by the pressure of the star's radiation—and this pushes the cold envelope outward. Hence nebulae of this kind expand, often breaking up into smaller clouds which move with velocities of some five or ten kilometers per second.

The atoms in cold regions of interstellar space may combine to form simple molecules, like CH, CH_4 (methane), NH_3 (ammonia), OH_2 (water), and these molecules may stick together to produce small grains of dust or smoke. The gas is highly transparent, but the dust grains are efficient absorbers of radiation. Hence they produce the intense obscuration observed in dark clouds and even in relatively open regions of the Milky Way. The dust particles do not only cut off a part of the light of very distant stars; since they absorb more violet light than red, they cause the transmitted light of the stars to appear redder. From this effect of selective absorption the sizes of the grains have been found to average about 1/100,000 of a centimeter.

Finally, the transmitted starlight is slightly polarized. The particles are not spherical in shape. They must be needlelike crystals, and they are oriented not at random, but in a preferential direction—at right angles to the lines of magnetic force between the stars.

In total mass, the dust grains amount to only 1 or 2 per cent of all interstellar matter; the rest is mostly hydrogen gas. The space distribution of the grains is similar to that of the gas. Where we observe dense gas concentrations, as in Orion, we also find great accumulations of dust. But the distribution of dust and gas is not identical in every detail. For instance, there is a small luminous nebulosity surrounding the B-type star Sigma Scorpii, part of the great complex of dark and bright nebulae in Scorpius and Ophiuchus. The small nebulosity shows hydrogen in emission on one side, while on the other side the glow we see is simply the light of the star reflected by the cloud of dust.

The interstellar clouds, containing about ten hydrogen atoms per cubic centimeter, have average diameters of thirty light years and motions of some five to ten kilometers per second. But some very compact clouds may have central densities of 1000 or even 10,000 atoms per cubic centimeter. And some of the smaller clouds travel through space, in different directions, with velocities of up to a hundred kilometers per second. Since many clouds are large, they often collide. This generates heat and causes evaporation of the grains. As a rule the grains do not have time to grow larger than 10^{-5} centimeter in diameter. Hence, the sizes of the particles are about the same in all clouds.

In 1953, at the Cambridge (England) symposium on gas dynamics of cosmic clouds, R. Minkowski remarked, "This picture is certainly an extreme oversimplification." And he went on to say, "If one looks at the central Milky Way, it becomes at once obvious that the schematic picture of separate clouds of 10-parsec diameter has little resemblance to reality. An entirely chaotic mass of dark clouds of all possible shapes and sizes appears projected on the background of stars and faint emission nebulosity. . . ."

Despite the chaotic appearance of the dark and bright galactic nebulosities, there are some interesting tendencies in the forms of these objects. Minkowski has pointed out that the nebulosities in the region of the star Gamma Cygni "seem to be part of one huge mass, cut in two main parts by heavily obscuring clouds along the galactic equator." On the western side of that nebulous mass the chaotic appearance "is replaced by filamentary structures and striations" which are many degrees long and which are approximately parallel to the galactic equator.

G. A. Shajn has repeatedly called attention to this tendency for the long filamentary structures in emission nebulosities, and in obscuring clouds, to lie parallel to the galactic equator. Among the latter, one of the most remarkable objects is the dark lane east of the star Rho Ophiuchi, which extends about 40 minutes of arc wide for more than 6 degrees, and which is oriented at a moderate angle to the galactic equator, as shown in Figure 49.

Two important questions arise immediately: Why are so many clouds greatly elongated? And why are they preferentially oriented parallel to the galactic equator? Shajn shows rather convincingly that the answer cannot be found in the shearing action of galactic rotation. An initially spherical cloud 15 light years across will be elongated in the plane of the Milky Way by such shearing, but even after 10 million years the longer axis will be only 20 light years, a relatively insignificant effect! In reality, the lengths of many clouds are 80 or 90 light years, while their cross sections measure only 15 light years. The ratio of length to cross section may be 6, or even larger.

In order to find a plausible answer to the two questions, Shajn has studied the orientations of many nebulae in different parts of the sky. Near the center line of the Milky Way both emission nebulae and dark clouds tend to be drawn out parallel to this plane. For example, out of 164 dark clouds there are five times as many making angles

FIG. 49. In this photograph, extending eastward (left) from Rho Ophiuchi, are several elongated dark nebulae. The direction of interstellar magnetic lines of force, deduced from the polarization of the light of six stars near Rho, runs from upper left to lower right, roughly parallel to the galactic equator. Antares is in the lower center, and the head of the Scorpion runs off to the upper right. (Harvard College Observatory photograph)

between 0° and 30° with the Milky Way as there are from 60° to 90°. That ratio is still larger when we compute the real distribution of the orientations in space, rather than the apparent orientations on the celestial sphere.

Measures of the planes of polarization of transmitted starlight also show that the magnetic lines of force lie preferentially parallel to the plane of the Milky Way. But to connect the two phenomena, Shajn had to find whether in those regions in which the nebulae make appreciable angles to the Milky Way the planes of polarization show similar departures.

The chart in Figure 50 shows this is indeed the case. Shajn has plotted the dark features from the Skalnate Pleso *Atlas of the Heavens*, and he has entered also the orientations of the magnetic lines of force inferred from the planes of polarization. The mean inclination of the elongated nebulae 1, 2, 3, 4, 5, 6, to the galactic equator is −35°, while in the same region the magnetic lines of force are inclined −41° ±3°. Thus it can hardly be doubted that the nebulae are drawn out along the magnetic lines of force.

In order to explain this phenomenon, Shajn makes the reasonable assumption that all nebulae tend to expand, with velocities of the order of 15 kilometers per second. If there were no magnetic forces,

FIG. 50. G. A. Shajn of Crimean Astrophysical Observatory here indicates the relation between dark nebulosities in the Perseus-Taurus region and the polarization observations by W. A. Hiltner and John S. Hall. Near the center is NGC1499, the California emission nebula. Parallels of galactic latitude are shown by dotted lines.

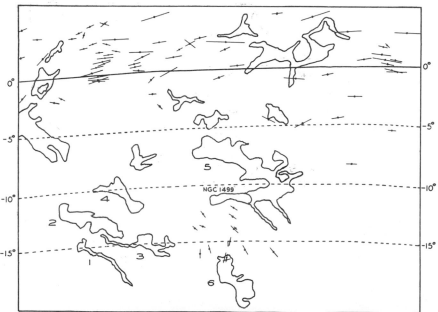

a spherical nebula would remain spherical (neglecting the galactic shearing effect), but in one million years its diameter would grow from 15 to 90 light years, a ratio of 6. The densities, of both hydrogen ions and free electrons, would therefore decrease by $6^3 = 216$ times. The surface brightness of a nebula is proportional to both the ion and electron densities, and to the thickness of the column of gas through which we look. The product of the changes in the two densities would be $1/6^6$, while the optical column in the expanded shell would be 6 times longer than in the original nebula. Hence in a million years the surface brightness would change by a factor of $1/6^5$, or $1/7776$. Even in 100,000 years the surface brightness would have decreased to $1/32$, while the nebula doubled in size. Such spherically expanding nebulae would become invisible in little more than 10,000 years!

But if the magnetic field is sufficiently strong, ionized gas cannot cross the lines of force, and the nebula can only expand along the lines. Our small spherical nebula 15 light years in diameter will, after a million years, resemble a cylinder whose cross section is still the same as before, 15 light years. But its length will now be 90 light years. The two densities, of the ions and the free electrons, will both have decreased merely to $1/6$, and the surface brightness by their product, $1/36$. Compare this with the factor $1/7776$ for the spherical expansion after a million years.

Figure 51 shows a region just east of Eta Cygni, together with a plot of the orientations of the magnetic force lines. Again the agreement is good. Apparently both the bright ionized and dark un-ionized clouds are drawn out along the lines of force. For the emission nebulae this is understandable; their electrical conductivity is high and their behavior resembles that of an iron ball in a magnetic field. If the field is weak, the ball will carry the magnetic lines with it. But in a strong field the ball experiences so much resistance against motion across the lines that it adjusts its motion to follow the lines of force.

But even the dark hydrogen gas clouds contain ionized atoms of elements other than hydrogen. Their ions and electrons produce a sufficient amount of electrical conductivity. Moreover, the dust grains collect small electrical charges on their surfaces. Thus the dark clouds as well as the bright ones are constrained to orientations along the force lines of the interstellar magnetic field.

Shajn argues that since we observe many bright nebulae they must be fairly old, on the average. If their expansion were always to proceed with spherical symmetry, the emission nebulae would fade so rapidly from sight that we should observe only a small number of them at any given time. Expansion into very elongated filaments therefore explains the fact that so many bright nebulae are seen at present.

FIG. 51. Complex wreaths of emission nebulosity fill this area of 3° × 2° in Cygnus, just south of the star 28 Cygni, which is near the top of the field. Here G. A. Shajn compares the orientation of the wisps of nebulosity with polarization observations (left) by W. A. Hiltner. The sloping line marks the galactic equator. (Crimean Astrophysical Observatory photograph)

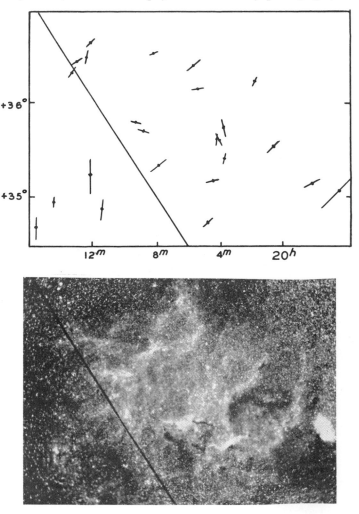

The Behavior of
Matter in Space

(*Sky and Telescope*, May 1954)

The two main questions considered by Lyman Spitzer, Jr., of Princeton University Observatory, who gave the seventh Henry Norris Russell lecture [at the December 1953 meeting of the American Astronomical Society], were: What determines the temperature of the interstellar gas? How can we explain the random motions of the interstellar clouds?

What we mean by the temperature of interstellar space depends on the "thermometer" we use and on our definition of temperature. A black body, heated by starlight, will be at the very low temperature of only three degrees above absolute zero when located far from any particular star; but in these same regions the energies of cosmic ray particles correspond to trillions of degrees.

TABLE 3.   OBSERVED CHARACTERISTICS OF INTERSTELLAR MATTER

HYDROGEN GAS

Density. About 1 atom/cm^3 in spiral arms, with much lower values outside the arms.

Physical State. Ionization nearly complete within 20-150 parsecs of B and O stars (H-II regions). Elsewhere predominantly neutral (H-I regions). Temperature greater than 1000°K in H-II regions; about 50°K in dense H-I clouds.

Velocities. Circular velocity of galactic rotation; turbulence between 5 and 10 km/sec (root mean square of radial velocity).

OTHER ELEMENTS IN GAS

Density. Mean density of neutral sodium and ionized calcium about 3 × 10^{-9} atoms/cm^3. Fe, Ti, K, CH, CH+, CN present with about the same density.

Velocities. Most clouds move with local circular velocity of galactic rotation, plus r.m.s. spread of 5 to 10 km/sec in radial velocity. About 1 per cent have high random velocities, from 25 up to 95 km/sec.

Distribution. Straight line in galactic plane near sun intersects 10 such clouds per kiloparsec. Ionized calcium present in clouds or currents of differing velocities, but its ratio to sodium is greater in high-velocity than in low-velocity clouds.

GRAINS

Size. Mean radius of optically important grains is about 3 × 10^{-5} cm. Distribution of radii very similar in different regions.

Density. Mean space density of optically important particles in local spiral arms is about 10^{-26} gm/cm^3; density is much less outside spiral arms.

Distribution. Spatial distribution is extremely irregular; concentrations ranging from 0.05 to 50 parsecs, with density varying by at least 10^4.

Polarization. Grains are somewhat elongated, and tend to be oriented perpendicular to local spiral arms.

Spitzer adopted the principle that most of the atoms in the interstellar gas have random velocities which can be expressed in terms of the temperature of a gas in the ordinary sense. That is, the distribution of the velocities in the interstellar gas can be shown to be Maxwellian, the way molecular velocities are distributed in a sample of air in thermal equilibrium. This condition holds certainly for those hot regions where the hydrogen is ionized (H-II regions), for unionized (H-I, or cold-hydrogen) regions in general, and also for dust grains.

The temperature of the gas depends upon the balance between the absorption of energy from starlight and the reradiation of this energy by the gas. Eddington pointed out many years ago that interstellar gas can gain heat from starlight by the photoelectric effect. An atom is first made neutral (if it was ionized previously) by capturing an electron; then a stellar photon of high energy strikes the neutral atom and is absorbed; its energy is acquired by the electron, which escapes with more energy than it had before it was captured. The additional kinetic energy is thus available for heating the gas. Most of the heating by this process must occur in the H-II regions near hot stars, for the ultraviolet radiation capable of ionizing hydrogen or helium is available only around such stars.

In the cooling of the gas, however, atomic hydrogen plays a very minor role, because this atom is a very poor radiator in visible and infrared light. The dominant process is excitation of an atom by electron impact, followed by radiation of a photon of light, which carries away into space the energy lost to the atom by the colliding electron. Atomic hydrogen cannot radiate under such electron bombardment unless the electrons have some 10 volts of energy, corresponding to a temperature well above 10,000° absolute. Most other atoms, however, have excitation potentials from a hundredth of an electron volt to several electron volts, and they can be important in the cooling process.

From calculated probabilities of the excitation of the oxygen atoms by electrons, Spitzer finds of great importance the 3.31-electron-volts excitation of ionized oxygen. After a wait of several hours an atom excited in this way will emit a photon of the "forbidden" line* at

* So called because this line never appears in the spectrum of oxygen at normal density in the laboratory. It is only emitted by ionized oxygen at very low density in interstellar space.—TLP

wavelength 3727 angstroms. If there is an appreciable amount of singly ionized oxygen present in H-II regions, the equilibrium temperature would appear to be about 10,000°K. There is a possibility that ionized nitrogen might play a similar cooling role, but it probably does not match ionized oxygen, as indicated by the considerable observed strength of the interstellar 3727 line.

The situation in the H-I regions differs because there is no heating by absorption of ultraviolet light by hydrogen atoms. The cooling processes are again dependent on low excitation potentials, and several kinds of atoms may take part. There may be a slight heating of neutral hydrogen by the impact of cosmic ray particles, but this is uncertain. Interstellar grains tend to lower the temperature, as neutral hydrogen atoms lose energy on collision with them. The presence of hydrogen molecules would also afford efficient cooling if any effect, such as the passage of a shock wave, were to cause a temperature rise. The combined effect of all these processes, while difficult to work out in detail, must lead to a temperature of the H-I regions of about 50° absolute.

In principle the temperature of these neutral hydrogen clouds can be found from the measured intensity of the hydrogen 21-cm line, and the first preliminary measures do confirm low temperatures.

The interstellar gas, besides sharing in the rotation of the galaxy, has also turbulent motions; the clouds have velocities averaging about five to ten kilometers per second, but occasionally motions of a hundred kilometers per second are observed. Collisions between clouds are relatively frequent—about once in ten million years for any one cloud. As the collisions are inelastic, the motions would die out quickly unless sustained by temperature differences between various parts of the gas.

High-temperature regions should expand at the expense of low-temperature regions until pressure equilibrium is attained, when the neutral hydrogen regions would have roughly 200 times the density of the ionized regions, since this is about the ratio of probable temperatures. The density of hydrogen in an H-I cloud is probably about ten atoms per cubic centimeter, but in the spaces between the interstellar clouds the density is probably less by a factor of a hundred or more.

Thermal effects that produce motions in interstellar matter may include heating by an early type star—this might cause heated gas to rise away from the galactic plane, buoyed up by heavier gas. The Dutch astronomer Jan H. Oort has suggested that when a star is formed by condensation within a cloud the rapid increase in radiation pressure as the star begins to shine might cause a violent explosion of the cloud.

Small clouds near which a very hot star passes may be accelerated to very high velocities by what Spitzer called "the interstellar rocket." The star's radiation would heat one side of the dense cloud, causing the heated material to expand toward the star; the recoil from this expansion would accelerate the remainder of the cloud away from the star. In this way, 1 per cent of a cloud, initially nearly stationary with respect to the star, could be accelerated to a speed of 80 kilometers per second. Spitzer regards all of these processes as likely to occur, with Oort's mechanism of an explosion around a newborn O star accounting for the bulk of cloud motions.

The expansion of a rarefied hot cloud into a denser medium is an unstable situation, and others have shown theoretically that thin spikes of cooler, denser hydrogen gas should project into the hotter and rarer expanding gas. This appears to explain what is frequently observed in emission nebulae, such as the Horsehead in Orion (see Fig. 52) and M16 in Serpens: tongues or "elephant trunks" of ob-

FIG. 52. This picture of the region of Orion's belt was made on October 3, 1948, by John C. Duncan with the 18-inch Palomar Schmidt camera. The third belt star is off to the upper right, and the Great Nebula in Orion's sword is off to the lower right. Near the center of the field Zeta Orionis is immersed in bright nebulosity. The lower of the two tongues of dark matter silhouetted against this nebulosity is the famous Horsehead nebula. (Mount Wilson and Palomar Observatories photograph)

scuring matter extend inward from surrounding dark nebulosity and point toward the exciting star or stars.

The effect of an interstellar magnetic field upon cloud motions must also be considered. Under the conditions in interstellar space, ionized particles cannot stray very far from a particular line of force. The field, if it is strong, will restrain the motions of the clouds, or if it is weak, will be distorted by them. Roughly uniform fields have been proposed by several investigators to explain the polarization of starlight.

Spitzer thinks that a uniform field in the galaxy is improbable; he believes the magnetic field is locally chaotic, with an average tendency for the lines of force to lie parallel to the spiral arms. Such a chaotic field would fit better the observed randomness of the motions of the interstellar clouds.

How Much
Molecular Hydrogen
in Interstellar Space?

(*Sky and Telescope*, March 1962)

Radio and optical observations have shown that the gas lying between the stars is mainly atomic hydrogen. They do not tell how much additional hydrogen may be there in molecular form. But from theoretical considerations, Robert J. Gould at Cornell University finds that hydrogen molecules are abundant in space.

The interstellar gas is so rarefied that two hydrogen atoms have no appreciable chance of combining to form an H_2 molecule unless they both collide with the same solid grain of interstellar material, sticking temporarily to it. In this way, the concentration of H_2 gradually builds up in an interstellar cloud until it passes near a hot star, whose ultraviolet radiation will dissociate some of the molecules.

Gould's most significant finding is that the rate of this photodissociation is only about 1/100,000 the previously computed value. Hence, instead of being drastically depleted, hydrogen molecules can accumulate, and the Cornell scientist computes that about 10 to 20 per cent of the interstellar gas should be molecular hydrogen.

A direct test will be possible by means of an artificial satellite carrying a spectrograph. Interstellar H_2 should produce an appreciable absorption in the far-ultraviolet spectra of stars.

In addition to direct observations of glowing H-II gas clouds and cold H-I gas emitting 21-cm radio waves, there is evidence of interstellar dust given by the reddening and polarization of light from distant stars. Moreover, the spectra of such stars often show interstellar absorption lines of sodium and ionized calcium. Because of different Doppler shifts (p. 319), due to different motions toward or away from us, the absorption lines of gas clouds are often separated from the lines of the same atoms or ions in the star's atmosphere.—TLP

....

The Interstellar Medium

(*Sky and Telescope*, September 1951)

It is well known that interstellar gases produce "detached" lines in stellar spectra; particularly noticeable are the lines of ionized calcium. A theory that interstellar matter tends to occur in a random pattern of essentially discreet clouds has been developed to account for the observations. However, Bertram Donn of Wayne University has proposed an alternative working hypothesis.

He suggests that the major part of the gaseous medium forms an extensive inhomogeneous cloud partaking of the galactic rotation. This cloud produces a fairly strong interstellar line in the spectrum of a distant star. In some cases there are different velocities among the density concentrations in the cloud, as well as the thermal motion of the atoms. Weaker components of the interstellar lines with a large velocity difference may arise from large-scale turbulence in the cloud.

A similar diffuse distribution is suggested for the interstellar dust, but with substantial differences in the density fluctuations for the two forms of matter, dust and gas.

Protostars and
Planetary Formation

(*Sky and Telescope*, March 1947)

Three stages in the evolution of his protostar model have been described by Lyman Spitzer, Jr. [of Princeton University], but he emphasizes the extremely preliminary character of the picture. In the first stage, atoms other than hydrogen and helium adhere together, forming the *smoke*, or interstellar dust, discussed by the European astronomers. This condensation should take place most rapidly in regions of low temperature (about 100° absolute) and high density. The diffuse clouds of dust and gas thus formed contain mostly gaseous hydrogen and helium at density about 10^{-24} grams per cubic centimeter.

Radiation pressure [on dust grains by outside starlight] acts in the second stage to increase the density to about 10^{-22} grams per cubic centimeter, and the absorption of starlight by the cloud becomes about one magnitude per kiloparsec. The cloud is now apparently similar to one of Bok's less dense "globules," observed principally away from the center of the Milky Way system.

As the cloud continues to contract, radiation pressure gives way in relative importance to gravity, and gas shares in the contraction with the dust grains. In each dense cloud, *one or more* prestellar masses, or protostars, less than a parsec in size, may form, and with sufficient density to be wholly stable gravitationally. The contraction of these protostars then leads to the formation of stars.

There is danger, however, that a protostar might break up because of rotational instability following contraction. Spitzer suggests that eddy currents, produced by a general magnetic field of the Milky Way, may counteract the excess rotational motions.

Collisions between large interstellar gas clouds should occur not more than once in ten million years per cloud according to Fred L. Whipple's analysis of measurements of the motions of interstellar gases producing "detached" lines in the spectra of distant stars. These lines furnished the original clue to the existence and nature of interstellar gas and have been found to have random displacements of their own of roughly five miles per second. The present diameters of these gas clouds are between one and two hundred light years. The collision frequency agrees well with that required by J. H. Oort to prevent excessive growth of the cosmic grains in the clouds.

Perhaps as many as 100 or 1000 million years would be required for clouds of this sort to collapse to radii of a few thousand astronomical units, but then the contraction process should speed up.

If the angular momentum (spin) is small, a planetary system should develop during such a final collapse; a double star is more probable otherwise.

Resultant planets would move in one plane, with nearly circular orbits, and the larger ones would be at greater distances from the sun. Whipple's theory also proposes to account for various other general features of the solar system.

By 1947 is was generally agreed that stars formed from contracting clouds of interstellar gas and dust. Spitzer's "protostar model" explained the initial contraction as due to radiation pressure on the dust particles even when the density was too low for gravitation to cause contraction. Spitzer showed that general starlight can do this because of shadows cast on one dust particle by another. Starlight is faint, but it adds a small pressure that concentrates the dust, which then pulls in the gas.

Since the sun probably started in this way, Whipple sought to explain how planets could form in our solar system as a cloud of gas and dust condensed to make the sun. The development of this theory by Kuiper, Urey, and others, is described in Volume 3 of this series, The Origin of the Solar System.—TLP

....

Formation of Stars

(*Sky and Telescope,* July 1956)

Most astronomers now believe that the stars were formed out of the very tenuous interstellar gas clouds of our galaxy. The birth of a star thus requires the contraction of a region of gas several parsecs in diameter to about a hundred-millionth of its size, with a corresponding increase in density.

G. C. McVittie, University of Illinois Observatory, has investigated the mathematically difficult problem of how such a gas cloud collapses to form a star. He uses a method of attack, in this problem of gas dynamics with gravitation, that is based on Einstein's equations of general relativity. To simplify the problem, he considers only two forces: gas pressure, which seeks to distend the cloud, and self-gravitation, which tends to contract it.

The solution obtained is not unique. McVittie found that there are many different ways in which a sphere of gas, at first at rest but not in equilibrium, can flow internally toward its center until all the gas finally comes to rest again in a relatively small volume, forming a body of comparatively high density at high temperature having the known properties of a star.

But all the different ways have two properties in common. During the collapse of the cloud, gas flows inward with a speed that is proportional to its distance from the center, and the flow is accompanied by the release of energy in the form of radiation. It can be proved that no shock waves occur; these might otherwise halt the shrinking of the mass of gas. The time required for the collapse into a star is about 100,000 to 100 million years, depending on the initial density of the cloud.

For the shrinking to begin, the temperature of the gas cloud must be very low, and McVittie suggests that "cold spots" in the interstellar medium may be necessary for star formation. He emphasizes that his solution indicates only that stars *may* form in this way, and that he has omitted several very important factors, such as the opacity of the condensing nebula to outgoing radiation and the viscosity of the gas.

....

Recession from Orion

DORRIT HOFFLEIT

(*Sky and Telescope*, November 1954)

The star AE Aurigae and its associated nebulosity, IC405, have been found by A. Blaauw and W. W. Morgan, Yerkes Observatory, to have a space motion directly away from Orion. These same investigators have also found that the star Mu Columbae is moving away from the Orion nebula at the same speed of 127 kilometers per second, but in nearly the opposite direction to AE Aurigae.

Extrapolated backward, the present motions strongly suggest that both stars originated in the vicinity of the Orion nebula 2.6 million years ago. They are very young blue stars that could hardly be older than this. At present they are each about 337 parsecs from their possible point of common origin, which is 500 parsecs from the sun.

The details of this work were published in the July [1954] issue of *The Astrophysical Journal*.

....

Moving Red Nebulae

(*Sky and Telescope*, May 1964)

While a guest investigator at Mount Wilson and Palomar Observatories, W. J. Luyten has been searching for stars of large proper motion by comparing photographs taken with the 48-inch Schmidt telescope several years apart. During the course of this work, a remarkable new kind of object has come to light: very small, very faint red nebulosities moving at high speed.

The first such object was found by Luyten in 1963. By now he has found three additional cases. Typical of them is LP1-474 in Ursa Minor—a tiny blob five seconds of arc in diameter, of the twentieth magnitude, that is traveling 0.25 second of arc per year.

Luyten notes that, with reasonable assumptions as to the distances of these strange nebulosities, they are about 100 to 500 astronomical units in diameter. This happens to be roughly the size of the primitive nebula from which our solar system is thought to have formed. The University of Minnesota astronomer therefore asks whether the newly discovered objects may not be evolving into planetary systems, or perhaps be planetary systems spoiled in the making. Details were published in Harvard *Announcement Card* 1642.

The Interaction
between
Stars and Nebulae

OTTO STRUVE

(*Sky and Telescope*, November 1954)

If the stars have been formed—or are even now being formed—out of interstellar gas and dust, we might expect that the interstellar clouds are more rare, or less dense, than they were, say, five billion years ago. But it is also possible that the stars, in the course of their evolution, may shed matter that ultimately augments the depleted nebulosities.

These ideas are not new. The Russian astronomer B. A. Vorontsov-Velyaminov has for many years favored the hypothesis that the stars actually shed more gas than they acquire, so that *all* of the nebulae we see now were once inside the stars. Other astronomers, for example, L. Biermann in Germany, have examined the possibility of an equilibrium state, in which the mass acquired by the stars from the interstellar medium is about equal to the mass they expel in the form of novalike explosions, rotational breakup, or corpuscular radiation.

Still others, especially G. A. Shajn and V. Hase, in Russia, have suggested that while exchange of material between stars and nebulae goes on all the time, this process is a very minor one. They propose that both stars and nebulae originated at about the same time, in some unspecified primordial medium whose properties may have been those of what the western astronomers describe as the prestellar state of matter, or what George Gamow calls "ylem."

It would be important to know whether the interstellar gas and dust that we now observe is the remnant of the original medium, retaining its original chemical composition, or whether it came from stars, modified in its helium content, and perhaps also in its content of the heavier elements, by the nuclear processes that went on in the stellar interiors.

Several observational results seem to indicate that very old stars are poorer in heavy elements than are recently formed stars. Thus, in July, B. Strömgren gave the following summary of the content of metals: in very young stars, 3 per cent; in medium-age stars, 2 per cent; in fairly old stars, 1 per cent; and in extremely old stars, 0.1 per cent.

This suggests that the interstellar medium out of which the stars in Orion, for example, are being formed at the present time is considerably richer in heavy elements than the original gas, five billion years ago, out of which the old stars in globular clusters or in the central bulge of the Milky Way were formed.

Further insight into these problems is offered by our present knowledge of how the stars transfer mass to the interstellar medium. We shall follow a compilation Biermann presented in July 1953. (His results differ only slightly from those presented in 1948 by Vorontsov-Velyaminov in his book on gaseous nebulae and novae, which is now available in a German translation.)

The interactions which lead to the loss of mass are:

1. Catastrophic explosions: (a) in supernovae and novae, (b) in planetary nebulae, (c) in P Cygni-type stars.

2. Slow, continuous corpuscular emission: (a) in Wolf-Rayet stars, (b) in supergiant stars, (c) in main-sequence stars of about the type of the sun, (d) by single early-type stars, (e) during rotational breakup in single stars and in close binaries.

If the matter in the universe is in equilibrium—in the sense that the masses of the stars and of interstellar matter combined remain constant, without of necessity being equal to each other—then the loss of mass from processes 1 and 2 must be balanced by the following reverse reactions:

3. Continuous accretion of interstellar matter: (a) by stars of large mass in average interstellar clouds ("rejuvenation"), (b) by ordinary main-sequence stars in very dense dust clouds (for example, T Tauri-type stars).

4. Formation of stars in very cold and dense regions of interstellar material.

Biermann remarks that processes 2 and 3 cannot be expected to occur simultaneously in any particular star. It can be shown that if conditions favor expulsion of atoms from stars, this process will be a very stable one; small changes in temperature or other physical conditions will not reverse it.

We shall now proceed to estimate the effectiveness of processes 1 and 2. No one really knows how much mass is ejected as nebulosity during a supernova explosion. A rough guess is about two solar masses, or 4×10^{33} grams. (To facilitate notation in the following discussion, numbers otherwise unlabeled refer to the mass of the sun as a unit.) If there is, on the average, one supernova in 200 years in our galaxy, the interstellar matter would gain at the rate of 0.01 (solar mass) per year. The ordinary novae lose much less matter per explosion, say about 10^{-5}, but about 100 novae occur in the galaxy each year. Thus they contribute 0.001 per year.

For the planetary nebulae [slowly expanding shells of gas around small, hot stars], K. Wurm estimated a loss of 3×10^{-5} per year. There are about 500 planetaries in the Milky Way at the present time—and thus presumably at any time—even though in any particular star the planetary-nebula stage may last only a few thousand years. Hence all planetary nebulae send out interstellar gas amounting to 0.015 per year.

For the P Cygni-type stars Biermann gives no estimate, but says, "It seems unlikely that these stars contribute more than the planetary nebulae." I believe a reasonable estimate is again 0.015 per year.

In the spectra of the Wolf-Rayet stars, we observe strong and exceedingly broad emission lines, probably produced in semipermanent expanding shells. These stars are about six times as large as the sun, and their luminosities are roughly 20,000 times greater. Their masses are about ten times the solar mass. From the intensities of the emission lines, Biermann adopts a loss of mass of 10^{20} atoms per square centimeter per second, or about 10^{-4} grams per square centimeter per second. The surface area is 2×10^{24} square centimeters, and one year contains about 3×10^{7} seconds; hence each Wolf-Rayet star loses about 5×10^{-6} solar masses per year. Biermann estimates that there are between 1000 and 10,000 such stars in the Milky Way at any one time. Their total annual contribution to the interstellar gas is thus of the order of 0.01 solar mass.

Vorontsov-Velyaminov makes this estimate 10 times larger—0.1 per year, or 5×10^{8} solar mass units in five billion years; and he suggests that the entire present diffuse constituent of the Milky Way can be accounted for by the expansion of the Wolf-Rayet stars. But it seems to me that this is based upon an underestimate of the present mass of the interstellar material. If it is equal to that contained in the stars, or 10^{11}, then only $1/200$ of the interstellar gas was once inside the stars if we adopt the Vorontsov-Velyaminov figure for the rate of ejection.

The ordinary supergiants do not change the picture appreciably. Although Biermann uses a value of 0.0001 for the annual loss of mass, this is clearly an overestimate, and he assumes that there are 50,000 such stars in existence. It seems better to adopt 0.01 for their total annual contribution.

The sun loses atoms in clouds of protons and other ions, whose effects we can observe in comet tails, magnetic storms, northern lights, and even in some relatively low-energy cosmic rays. Biermann had previously estimated the intensity of this corpuscular outflow as 10^{-12} solar masses per year. But undoubtedly many stars, such as those with flares, are much more powerful emitters of particles. Hence we shall use 10^{-11} for each star. Since there are about 10^{11} such stars in the Milky Way, we find here a really powerful source of interstellar gas, about one solar mass annually.

A star of early spectral type undoubtedly emits particles much more copiously than does the sun. The work of the Russian astronomers V. G. Fessenkov and A. G. Massevich has indicated that the rate of loss of mass is proportional to the luminosity of a star. A Bo star is about 5000 times more luminous than the sun, but there is perhaps only one such star in our galaxy for every 5000 stars like the sun. Even so, the B stars should contribute at least as much as all the solar-type stars.

Biermann declines to estimate the loss of mass from rotational or orbital instability. The shell around a rapidly rotating star is tenuous, and I once estimated that its mass might amount to 10^{-8} at any given moment. Few shells show large motions of expansion, but a replenishment of the entire shell (or ring) in about a year is a reasonable guess. Each of the most rapidly rotating stars would then contribute 10^{-8} per year. But their number is relatively small, and their total contribution probably does not exceed 0.01 per year.

The close double stars, especially of the Beta Lyrae and Algol types, may lose mass more rapidly, perhaps at the rate of 10^{-4} or 10^{-5} per year. But they are not sufficiently numerous in the galaxy to upset our rather shaky apple cart of estimates. Let us allow for them a contribution of the order of 0.1 per year.

TABLE 4. ANNUAL LOSS OF STAR MASS TO THE
INTERSTELLAR MEDIUM

Type of object*	Solar mass units
1. a. Supernovae	0.01
a. Novae	0.001
b. Planetary nebulae	0.015
c. P Cygni stars	0.015
2. a. Wolf-Rayet stars	0.01
b. Supergiants	0.01
c. Main-sequence stars (solar type)	1
d. Main-sequence stars (O and B)	1
e. Shell stars	0.01
f. Close binaries	0.1
Sum	2.2

* See p. 140.

Our foregoing estimates are listed in Table 4. All the values are rough, but we have been quite conservative in our computations, and we can infer that the annual gain of interstellar matter may be between one and ten solar masses. Hence, in the lifetime of the galaxy, say 5×10^9 years, the total amount of gas expelled by the stars may have amounted to as much as 5×10^{10}, or 50 billion times as much matter as in the sun.

This would be a considerable fraction of the present amount of diffuse interstellar material, and might justify the belief that some, but probably not all, of this matter had at one time or another been inside stars. It also makes more plausible the idea that the stars and the interstellar matter are in equilibrium with each other, for it is not unreasonable to suppose that on the average between one and ten fresh (or rejuvenated) stars are produced annually in the Milky Way.

Let us consider, for example, a typical "young" association of stars. It may contain some one hundred stars, none older than about one million years. Hence within a single association fresh stars appear at an average rate of once in 10,000 years. V. A. Ambartzumian has estimated that the number of T Tauri associations in the Milky Way may be over 10,000. The associations of O and B stars are less frequent, but the galaxy may contain as many as a thousand of them. Thus it is possible that the present star birth rate may lie between one and ten each year, and this would use up the loss of mass from other stars.

It would, however, be wrong to infer from this that all or most of the gaseous nebulosities are recent products of stellar ejection. This has become especially clear from the work of Shajn and Hase. We summarize and comment on their conclusions in the remainder of this article.

1. Several diffuse nebulosities have masses of the order of 1000 or 5000 suns. Yet these nebulosities contain only relatively few stars, between ten and a hundred, and such large nebular masses could not possibly have been expelled from the stars now associated with them. In addition to the one in Orion, these giant nebulae include the Lagoon nebula in Sagittarius (M8) with a mass of 3200, and the Rosette nebula in Monoceros (NGC2237) with a mass of 5800. For

FIG. 53. The Rosette nebula in Monoceros, photographed with the Palomar 48-inch telescope. Against the background of bright nebulosity are black wisps and tatters of dust clouds and, in particular near the center of the photograph, minute dark round blots. These are globules— dust clouds only a few thousand astronomical units in diameter, which may be contracting to form stars. South is above, east to the right; the scale is about 1 minute of arc per millimeter. (Mount Wilson and Palomar Observatories photograph)

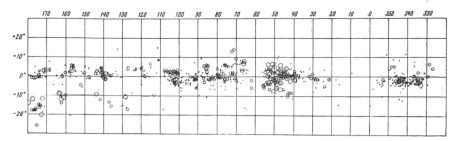

FIG. 54. To test the relationship between galactic nebulae and early-type stars, G. A. Shajn and V. Hase have plotted their positions on this chart of the northern Milky Way. The horizontal and vertical scales are galactic longitude and latitude. Diffuse nebulae are denoted by circles, and the dots are for stars of spectral types O, Bo, and B1, as well as for Wolf-Rayet stars. The early-type stars and the diffuse nebulae both show a strong tendency to clumping, but there appear to be many nebulae, especially in the lower left part of the chart, that have no evident connection with stars of these varieties.

the last, in 1949 R. Minkowski even gave a mass of as much as 10,000 suns. His photograph of this object (Fig. 53) reveals many typical globules, those tiny dark nebula that Bart J. Bok regards as stars in the making. They are so numerous that I feel we are justified in believing that here, at any rate, the process of new-star formation greatly exceeds that of loss of mass by the existing stars.

2. If we plot, as Shajn and Hase did in Figure 54, the galactic coordinates of the Wolf-Rayet, O, Bo, and B1 stars and nebulae, we find that there are many early-type stars without nebulae near them, and many nebulosities without early-type exciting stars near them. According to Hugh M. Johnson's recent work at the Yerkes Observatory, probably every O star has a luminous II-II sphere of nebulosity around it. But it is also certain that one O star may be associated with a very bright nebula, and another with a nebula of exceedingly low surface brightness.

3. The emission-line stars of spectral classes O and early B certainly rotate very rapidly, and many of them are near the point of equatorial instability. They might be expected to shed gas more rapidly than the ordinary absorption-line O and B stars. Yet Shajn and Hase find that the emission-line stars are less apt to be associated with gaseous nebulae.

4. There is no greater tendency among the Wolf-Rayet stars to be associated with nebulosities than among O and B stars. Yet the individual Wolf-Rayet stars are the more copious suppliers of interstellar gas.

5. In some of the widely dispersed fields of nebulosity, especially

near the stars Alpha and Gamma Cygni, the filaments of nebulous matter show a tendency to be oriented parallel to the plane of the Milky Way [see Fig. 49]. It may well be that this arrangement has some relation to the orientation of the magnetic lines of force in interstellar space. It suggests the action, over long intervals of time, of forces that are unrelated to any particular stars.

6. Finally, Shajn and Hase have discovered several extraordinary filamentary nebulosities, such as the one in Auriga, which they have aptly described as "a tangled ball of thread." The peculiar structure would seem to call for forces other than those that expel material from the outer layers of stars.

Struve's summary in Table 4 shows that a considerable fraction of the interstellar material is "secondhand"—already used in stars. His comments on the work of Shajn and Hase show that there may be old nebulae as well as ones recently formed from matter ejected from stars.

Whether or not the composition of this ejected matter has been altered by nuclear processes in the stars is still open to question. Most of the ejection is estimated (Table 4) to come from the surfaces of ordinary single stars, in which the nuclear reactions are going on far below the surface. As shown in Chapter 2, the helium and heavy element products of such nuclear reactions form a central core which would only be spewed out in the violent explosions of supernovae. It is possible that turbulence in intermediate layers could mix the core material with material in the outer layers, but this had not been firmly established in 1954.—TLP

....

Evolution in the Galaxy

(*Sky and Telescope*, January 1957)

Under the chairmanship of Jesse L. Greenstein, Mount Wilson and Palomar Observatories, a symposium was held [at the joint meeting of the American Astronomical Society and the Astronomical Society of the Pacific in August 1956] on evolution in the galaxy. It was followed by a panel discussion featuring the symposium members, who were A. Blaauw, Leiden and Yerkes Observatories; A. R. Sandage, Mount Wilson and Palomar Observatories; L. G. Henyey, Leuschner Observatory; and W. A. Fowler, California Institute of Technology.

Under the title "Kinematics, Duplicity, Luminosities, and Ages of Early-Type Stars," Blaauw dealt mainly with the properties of stars of spectral types O to B3 lying on and above the main sequence of the H-R diagram. Only a fraction of the present stellar population has evolved from these massive stars, but they are the most accessible ones for detailed study and are also those in which the most rapid evolutionary changes take place.

Blaauw pointed out that in many stellar associations there are different ages—from one to ten million years—for different parts of the same association. In the Orion association the densest part has stars of earliest spectral type, associated with nebulosity. He concludes that the loose outer regions are the oldest parts of the association.

A surprisingly large number of high-velocity O and early B stars are produced in associations; some of these are of such high velocity that they may even escape from the galaxy's gravitational field.

Many of the early-type stars are double or multiple stars, and there is a relation between the space velocity and the occurrence of such systems. Young stars with high initial velocities are seldom double, whereas those for which such velocities are small are quite often double. This distinction may have an important bearing on the process of star formation.

Referring to the Hertzsprung-Russell diagram of spectral types and luminosities for galactic clusters of all ages [see p. 109], Sandage asked questions that must be answered by theories on the evolution of stars. Why does the shape of the evolutionary track of an individual star depend on its mass? . . . Why is the Hertzsprung gap wedge shaped? . . . It is believed that stars evolve across the gap from the main sequence to the giant branch. There is no gap for M67, while it is wide for the Perseus Double Cluster. . . .

In the discussion of Sandage's work, W. P. Bidelman, Lick Observatory, pointed out that the Beehive cluster has one star in the middle of the gap—a G-type giant. He said that this and other similar G stars are often peculiar, with very broad spectral lines. Henyey suggested that the formation of an expanded outer envelope is what stops the rapid expansion and evolution of a main-sequence star at the giant stage.

Concerning his own paper, "A Summary of Calculations on Stellar Evolution," Henyey emphasized that his model stars exist only in the high-speed electronic Univac calculator of the Atomic Energy Commission facility at Livermore, California. He described computations dealing with hotter stars in which the outer convective regions are relatively unimportant. The masses involved range from 1.5 to 20 times the sun's and the time scale for hydrogen depletion was determined. The rate of hydrogen consumption slowly increases with the temperature while the star is on the main sequence. Stars of spectral type O8, with 20 solar masses, evolve the most rapidly; in their original formation they contract in a very short time to the main-sequence. There they spend a few million years and are relatively stable before the loss of their hydrogen makes them move to the right toward the giant branch. They end the hydrogen-depletion stage just when the more slowly evolving stars of mass 6 (type B5) are beginning it. In contrast to these rapidly evolving stars, those of the sun's type and mass spend at least a billion (10^9) years on the main sequence.

Fowler's talk dealt with several problems of nuclear energy production and element formation in stars, a subject of great complexity and rapid change. During his work at the Kellogg Radiation Laboratory, Fowler calculated a possible time scale for element synthesis in the galaxy before the formation of the solar system.

Two isotopes of uranium were compared, those of atomic weights 235 and 238; they now have an abundance ratio of 1 to 139, whereas the element-building process of neutron capture indicates that originally there was as much or more U^{235} than U^{238}. The former isotope decays radioactively at a much faster rate than the latter; from the known rates of decay it is possible to compute the time elapsed since the original abundances were nearly equal. On this basis, the age of the galaxy is of the order of 7.5×10^9 years or more.

Theories of stellar evolution must take into account the existence and peculiarities of white dwarf stars, which were the subject of Greenstein's paper in the symposium. He emphasized the need for more observations of the distances and motions of white dwarfs and other very faint stars. For instance, a scant nineteen binary systems are known to contain white dwarfs, yet it is only from such cases that we can obtain direct information about the masses of these stars. The companion of Sirius is one of the few examples of a white dwarf with an accurately known mass.

Greenstein has studied forty white dwarfs with the 200-inch telescope, and with it he expects to get spectra for all such objects to a magnitude limit of 16.5. He has been aided by observing lists and charts from W. J. Luyten, University of Minnesota.

The hottest white dwarfs appear to have surface temperatures of about 25,000° absolute. Their masses average half that of the sun, ranging from about 0.2 to 0.8, except for the companion of Sirius, which is greater. The central density of a typical white dwarf is about 2×10^6 grams per cubic centimeter, or about 30 tons in each cubic inch, the densest matter known anywhere in the universe.

All white dwarfs have lost an enormous amount of mass—more than two thirds if they are of Population II, about 90 per cent if of Population I. As these stars appear now to be mostly helium and heavy elements, a large fraction of the stellar mass that has evolved in either population has been returned to the interstellar medium, presumably with an enrichment of its heavy-element content. Greenstein said this was a "wonderful way of feeding matter back to the interstellar medium."

The white dwarf stage for a star is one of very slow cooling, requiring billions of years. The great ages of some reddish white dwarfs indicate that there has been a long interval between the formation of the Milky Way Galaxy and the birth of our sun. This, in turn, implies the existence of large numbers of extremely faint, reddish degenerate stars.

T Tauri Stars and Associated Nebulosities

OTTO STRUVE

(*Sky and Telescope*, October 1961)

Today many astronomers are paying special attention to the T Tauri stars—dwarf irregular variables occurring in dark nebulae and characterized by emission lines in their spectra. The most famous member of this group is T Tauri itself, which illuminates a reflection nebula discovered by J. R. Hind in 1852.

This nebula, NGC1555, is remarkable because its brightness changes. Its history has been summarized by G. H. Herbig in *Leaflet* 293 (September 1953) of the Astronomical Society of the Pacific. Hind's discovery was made with a 7-inch refractor, and between 1852 and 1861 several astronomers observed the nebula. In the latter year H. d'Arrest reported that the object had disappeared, although he had seen it easily several times in 1855 and 1856. In the largest existing telescopes, however, faint traces were discernible until 1864.

Hind's variable nebula was not again detected until 1890, when E. E. Barnard and S. W. Burnham found it with the Lick 36-inch refractor as an exceedingly faint object. Beginning in 1899 there are photographic records of NGC1555. About 1920 it began to brighten gradually, and now is readily visible in large telescopes. More recent changes are shown in Figure 55 by the Lick Observatory photographs of nebulosity near RY Tauri.

These alterations in the brightness and form of Hind's nebula are due to varying illumination from the star T Tauri. As Herbig remarked, "It seems likely that the clouds, which a century ago were so brightly lit up by T Tauri, were not dissolved about 1861, but rather they disappeared when the shadow of something nearer the star swept across them. We are probably witnessing no more than the play of light and shadow on a relatively fixed curtain of dust clouds."

Most of our knowledge of the T Tauri variables has come from the work of three astronomers, A. H. Joy at Mount Wilson and Palomar, Herbig at Lick, and G. Haro at Tonantzintla Observatory in Mexico. In recent years Herbig has thoroughly discussed physical properties

FIG. 55. RY Tauri and its variable nebulosity, discovered by E. E. Barnard, as photographed on January 1, 1957 (left) and March 18, 1960, by George H. Herbig with a 36-inch reflector. Both photographs were 30-minute exposures in blue light. The fading of the nebula is conspicuous. (Lick Observatory photographs)

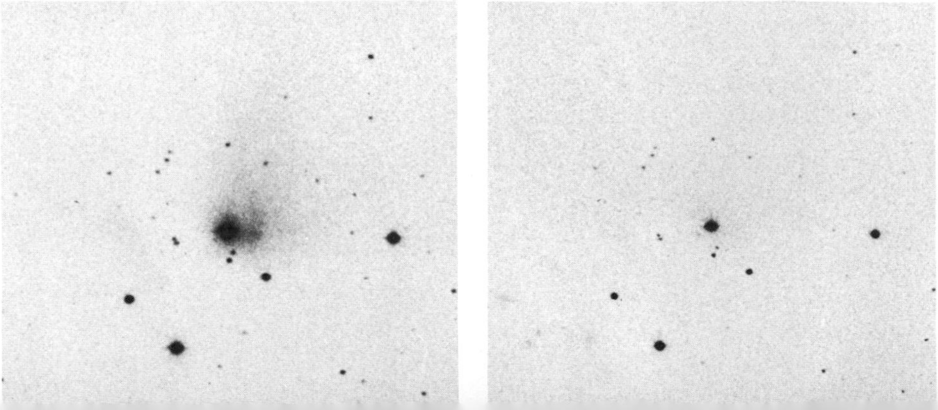

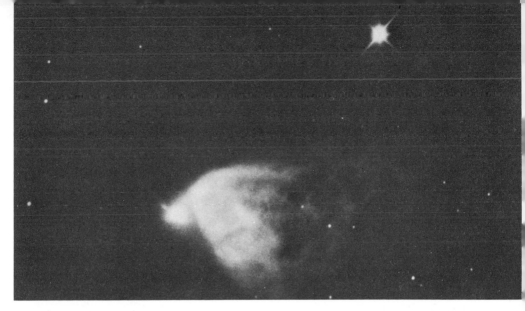

FIG. 56. Hubble's variable nebula, NGC2261. (Lick Observatory photograph)

of these stars derived from their spectra. The light curves are irregular, often with long intervals of quiescence, but there are many other kinds of irregular variables, and it is not possible to assign a particular variable to the T Tauri class on the basis of its light curve alone. All of the real T Tauri stars have low-temperature spectra with strong emission lines of hydrogen and ionized calcium. In addition, they often show weaker emissions of helium, iron, and a few other chemical elements.

Confirming earlier work by Joy, Herbig has concluded that the T Tauri variables are always associated with obscuring clouds of interstellar dust. They are particularly numerous in such great aggregations of interstellar material as the Taurus-Auriga clouds, the Orion nebula, and the region of NGC2264 in Monoceros. Often these stars occur in the fringes of dark clouds, and some are involved in dust that produces reflection nebulae. A few of these nebulosities are known to vary in brightness, six cases being listed by Herbig in *The Astrophysical Journal* for January 1961. One is Hind's nebula, associated with T Tauri; another is Hubble's nebula NGC2261, connected with the variable star R Monocerotis, shown in Figure 56. The star is inside the "head" of this comet-shaped nebulosity.

The spectra of T Tauri stars show several remarkable features. At certain stages of the light variation a strong continuous spectrum is present, appearing to veil the underlying late-type (low-temperature) absorption lines. In some stars, this blue and violet continuous emission almost completely obscures the absorption spectrum. The physical explanation of this continuous emission has not yet been found.

In certain T Tauri variables the spectrum shows shell-like absorption lines displaced toward the violet, indicating an outflow of gas from the atmosphere of the star. Herbig believes that there is no evidence in any well-observed variable of this type for an *inflow* of gas, which would occur if the star were pulling in matter from the surrounding nebulosities.

The spectra of a few of the brightest T Tauri stars have been observed by Herbig and Joy with sufficient dispersion to show conclusively that the underlying absorption lines are broad and diffuse. This line broadening, according to Herbig, is probably due to axial rotation of the stars. RY Tauri, for example, has a rotational velocity at its equator of the order of 50 kilometers per second, while its spectral type is dwarf Goe. No main-sequence star of solar type—apart from components of binaries—has a rotational velocity this great.

In visual absolute magnitude all T Tauri objects are considerably brighter than main-sequence stars of similar spectral type. Herbig has suggested that the T Tauri stars are relatively young and still in the process of gravitational contraction. If so, RY Tauri, at present a G star, would reach the main sequence in about ten million years as an A7 object in accordance with the theoretical work of L. Henyey and his colleagues at Berkeley. Thus RY Tauri would become hotter and smaller. Herbig's computations show that its radius would be halved, and conservation of angular momentum would double its rotational velocity. Hence RY Tauri on reaching the main sequence would have an equatorial velocity of rotation of about a hundred kilometers per second—a plausible value for a main-sequence A star.

There are many T Tauri stars whose present spectral types are between Ko and Mo, and Herbig has pointed out that after evolving to the main sequence they would be Go or later. He expects that these now very cool T Tauri objects, as they contract further, will result in slowly rotating main-sequence stars with equatorial velocities similar to the sun's two kilometers per second. It appears that the angular momentum of such a star may be conserved over a long interval as the star evolves, but the observations are insufficient to prove this conclusively.

As several authors have pointed out, complete conservation of

angular momentum is unlikely during the earliest stages of the contraction of a large gas sphere. Theories of the origin of the stars, such
as W. H. McCrea's, indicate that an interstellar gas cloud of mass
equal to the sun's would have an angular momentum greater than
that known for any star. Consequently if stars evolve by contraction,
the earliest stages of the process must be accompanied by a very
drastic reduction of angular momentum, and this must happen at an
evolutionary stage earlier than that represented by the T Tauri stars
we observe.

An unexpected spectroscopic feature of T Tauri variables is the
great strength of their lithium absorption lines. In these stars there is
one lithium atom for every 10,000 of calcium, as estimated by Herbig.
By contrast, the solar atmosphere contains only one atom of lithium
per seven million of calcium, according to Greenstein and R. S.
Richardson. But in stony meteorites and in the earth's igneous rocks,
the abundance ratio is approximately the same as in the atmospheres
of the T Tauri stars.

Why so much lithium in these stars? Herbig seems to favor the explanation that their abundance of lithium is normal, and that there
is now little of this element in the sun because of depletion by nuclear
processes over billions of years. Greenstein supports an alternative
hypothesis: in the atmospheres of the T Tauri stars a nuclear mechanism replenishes their lithium, a mechanism that does not work in
the sun.

The light variations of T Tauri variables have been studied chiefly
by German and Russian astronomers. A particularly valuable summary of observations was published in 1951 by P. N. Kholopov in the
Soviet journal, *Variable Stars*. Among the variables he studied were
some stars described by A. H. Joy in 1949 as having bright lines of
hydrogen. Two of these variable stars are less than 30 seconds of arc
apart on the sky. The northern component, CZ Tauri, is about magnitude 16 and is of spectral type dM2e; the southern, DD Tauri, is
about 15 and has a dK6e spectrum.* The original discovery of their
light variations was by the German astronomer K. Himpel in 1943.

I became interested in these two stars about twenty-four years ago
because they lie within the confines of the faint but fairly large re-

---

* The letter d in these spectral types stands for "dwarf star," the letter e for
emission lines in the spectrum.

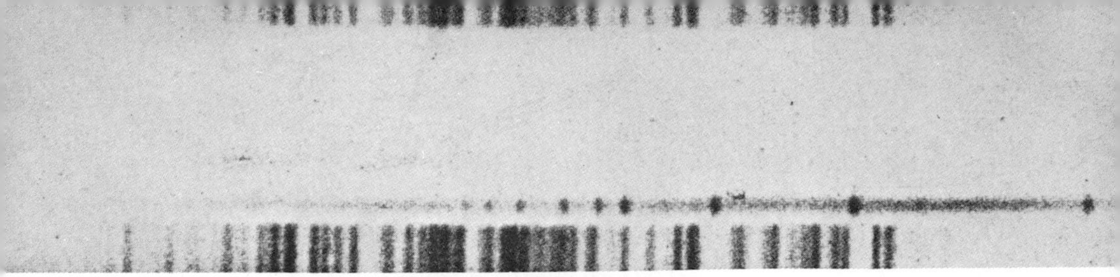

FIG. 57. Numerous emission lines appear in this spectrum of DD Tauri, taken by Otto Struve with the 82-inch McDonald reflector. The two lines on the right are due to hydrogen; two in the center are from ionized calcium. This T Tauri-type star lies in the nebula B10. (From *Stellar Evolution* by Otto Struve, Princeton University Press, 1950)

flection nebula known as Barnard 10. This is a luminous patch in the central part of Barnard's dark cloud B7. With the 82-inch McDonald reflector I obtained spectrograms of both stars. P. Swings and I found that the southern one had a strong emission spectrum of hydrogen and ionized calcium (as shown in Fig. 57), with a few weaker emission lines of helium and possibly other elements. The fainter, northern component could be classified as type *K*, with bright lines of ionized calcium and with strong absorption bands of CH.

The nature of the emission nebulosity Barnard 10 posed an interesting problem. At my request, O. C. Collins photographed it in 1937, and found that this nebula is distinctly blue. At the time I was inclined to believe that B10 owes its light to DD Tauri, whose continuous spectrum is strong in the blue, violet, and ultraviolet regions.

An examination of the Palomar Sky Survey photographs fully confirms Collins' result; the nebula is distinctly bluer than other reflection nebulosities connected with T Tauri stars. As far as can be judged from a comparison of these pictures with earlier ones by Barnard and F. E. Ross, there has been no noticeable change in the brightness or color of B10. . . .

In 1948 Swings and I noted the fact that B10 is much too luminous to owe its brightness to the reflected radiation of DD Tauri. This is easily shown by an argument first developed by E. Hertzsprung in 1913 for the reflection nebulosities in the Pleiades. A perfectly white, diffusely reflecting hemisphere, located some distance from the star, would possess a surface brightness equal to that of an extrafocal image of the star having an apparent diameter the same as the hemisphere. If the image of DD Tauri were spread out over several minutes of arc, the size of B10, the surface brightness would be far less than the nebula's.

Even so, there is still the problem of explaining the bluish appearance of B10. As far as I know now, B10 is the only blue reflection nebula associated with a late-type star. It seems improbable that some special mechanism is at work without producing similar effects in other cases.

Another puzzle is presented by the luminous nebula B14, which is quite clearly shown on early Milky Way photographs by Barnard and Ross. This nebula is distinctly red, but there is no star in its immediate vicinity that could account for its light—two facts evident from both Collins' photographs and the Palomar Sky Survey. There is some indication that the brightness of B14 has changed in the past quarter century, and perhaps its shape. It may be that in this case there is a T Tauri star so deeply involved in the obscuring cloud that it has not been recorded with even the most powerful telescopes. This phenomenon would be analogous to the effect of a terrestrial cloud layer that is dense enough to blot out the sun's disk, showing only a large luminous patch of scattered sunlight.

The rotation of T Tauri stars poses a problem. As Struve says, there must be some braking action ("drastic reduction of angular momentum") if they are to evolve into normal G stars. One possibility is that some interaction with the surrounding interstellar materials could slow down the spin of the newly forming star (passing the angular

FIG. 58. In this Crossley photograph of the B10 nebula, CZ and DD Tauri form the wide double star above the center of the nebulosity. DD is the brighter component. Northeast (below and to the left) of the nebula is the brighter, fuzzy star called "b" by P. N. Kholopov. (Lick Observatory photograph)

momentum to distant gas clouds). Another is that planets or a double star might form, as discussed in Chapter 5.

The strange blue nebula Barnard 10 is not explained by Struve. It is possible, though unlikely, that a more luminous star, such as the one to the lower left in Figure 58, is shining on it from behind a dark cloud. Struve's discussion shows the complex structure of dark and bright nebulae in which new stars may be forming.—TLP

....

Evolution of Protostars

(*Sky and Telescope*, November 1962)

Most astronomers are agreed on the broad picture of star formation. An extended, very tenuous cloud of interstellar gas and dust gradually contracts, growing denser and warmer, and finally becomes a star when thermonuclear liberation of energy begins in its interior. The object is called a protostar in its intermediate stage.

As plausible physical properties of a protostar, John E. Gaustad of Princeton University cites temperatures in the range of 50° to 3000° Kelvin, and mean densities of 10^7 to 10^{17} hydrogen-atom masses per cubic centimeter. For a protostar of the same mass as the sun, these values correspond to a range in radius all the way from 5000 astronomical units down to one.

A protostar contracts by spending its gravitational potential energy as radiation, and thus the contraction rate is controlled by the opacity of its material, through which radiation must flow in escaping from the interior. Gaustad has investigated in detail the effectiveness of this restriction on the rate of protostar evolution.

At temperatures below 100°, the opacity is due primarily to solid grains, composed largely of the ices of water, methane, and ammonia. At higher temperatures, these ices evaporate, leaving smaller grains of less volatile compounds, such as iron oxide and silicon dioxide. For a temperature of 1600° or higher, these grains too will have evaporated, leaving only hydrogen as a significant agent to dam the outward flow of radiation. Its opacity is due to scattering by hydrogen molecules that are interacting with free electrons.

The Princeton astronomer has calculated the behavior of contracting protostars of 0.01, 0.1, and one solar mass, disregarding magnetic fields and angular momentum. For the first two of these models, the opacity is great enough to slow down the escape of energy to an orderly process. Thus a protostar of a tenth the sun's mass or less would be in quasi equilibrium, contracting in the manner Helmholtz suggested a century ago to account for the sun's light and heat [see p. 37].

However, a more massive protostar would have insufficient opacity to check significantly the outflowing radiation and would probably collapse in free fall from an interstellar cloud to a star. Hence the contraction stage in the early evolution of a star of solar mass may be much shorter than had been thought.

••

Jeans' Criterion of Gravitational Instability

SU-SHU HUANG

(*Sky and Telescope*, August 1963)

On December 10, 1692, five years after he had published his law of gravitation, Sir Isaac Newton wrote in a letter to Richard Bentley:

"It seems to me that if the Matter of our Sun and Planets, and all the Matter of the Universe, were evenly scattered throughout all the Heavens, and every Particle had an innate Gravity towards all the rest, and the whole Space, throughout which this Matter was scattered, was but finite; the Matter on the outside of this Space would by its Gravity tend towards all the Matter on the inside, and by consequence fall down into the middle of the whole Space, and there compose one great spherical Mass. But if the Matter was evenly disposed throughout an infinite Space, it could never convene into one Mass, but some of it would convene into one Mass and some into another, so as to make an infinite Number of great Masses, scattered at great Distances from one to another throughout all that infinite Space. And thus might the Sun and fixt Stars be formed, supposing the Matter were of a lucid Nature."

Thus Newton, with his physical insight, anticipated the theory of condensation of matter in the universe more than two hundred years before Sir James Jeans gave it an exact mathematical treatment in 1902. Jeans' discussion is highly involved, so we will only describe the underlying physical ideas, and a very recent criticism by David Layzer of Harvard Observatory.

Jeans considered what would happen if waves of disturbance should be created in an extended gaseous medium. When a steeple bell chimes, it can be heard miles away. Vibrations in the bell start a series of sound waves, or disturbances in the surrounding air, which carry the vibrations over large distances, just as waves spread out from a pebble dropped into a still pond. The waves that Jeans treated were nothing more than a kind of sound wave.

These oscillations are composed of alternate condensations and rarefactions. One of the condensations temporarily holds together a large number of particles in the medium, which are then dispersed into a rarefaction as the wave passes. A condensation, because of the concentration of mass within it, exerts a greater gravitational attraction on neighboring particles than does the same volume of undisturbed medium.

In ordinary sound waves in air, this excess in gravitational pull is infinitesimal and has no perceptible effect. But when the same phenomenon happens on a far larger scale, the gravitational forces may become very important. The attraction within each condensation becomes so strong that no subsequent rarefaction can occur. When this happens the extended medium is said to be *gravitationally unstable*. According to Jeans it will then collect into many big lumps, as Newton had supposed.

The size of a condensation is proportional to the wavelength of the disturbance, since the wavelength is the distance from one condensation across a rarefaction to the next condensation. From a long mathematical analysis, Jeans found a formula for the shortest wavelength of density fluctuation, λ_0, that will cause instability in an extended medium:

$$\lambda_0{}^2 = \pi\gamma V^2 / 3G\rho.$$

Here V is the mean velocity of the particles, ρ is the density of the medium, and γ is the ratio of specific heats (which depends on the nature of the gas in the medium). G is the gravitational constant.

From this equation *Jeans' criterion of gravitational instability* states: any disturbance that has a wavelength equal to or greater than λ_0 will produce a collapse of the extended medium.

The gas in interstellar space is dominantly atomic hydrogen, so γ may be taken as $5/3$. Also, the radius R of a condensation is roughly half the wavelength, the other half being the rarefaction. Hence Jeans' criterion may be expressed in the following form: for a permanent condensation, R^2 must not be smaller than $0.44\, V^2/G\rho$. (The coefficient is 0.44 only if we use centimeter-gram-second units.)

This Jeans formula can be derived approximately in a simple way from basic ideas. Consider a homogeneous spherical condensation of mass M and radius R. What is the minimum velocity a particle on the surface must have to escape from the condensation? This escape velocity is $(2GM/R)^{\frac{1}{2}}$. For a particle at the surface of the earth it is 11 kilometers per second, but it is only 2.4 kilometers per second on the moon (or at the edge of a protostar).

If the condensation is to hold together, the particle velocity, V, must be smaller than the escape velocity. That is, $2GM/R$ must be larger than V^2. Remembering that mass is volume times density, or that $M = 4\pi R^3 \rho / 3$, we see that this means R^2 is more than $0.12\, V^2/G\rho$ for a stable condensation. This is approximately Jeans' criterion. Our coefficient differs from his because we have simplified the problem, but we are primarily interested in the physical ideas involved.

The total mass of the condensation can be found directly from the original Jeans formula, using the relation $M = 4\pi R^3 \rho / 3$. Instead of density, astronomers often specify the mass concentration of the interstellar medium in terms of the equivalent number of hydrogen atoms per cubic centimeter, N. (This means that the mass in that volume equals the mass of N hydrogen atoms, and does not imply that all the matter is hydrogen, though it is indeed the dominant constituent.)

It turns out that the lower limit to the total mass, M, of a stable condensation is $27,300\, V^3/N^{\frac{1}{2}}$, where V is expressed in kilometers per second, and M in solar masses. We see that a larger mass is needed to hold a condensation together in a less dense medium (smaller N).

In the interstellar medium, density varies greatly from one region to another, with N ranging from one to well over 1000 hydrogen atoms in each cubic centimeter. A further complication is that the interstellar matter is in turbulent motion, which may be regarded as the cause of the disturbances that lead to density waves in the medium.

It is hard to tell the turbulent velocity, but in neutral hydrogen clouds it seems to be about one or two kilometers per second, corresponding roughly to a temperature between 10° and 100° Kelvin. The effect of turbulence is to increase the minimum mass, and consequently the masses of actual condensations in space could well be much greater than the lower limits tabulated here.

TABLE 5.   MINIMUM NUMBER OF SOLAR MASSES IN STABLE CONDENSATIONS (ACCORDING TO JEANS' CRITERION)

Average Particle Velocity	Density (hydrogen atoms per cubic centimeter)			
	1	10	100	1000
1 km per sec	2.73×10^4	8.63×10^3	2.73×10^3	8.63×10^2
2 km per sec	2.18×10^5	6.91×10^4	2.18×10^4	6.91×10^3
4 km per sec	1.75×10^6	5.52×10^5	1.75×10^5	5.52×10^4

Table 5 demonstrates that the first fragmentation of the gaseous medium that was to become our Milky Way system could not have resulted in stars, but in much more massive condensations. The large masses suggest conglomerations that later evolved into star clusters. Perhaps the clumps that were to become globular clusters first condensed in this way when the material of our galaxy was still in a spherical shape. They would contract under their own gravity and become denser. Then a second fragmentation might occur in accord with Jeans' criterion. Because of the higher densities of the contracting clouds, their breakup would result in smaller masses, perhaps comparable with a star's mass (½ to 10 solar masses). But astronomers disagree as to whether the stars are indeed formed in such a second Jeans process.

While fragmentation is going on, the atoms in the galactic gas suffer numerous collisions. If the matter does not possess a net angular momentum, such collisions will not affect its general shape. But if the primeval galaxy did have net angular momentum, the collisions would gradually tend to change its shape from a sphere to a disk. Thus when two streams of particles moving parallel to the rotation axis collide, their velocities can neutralize each other, and their energy is radiated away. But if the collision is between two streams moving in the rotational plane, the velocities cannot cancel completely, because angular momentum must be conserved. In this way, vertical motions diminish, while material in the central plane continues to circulate rapidly around the center. In the neighborhood of the sun, this rotational velocity is about 250 kilometers per second according to observation.

Globular clusters and stars formed early in the history of our galaxy would not collapse into the disk because they do not collide frequently among themselves. To this day, globular clusters and other old Population-II objects maintain a spherical distribution [see Fig. 1].

Once the gas and dust have collapsed into a flattened disk, the medium may again become gravitationally unstable. Perhaps the condensations thus formed are the interstellar clouds that we now observe in the galactic plane.

In a paper in *The Astrophysical Journal*, Layzer has shown that fragmentation of a contracting cloud cannot lead to the formation of stars. He bases his argument on the limitation to contraction imposed

FIG. 59. The spiral galaxy NGC253 in Sculptor, about five times as distant as M31 in Andromeda, is streaked and dappled with dust clouds. (Harvard College Observatory photograph)

by angular momentum. Gravitational interactions among condensations early in their evolution impart some angular momentum to each. As they contract, the transfer of angular momentum becomes smaller and smaller until each condensation behaves independently, conserving its angular momentum.

Since angular momentum is the product of angular velocity and the square of the radius, a condensation will spin faster as it contracts until centrifugal force balances internal gravitational force. Then no further contraction is possible. On the other hand, the cloud from which the condensations were formed can contract much more. Therefore, Layzer concludes, even "if the growth of initial density fluctuations in a contracting cloud were to result in the formation of stable condensations, these would be obliterated by the subsequent contraction of the cloud."

Jeans' original theory of gravitational instability has been generalized by S. Chandrasekhar of Yerkes Observatory. In his recent book *Hydrodynamic and Hydromagnetic Stability* he has shown that "Jeans' criterion for the gravitational instability of an infinite homogeneous medium is unaffected by the presence, separately, or simultaneously, of a uniform rotation and a uniform magnetic field."

Magnetic lines of force repel one another, while along each line there is a tension like that of a stretched string. At the same time, charged particles are constrained by the lines of force, but are free to move along them. Hence we might intuitively expect Chandrasekhar's result.

On the other hand, sound waves moving perpendicular to the magnetic field will interact with the lines of force to which the charged particles are "glued." When the wind blows through stretched strings it produces vibrations of the strings themselves. Similarly, when sound waves pass laterally through magnetic lines of force they cause vibrations of the lines. Actually, density fluctuation will be coupled to magnetic vibration to form what are known as magnetohydrodynamic waves.

With the introduction of the magnetic field, angular momentum will no longer be conserved, since magnetic damping of axial rotation is a very efficient process. Even without a magnetic field, a condensation can lose some angular momentum as it sheds mass, while the remaining part spins like a top. Indeed, the newly formed O- and B-type stars are observed to be rotating rapidly. Otto Struve and I proposed in 1954 that the rotation of these stars results from collisions between protostars at an early stage when they are still very large. All these considerations show that it is possible for stars to form in accordance with Jeans' ideas.

Many astronomers, including Jeans himself, have suggested that galaxies are formed from fragmentation of a primeval medium that is gravitationally unstable in Jeans' sense. This is essentially what Newton conjectured in the letter quoted. However, the manner in which galaxies were formed depends on the structure of the universe. Furthermore, any application of Jeans' criterion to the formation of galaxies is complicated by the expansion of the universe. Therefore Jeans' ideas about gravitational instability may not have as wide a range of astrophysical applications as he had thought. But his criterion remains a fundamental concept every astronomer should remember.

These ideas about angular momentum, magnetic fields, turbulence, and the stability of condensations in interstellar material are basic to any discussion of star formation, or of galaxy formation (a topic reserved for a later volume in this series). The influence of magnetic fields on visible nebulae is well demonstrated on p. 126; the existence of turbulence in interstellar clouds is obvious in Figures 51, 52, and 53, and the formation of stable condensations seems to explain the T Tauri objects and probably all the stars we can see.

Getting rid of angular momentum from a contracting protostar remains a problem, involving observations of rotating stars, double stars, and possible planetary systems.—TLP

The History
of Spinning
Material

It should now be clear that spinning material has a special significance: over long periods of time the angular momentum must remain constant unless there is some outside braking force. The total angular momentum is "conserved," and this conservation law applies to all matter, from atoms and subatomic particles to stars, nebulae, and galaxies.

"Spin" implies rotary motion about an axis, and angular momentum (a measure of the amount of spin) must be referred to an axis. It is defined as the sum of $Mv_c r$ for all the individual masses, M, at distance r from the axis moving with a velocity that has some part or "component," v_c, along a circle of radius r around the axis. In a rotating star, this sum must include all parts of the stellar material at various distances from the axis and moving at different speeds (from zero on the axis to the largest velocity on the equator). In solid-body rotation, like the earth's, v/r is a constant called the "angular velocity," ω, proportional to the number of turns per year, and the angular momentum is the sum of $M\omega r^2$, which can be easily calculated if the mass is known in each shell of radius r around the axis. This shows that when a rotating star contracts to smaller r, the angular velocity must increase as $1/r^2$ in order to conserve angular momentum.

In a double star the orbital angular momentum is $M_1 \omega r_1^2 + M_2 \omega r_2^2$ (subscripts 1 and 2 referring to the two component stars) and there is in addition the rotational angular momentum of each star, which may or may not have its rotational axis lined up with the orbital axis. In fact, if the rotations are opposite to the orbital revolution, the total angular momentum may be zero. This illustrates the difficulty of applying the conservation law to the angular momentum of a turbulent nebula condensing into stars. The nebula may have very small total angular momentum and yet contain two or more rapidly rotating eddies that condense into stars rotating in opposite directions. Once a protostar has condensed far enough to break its ties to the nebula, its angular momentum should thereafter remain constant. The significant question is, what "ties" must we consider? There is a frictional drag in the gas, tidal action due to gravitation, and magnetic interaction in ionized (hot) gases.

Although these theoretical considerations are complex, the observation of double stars and rotating stars provides a wealth of data that have a bearing on stellar evolution, as shown in the next article.—TLP

....

Double Stars

GERARD P. KUIPER

(*The Telescope*, January–February 1936)

Among the stars that compose our galaxy there are two classes of stars that deserve particular interest, variable stars and double stars.

In considering variable stars one deals with but a single star in the majority of cases and, through observations that give the nature of its cycle of light variation, obtains the properties of a single star of given mass. In considering binary stars one deals with two different stars that in all probability are of the same age. In the case of some close binaries the orbits of the components about each other may be so oriented that the stars will transit each other either partially or totally as seen from the earth, and the system is then seen as an eclipsing binary. Such binaries are of particular interest to the observers of variable stars, and through their assiduous observation, the properties of eclipsing binaries have become probably more completely known than those of any other stars except the sun. Here we are particularly concerned, however, with binary systems in general, including systems that can be seen as two individual stars and those in which the existence of two stars in orbital motion may be detected spectroscopically.

The early history of double-star observation deals entirely with micrometer measurements of visual binaries. One may refer in particular to the excellent work of Sir William Herschel and Wilhelm Struve in the nineteenth century and of R. G. Aitken and W. J. Hussey at the turn of the present one, that resulted in the accumulation of a tremendous amount of observational material concerning the angular separation and position angle of the components of many visual binaries. From their observations and from those of other observers a fair knowledge of the masses of the stars involved and of the orbital characteristics has been derived. Of these the knowledge of stellar masses is the most important. Recent observers have frequently confined their micrometer measures to close visual binaries with short periods of revolution. . . . Such selected observations do not give a sufficiently complete picture of stellar properties, such as the relation of binary stars to single stars and the origin of binary systems. More data, data of a different nature, are needed in the solution of these problems.

To discuss the origin and the nature of binary systems statistically, a selection and subdivision of the observational material is necessary. The selection of material may be made on the basis of a certain region of space in the neighborhood of the earth. The radius of this volume of space cannot be too small, for then it will include an insufficient number of binary stars to make possible a critical analysis of their properties. It cannot be too large, for then the properties of a system will be difficult to observe in the case of the more distant binaries. It will, for example, be impossible to separate close binaries visually or to investigate them spectroscopically because they will be too faint.

The binaries that fall within such a volume of space in the vicinity of the earth and sun may be further subdivided in two ways: firstly, according to real separation, and secondly, according to the difference of brightness of the two component stars. Concerning the former, the linear distance between the two components cannot be directly

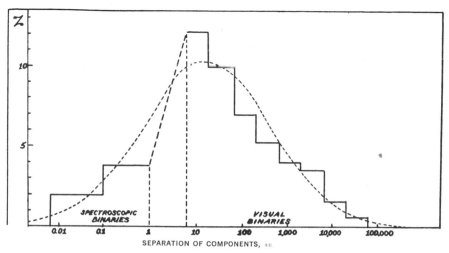

FIG. 60. The linear separations of the components of double stars. The heights of the various steps show the relative numbers of binaries with the separations given at the bottom of the diagram. The dashed curve shows the way in which the separations would be distributed if the law of probability were solely responsible.

observed; one can only observe the angular separation. A nearby pair of small linear separation may have the same appearance as a remote pair of large linear separation. Only from a knowledge of the distance of the pair from the earth can the true linear separation of the pair be determined, and inasmuch as the distances of the nearer pairs may be found with reasonable exactness, the knowledge of the true linear separation of these stars is quite complete.

The result of the investigation of the true separations of nearby binary systems appears in Figure 60. It is to be noted that the separations fall between two limits. The lower limit is about 1/100 A.U.,[1] or 900,000 miles. A separation of less than this would, in general, mean that the two stars were in contact, and hence did not form a true binary system. The upper limit is in the neighborhood of 20,000 A.U. Stars separated by this distance are so loosely bound that the effect of foreign stars passing nearby would be to disrupt the system. The effect of such transient stars upon close systems, tightly bound, would be minor.

It is entirely possible that binaries separated by more than 20,000 A.U. do exist. A few such pairs have been detected through common motion of the components in space, but the number is small. These few wide binaries have probably fortuitously escaped the perturbing

[1] A.U. = astronomical unit, the mean distance of the earth from the sun.

influence of passing stars during these early years of their life, but they may not survive the future unscathed.

In collecting the material for discussion, spectroscopic observations are required for the data concerning binaries with components separated by less than 5 A.U., and visual observations for binaries of larger separation. Actually, for the particular interval between 1 and 7 A.U., both the spectroscopic and the visual observations are scarce. In dealing with more distant binaries, excluded in this discussion, the inobservable region between spectroscopic and visual data would be larger. The reason for this is that the more distant the system, the less the chance that the two stars may be seen visually; spectroscopic observations will also be more difficult because of the apparent faintness of the stars.

The surprising fact about the frequency in Figure 60 is that between the two limits impressed upon it by the considerations of contact and instability (0.01 A.U. and 20,000 A.U.), the separations form a symmetrical curve (a normal distribution in the logarithm of the separations), with a most frequent separation near 20 A.U. Curiously, the situation within our solar system is similar; the large planetary masses from Jupiter to Neptune are at distances from the sun of 5 A.U. to 30 A.U., or about 20 A.U. The only possible interpretation of the frequency curve is that it bears some relation to the way in which binary stars have been formed; it does not seem possible that outside influences can have since changed the frequency curve (except in reducing the number of very wide binaries).

Some further light is shed upon the question of origin by the differences of brightness of the component stars in binary systems. The difference in brightness is directly related to the difference of mass of the two stars involved. The relation between the mass of a star and its intrinsic luminosity [see p. 50] became of special significance through Eddington's research. The relation is such that if two stars differ by a certain amount in absolute magnitude,[2] the ratio of their masses will have the same value, regardless of whether the two stars are relatively bright or relatively faint. Only for the very luminous stars will this mass proportion be somewhat different.

This relation may be immediately applied to binary systems, for, inasmuch as the two stars are at the same distance from the earth, the difference of their apparent magnitudes is the same as the differ-

[2] A measure of intrinsic luminosity.

ence of their absolute magnitudes, and hence the ratio of the masses of the two stars is known.

A second, surprising result can also be derived from the consideration of the difference of brightness. On the basis of temperature and absolute magnitude, stars may be divided into two main groups, as shown in Figure 61: a group of very luminous stars with low surface temperatures (the "giants"), and a larger group of stars, covering a large range of surface temperature (the "dwarfs" or "main-sequence stars"). The names "giant" and "dwarf" are adequately descriptive of the relative sizes of the stars forming the two groups. If all the stars composing these two groups are mixed together and then sorted according to intrinsic brightness, one finds a steady increase in number as one proceeds to stars of low intrinsic luminosity. If binary stars were formed by picking pairs at random from all the stars and were then arranged in groups according to the intrinsic luminosity of the brighter component, one would expect to find in every case a preponderance of companions possessing low intrinsic luminosity. Such, however, is not the case.

It will be noted from Figure 61 that the giant stars of low temperature (spectral classes K and M) possess the same intrinsic luminosity as main-sequence stars of type A. If one sorts binary stars into two groups, those in the one group having a giant K or M star as the brighter component, and those in the other group having a main-sequence A star as the brighter component, one finds for the first group a distribution of luminosities of the companions that is a near duplicate of the distribution of luminosities for the stars in general, as shown in Figure 62. But for the second group there is a totally different distribution of luminosities of the companion; there is a surprising lack of companions of low luminosity. It is as though a giant star chose its companion from the stars in general, whereas a

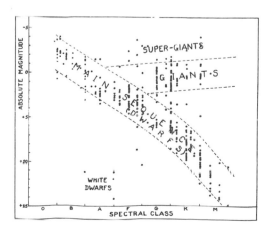

FIG. 61. The relation of the absolute magnitudes of stars to their temperatures. The vertical gaps in the diagram arise solely from the roughness of the classification of stellar spectra. The temperatures decrease from 50,000°F for class-O stars to 5500°F for class-M stars.

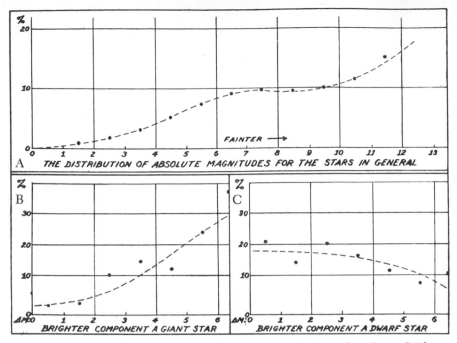

FIG. 62. A. Curve showing the relative numbers of stars of various absolute magnitudes. Note the increase in number of stars of low luminosity. B. and C. Curves showing the distribution of magnitude differences in double stars. The curve in B is for binaries in which the brighter component is a giant star; that in C is for those in which the brighter component is a main-sequence star. Note that the curve in B follows the curve of luminosity of the stars in general, while the curve in C departs greatly from it.

main-sequence star preferred to select a star of reasonably high luminosity, almost completely disregarding dwarf stars of low luminosity.

This selective effect in the luminosities of the components of binaries holds for both close pairs and wide doubles. One also finds in star clusters a closely analogous situation: a star cluster that possesses in its membership a number of giant stars possesses as well a large number of faint stars, while a cluster that possesses no giant members lacks faint stars too.

It has been generally considered that the fission theory is unable to explain the origin of the binaries separated by more than a few astronomical units, whereas the close binaries might have been formed by fission. The observed similarity between the close and the wide doubles, mentioned above, throws considerable doubt on these hypotheses about the origin, since it is highly improbable that two different ways of forming binary systems would yield exactly the same luminosity distribution. Moreover, the distribution of the separations in the binaries shows a single frequency curve (Fig. 60), not a double one, as would be expected if two processes of formation were acting.

We are forced to conclude that the binary systems are one class of objects, not two (wide and close pairs). Furthermore, since the fission theory cannot apply to the wide binaries, it must be abandoned. The capture theory for the origin of binaries has never been seriously considered and is not an alternative, since it is not difficult to show that it is unsatisfactory.

The similarity of composition of binary stars and of star clusters leads to the conclusions that the formation of these systems was accomplished in a comparable fashion, and that they were probably formed simultaneously with the formation of the whole stellar universe. Binaries, single stars, and star clusters thus in all probability possess the same age.

It is highly improbable that new binaries are still being formed; on the contrary, as time progresses, wide binaries will dissolve into two single and independent stars, on account of the perturbing effects of passing stars. The number of binaries is therefore steadily decreasing, and if the stellar system will live long enough, no binary systems will have survived. Conversely, the fact that we still observe so many binaries proves that our stellar system is not very old, probably not more than ten billion years.

Frequency of Binary Stars

(*Sky and Telescope*, November 1962)

"The available observational evidence indicates that a large fraction, probably a majority, of stars exist in binary or multiple systems," commented Charles E. Worley, U.S. Naval Observatory [at the August 1962 meeting of the American Astronomical Society]. However, an estimate of this fraction may be very misleading unless due allowance is made for the effects of observational selection.

For example, our counts of visual binary stars are much less complete for distant than for nearby stars. If Sirius were several times more remote than it is, no existing telescope could show its famous white-dwarf companion. In another selection effect, spectroscopic binaries of spectral type *B* are more liable to escape discovery than similar binaries of type *A*. The reason is that many *B* stars have spectrum lines too broad and indistinct for accurate radial-velocity measurements.

Worley pointed out three very thoroughly observed categories of stars for which some measure of completeness has been attained in the search for companions. One is the 30 nearest known stars; 17 of them are single, whereas the other 13 together have 29 components. Hence of the total of 46 objects, 63 per cent belong to binary or multiple systems.

Similarly, among the 30 apparently brightest stars in the sky, 15 are made up of 41 individual components. In this case, the percentage of objects belonging to systems is 73.

In recent years, Worley has been systematically examining *M* dwarf stars for visual companions. Of 561 such nearby stars, 119 are already known to be composite, with 261 components. The percentage of objects that are members of binary or more complicated systems is 37, and undoubtedly this number will be increased as more data come in.

The implications were outlined by the Washington astronomer: "If the above statistics are generally valid, then theories of star formation must start with the assumption that the normal star is formed and exists in a binary system, and then explain the existence of 'abnormal' single stars."

In a paper presented at the same meeting, J. Allen Hynek of Dearborn Observatory called attention to two notable anomalies in the statistical properties of binary stars. One is the fact that among *G*, *K*, and *M* giant stars the proportion of spectroscopic binaries is only about half that for *B*, *A*, and *F* main-sequence stars. This difference is just the opposite of what observational selection would cause. The other point underlined by Hynek was that the average orbital period for the *G*, *K*, *M* binaries is very many times longer than for those with *B*, *A*, or *F* components.

According to widely accepted ideas of stellar evolution, the giant stars of which Hynek spoke have evolved from main-sequence stars that were probably largely of types *A* and *F*. Hence it is very striking that the giants are observed to differ, as far as their percentage of binaries is concerned, from the present main-sequence stars, which should be very similar to the giants' progenitors.

As the primary of a binary evolves away from the main sequence it expands greatly and engulfs any close spectroscopic companion. Hynek suggests that this alters the subsequent evolution of the primary to such an extent that it never becomes a normal giant. This would account for the observed absence of short-period spectroscopic binaries among giant stars.

The Dearborn astrophysicist notes that this mechanism could also have some effect on the statistics of visual binaries. Consider a system like Mizar, in which a bright star has both a close spectroscopic companion and a distant visual one. The engulfment of the closer secondary would change the primary's evolution, preventing the later occurrence of a normal giant with a visual companion.

In the twenty-six years between the last two articles, interest shifted from the fission and capture theories of double star formation to the effects of evolution on the components of a binary. Hynek's suggestion that evolution of one component to the giant stage might engulf its companion may also provide an explanation of the differences Kuiper noticed between binaries containing giants and binaries containing dwarf stars only. When a binary is first formed, both components are dwarfs, and the distribution of differences in magnitudes is not as wide as the distribution of absolute magnitudes for stars in general. However, one of the components will eventually evolve to the giant stage, increasing the magnitude difference by several magnitudes. Binaries in which this has happened therefore have a different distribution of magnitude differences, as shown in Figure 6a. Somewhat greater spread is introduced by the second component also evolving to the giant stage. The interval of time between these two departures from the main sequence will generally be quite large— several billion years if the stars were originally one A and one F star, differing by two or three magnitudes—and this makes giant-dwarf pairs much more likely than pairs of giants.—TLP

....

Axial Rotation and
Stellar Evolution

OTTO STRUVE

(*Sky and Telescope*, November 1955)

In 1929 Sir James H. Jeans wrote in his famous book *The Universe Around Us*, "In discussing the way in which nebulae might be born out of chaos, we noticed that the existence of currents in the primordial medium would endow the resulting nebulae with varying amounts of rotation. For the same reason the children of the nebulae, the stars, must also be endowed with rotation at their birth. There is a further reason for such rotation. The general principle of the 'conservation of angular momentum' requires that rotation, like energy, cannot entirely disappear. Its total amount is conserved, so that when a nebula breaks up into stars, the original rotation of the nebula must be conserved in the rotations of the stars. Thus the stars, as soon as they come into being, are endowed with rotations transmitted to them by their parent nebula in addition to the rotations resulting from the currents set up in the process of condensation."

While Jeans was writing these words several astronomers were at work at Yerkes Observatory studying the absorption lines in stellar spectra. In some stars, such as the sun, Procyon, Sirius, Vega, and Tau Scorpii, the lines are narrow and sharp. In other stars of similar temperatures and luminosities, like W Ursae Majoris, Altair, and Eta Ursae Majoris, the same spectral lines appear broad and diffuse (Fig. 63). The Yerkes astronomers concluded that the latter stars rotate rapidly around their axes—with periods of a few hours—while the stars of the first group either do not rotate appreciably or are so oriented that their axes lie close to our line of sight (Fig. 64).

Notice in Figure 63 that the sharp, deep line in Vega's spectrum at wavelength 4481 (due to the ion of magnesium) is only a blur in the spectrum of Altair. Measurements of the widths of this line show that the component of the rotation of Vega in the line of sight is zero, while in Altair it is 240 kilometers per second at the star's equator. Since we do not know whether the axis of Altair is exactly perpen-

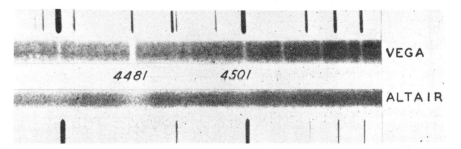

VEGA

4481   4501

ALTAIR

FIG. 63. These short sections of the spectra of Vega and Altair, both A-type stars, illustrate the differing shapes of their spectral lines. Notice how the blue magnesium line (4481 angstroms) appears much broader in Altair, due to the rapid rotation of this star. (Yerkes Observatory photograph)

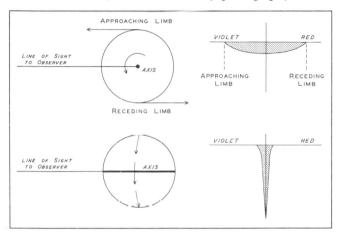

FIG. 64. A. The axis of a rapidly rotating star is at right angles to the line of sight, and the spectrum line is widened due to the Doppler effect. B. No line broadening results where the axis of a rapidly rotating star points directly at the observer.

dicular to the line of sight, this value is a lower limit to that star's true equatorial velocity of rotation. But let us assume that the axis is actually at right angles to the line of sight.

The radius of Altair is about three times the sun's, or 2,100,000 kilometers. Hence the circumference at its equator is 13,200,000 kilometers. A point on Altair's equator, carried by rotation at 240 kilometers per second, would require fifteen hours to complete one revolution. This is very much shorter than the rotation period of the sun, which is about one month! If the axis of Altair were inclined at an angle of less than 90 degrees to the line of sight, its rotational period would be even shorter.

In the case of Vega, we do not know whether its rotation is unobservably slow or whether its pole is turned almost exactly toward us, as in Figure 64B. But as observations accumulated for more and more stars it became clear that some, at least, really have very slow rotations. It seems reasonable to suppose that the axes of the stars are pointed at random, in all directions. Then there should be very few stars with their axes in the line of sight, and a great many with their axes nearly at right angles to it.

I have often demonstrated this to lecture audiences by asking each person to point his pencil in any direction that first comes to his mind. I then tell the members of the audience that I am the observer, and their pencils represent the orientations of the rotational axes of the stars. Each person estimates the angle between my line of sight and the orientation of his pencil, and I record on the blackboard the numbers with angles between 80° and 90°, 80° and 70°, and so on. The result demonstrates the statistical preponderance of the larger angles. (However, this experiment is beset by a systematic error: even before the audience members know that I shall designate the direction to me as the "line of sight," they seem to be reluctant to point their pencils directly at the speaker, and the preponderance of large angles appears exaggerated in the actual count. The mathematical form of the random distribution is, of course, known from statistical theory.)

At any rate, it is certain that there are many stars which do not rotate rapidly. If we correct the measured (foreshortened) velocities of rotation for the statistical effect of the random orientation of the axes, we obtain, for stars of different spectral types, the graphs shown in Figure 65.

FIG. 65. The relative numbers of rapidly and slowly rotating stars are shown here for different spectral types. The curves, by K. H. Boehm, allow for varying axial orientations of the stars, so the abscissae are equatorial rotational velocities.

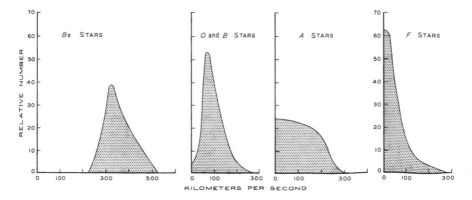

We see at once that the B stars with emission lines in their spectra (type Be) all rotate rapidly between about 200 and 500 kilometers per second at the equator. Among the O and B stars, about 10 per cent have no perceptible rotation, while nearly half rotate at 100 kilometers per second, and relatively few have rotations as large as 175 kilometers per second. For the A stars the rotations are somewhat the same, but among the F stars about 60 per cent have no observable rotation, and only 10 per cent have rotations of around 125 kilometers per second.

The remarkable decline of the rotational velocities as we pass from the early spectral types to the later ones was already known thirty years ago, from the work of C. T. Elvey and myself. It poses an interesting evolutionary problem when we consider that presumably all stars which are now located on the main sequence of the H-R diagram have been formed by the gravitational contraction of globules of interstellar matter. These nearly spherical dark cloudlets were discovered by Bart J. Bok at Harvard in gaseous nebulosities [such as those shown in Figs. 48 and 49]. Globules have diameters of the order of 10,000 astronomical units. Their masses are not known, but they presumably range between one and fifty solar masses, similar to the masses of the stars. They are sufficiently compact to resist disruption by tidal effects of the Milky Way as a whole, and of neighboring stars. They contract fairly rapidly [see p. 135]. . . .

L. G. Henyey, R. LeLevier, and R. D. Levee have recently shown that a protostar of solar mass takes about 30 million years to reach the present position of the sun in the H-R diagram. . . . This time is short compared to the 100 billion years that the sun will presumably need for its later development. No wonder that among the stars observed at random we find few, if any, that are now in the early, contracting stage of evolution.

Nevertheless, if our ideas are correct, we should expect all individual stars that are now located on the main sequence to retain the rotation (angular momentum) of the original globules. There is no reason to suppose that globules of small mass had, to begin with, less than their normal supply of angular momentum per unit of mass. Therefore, we should have predicted that the frequency distributions in Figure 65 should have been the same for stars of all spectral types.

The slow rotation of the later F-type stars, and of classes G, K, and M, must be the result of an evolutionary phenomenon not considered in the theory of contracting globules. I have previously suggested that this phenomenon is the formation of systems of planets. If, as seems likely, many main-sequence stars have developed not as single bodies but as planetary systems, a large part of the original angular momentum of the globule would now reside in the orbital motions of the planets.

The sun, for example, if it could absorb within its body all of its attendant planets, would spin around its axis at some sixty kilometers per second—becoming a fairly rapidly rotating single star. In reality, its equatorial rotational velocity is only two kilometers per second; and the remainder of the angular momentum is shared among the planets. To me, this is a very strong argument in favor of the hypothesis advanced by Kuiper and others, on different grounds, that planetary systems are the rule and not the exception among stars of spectral classes F, G, K, and M.

But what of the stars of early spectral class? Presumably they have developed from the contraction of the more massive globules, as single, double, or multiple stars (without planets). They possess, even now, the large angular momenta that were originally present in the globules. What will happen to the rotation of these stars as they subsequently evolve by the conversion of their hydrogen into helium?

In the first place, the contracting stage of evolution of these massive globules and protostars is even shorter than for the globules of solar mass. According to Henyey and his collaborators, Sirius, with a mass of 2.3 suns, required only three million years to change from a protostar of temperature 4000° absolute to its present state with a temperature of 10,000°. An even more massive star, like Tau Scorpii, may have needed only a few hundred thousand years. These intervals are so short that our chances of actually observing a protostar of large mass in the contracting stage are quite poor.

But we do observe many early-type stars which are subgiants, a little more luminous than main-sequence stars of the same spectral types. These are believed to have evolved appreciably from the main-sequence stage, because they have had enough time to use up a large fraction of their original supply of hydrogen by converting it into helium. These stars of advanced evolutionary age occur in certain galactic clusters, such as the Pleiades and the Hyades, and also among the single or binary subgiants.

The evolutionary tracks of stars in this second stage of their development are known from the theoretical work of Allan R. Sandage and M. Schwarzschild [see Fig. 33]. For example, the star Xi Geminorum is now a subgiant of spectral class $F5$; its visual absolute magnitude is $+1.9$, and its observed rotational velocity is, according to J. B. Oke and J. L. Greenstein, 73 kilometers per second. Its present spectral type implies a surface temperature of about 6500°. If we locate this star on an H-R diagram [like Fig. 33] by its temperature and its absolute magnitude, we find that the mass is about 1.5 suns, and that, to begin with, Xi Geminorum had an absolute magnitude of about $+3.3$ and a temperature of about 7500°. It is now about four times more luminous and 1000° cooler than when it was located on the main sequence. Now, as the temperature decreases from 7500° to 6500°, the light emitted by every square centimeter is less by a factor of $(6500/7500)^4 = 0.56$. But the total luminosity is now *greater* than before by a factor of four. Hence, its surface area has increased about seven times and its radius by a factor of 2.5, which is roughly in agreement with a more exact calculation by Oke and Greenstein giving nearly 2.

The present rotational velocity of 73 kilometers per second is statistically improbable for a main-sequence star of class $F5$. But if Xi Geminorum was originally a main-sequence star having a temperature of 7500° (corresponding to spectral class A8), its rotational velocity would have been $2 \times 73 = 146$ kilometers per second (because of its smaller original size), and this larger velocity of rotation is not at all unusual among main-sequence stars of class A8. Thus Xi Geminorum seems to fit our ideas concerning the conservation of angular momentum during the evolution of a star without planets.

In recent years a vast amount of new information on stellar rotation has become available through the work of Su Shu Huang, G. H. Herbig, J. F. Spalding, and A. Slettebak. Slettebak has systematically observed all accessible stars brighter than the fifth magnitude, of spectral types B2 to G0. The resulting distributions of the observed foreshortened axial rotations of those stars that lie on the main sequence are shown in the upper parts of Figure 66. These patterns are substantially similar to those derived from previous measurements.

But Slettebak has also measured the rotational velocities of many subgiant stars. For these Sandage has computed the ratio of the present radius to the original one, using substantially the same procedure

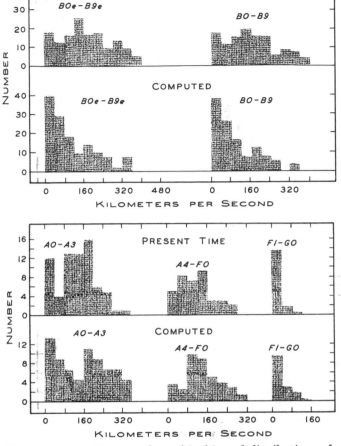

FIG. 66. The two upper diagrams show the observed distributions of rotational velocity for stars of different spectral types. Be stars (those with bright spectral lines) are separated from ordinary dark-line B stars. The lower diagrams give the corresponding distribution of rotations, computed by Allan R. Sandage for the remote past, when stars that are now subgiants were presumably on the main sequence. (Mount Wilson and Palomar Observatories diagram)

we employed for Xi Geminorum. This has enabled him to compute for each star the original, faster axial rotation—referred to the time when each star was a main-sequence object. The resulting values, using certain assumptions concerning the arrangement of mass within the evolving star, give a set of computed distributions, in the lower parts of Figure 66.

The computed frequencies should resemble those observed at present if recently formed stars on the main sequence rotate like those that were on this sequence some 10 or 100 million years ago. Actually, the computed patterns closely resemble the present ones for spectral classes Ao to Go, on the right of Figure 66. But among the B-type stars, on the left, the present distribution contains many more rapidly-rotating stars than the computed distribution.

Sandage remarks that this discrepancy may mean that the B stars have not conserved their original mass during their evolution. Actually, the nuclear conversion of hydrogen into helium reduces the mass of a star, at most, by only 0.7 per cent—an insignificant amount. But if other processes, such as loss of mass by rotational instability or corpuscular radiation, are at work, the original radius may have been much larger than that found by tracing its past history along a Sandage-Schwarzschild track.

Thus a subgiant star that now has a small observed rotational velocity may actually have possessed an even smaller velocity when it was on the main sequence, because with its larger initial mass its radius would also have been in excess of that computed with the Sandage-Schwarzschild values. In this case the computed histograms would show still more B stars with rapid rotation, and at first sight the agreement with the present distribution would become worse, not better. But in the distant past these more massive, original stars would have had earlier spectral types. A star shown in Figure 66 as being of class B might actually have been an O-type star, and we should compare the computed distribution with the present distribution of the O stars. In Slettebak's earlier work there was some indication that the O-type stars indeed show a greater proportion of slowly rotating objects than do the B and A stars. Slettebak remarks, "On the main sequence axial rotation appears to reach a maximum for the middle B-type stars."

Some Problems of Stellar Rotation

OTTO STRUVE

(*Sky and Telescope*, December 1960 and January 1961)

A good example of how a new field of astronomy can arise from a spark of scientific imagination is provided by a pioneer paper on the interpretation of stellar spectra, written by the English astronomer Captain W. Abney in 1877. If a star were rotating around an axis nearly at right angles to the line of sight, he asked, what observable changes would be produced in its spectrum?

Abney correctly pointed out that the observed spectrum is actually a composite of light from all portions of the star's disk. Because of the Doppler effect, wavelengths in the light of the receding edge of the star would be shifted toward the red; those from the approaching edge toward the violet. The net effect would be to broaden every line in the spectrum [see Fig. 64]. . . .

The actual effect of stellar rotation is illustrated in Figure 67 by diagrams of how a line would look in the spectra of stars with different rotational speeds. . . .

In the case of an individual star, the direction of its rotational axis is unknown, and the measured speed of rotation is only a minimum value of the true equatorial velocity. [See p. 174.] . . .

Astronomers have known for almost forty years that there are many stars in our Milky Way system that have rotation periods of only a few hours. Most of these fast-turning bodies, whose equatorial velocities may in exceptional cases be as great as 500 kilometers per second, belong to early spectral types—O, B, A, and early F. Single stars (those not members of binary systems) of the later spectral types, late F, G, K, M, N, R, and S, usually turn slowly. The sun belongs to this second group because its rotation period is nearly one month, with an equatorial speed of only two kilometers per second.

The fastest rotations of all occur among some emission-line stars of spectral class B. In such a very rapidly spinning object the centrifugal force at the equator approximately balances the gravitational force of the star, as has been pointed out by A. Slettebak and others.

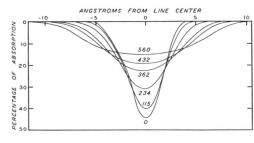

FIG. 67. The deepest curve, labeled 0 (kilometers per second) is for the 4026 helium line of Epsilon Cassiopeiae. The other curves are computed from it to show how increasing spin produces broadening. (Adapted from diagram by A. Slettebak in *The Astrophysical Journal*, The University of Chicago Press)

FIG. 68. Among the bright Pleiades, shown with surrounding nebulosity, are some of the most rapidly rotating stars known. (Lick Observatory photograph)

The equatorial layers of its atmosphere are highly unstable, and clouds of gas may escape to form a tenuous ring around the star.

Pleione, like some other rapidly rotating early-type stars in the Pleiades, has emission lines in its spectrum, and these have been explained as due to just such a gaseous ring. However, Pleione is not what astronomers call a zero-age main-sequence star; it has had time enough to convert much of its hydrogen into helium, thereby moving away from the main sequence in the H-R diagram toward the giant-star domain. It has long been a puzzle how such a star can now produce an equatorial ring, for it should have been smaller, and hence spinning faster, when on the main sequence. It would seem that Pleione should have relieved its instability long ago, and now be stable.

This paradox has been cleared up in an article published early this year by J. Crampin and F. Hoyle in the *Monthly Notices* of the Royal Astronomical Society. The two British astronomers show that the internal structure of a star undergoes a significant change during the transition from the zero-age main sequence to the giant stage. A fairly dense isothermal core forms inside the star, causing its equatorial regions to become more sensitive to centrifugal forces. Thus even though the rotation is slowing down, the increased sensitivity may allow new gaseous rings to form.

Crampin and Hoyle find that when an A- or B-type star on the main sequence ejects material from its equator it soon becomes stable for an interval of some millions of years. Then a second, brief stage of ejection sets in, followed by more millions of years of stability, and the process repeats. In this way, the star can continue to shed rings of gas long after it has left the zero-age main sequence.

An important observational result concerning young stars is due mainly to the work of G. H. Herbig, at Lick Observatory, on T Tauri-type variables [see p. 149]. As we have mentioned, normal main-sequence stars of late spectral type turn very slowly on their axes, but the T Tauri stars usually have broad absorption lines, indicating rotational velocities of the order of fifty or a hundred kilometers per second. These variables seem to be single stars and are believed to be very young. Still in the process of contraction, they have not yet reached the main sequence. Though such rotations are not exceptionally fast, and may not cause equatorial instability, they do suggest that very young stars often spin faster than those that have already arrived at the main sequence.

Consider, for example, a T Tauri star of spectral type G, with an equatorial rotation of seventy-five kilometers per second, in contrast to the two kilometers per second of a main-sequence G star like the sun. As the T Tauri variable contracts, it does not become a solar-type star. Instead, its evolutionary track in the H-R diagram carries its representative point leftward and slightly upward. Preserving angular momentum[1] while contracting, it may end up as an A or early F main-sequence star, whose rotational velocity could easily be around two hundred kilometers per second. Hence no contradiction is involved, at least for the present.

Rotation is an important factor in the problem of star formation. A principal difficulty has been to explain how a vast, diffuse cloud of gas and dust can ever contract into a star that has as little angular momentum as the 10^{53} units characteristic of a very rapidly spinning

---

[1] Angular momentum is a measure of the quantity of rotation. For a mass point it is mvr, where m is the mass, v its velocity, and r its distance from the center of motion. For an extended body, such as a large cosmic dust cloud, the angular momentum is the sum of the values for all the individual particles. In this article, angular momenta are expressed in units of gram centimeter^2 per second.

A- or B-type star. The whole solar system's angular momentum is only 3×10^{50} units. This stumbling block has been recognized for over a century in connection with Laplace's nebular hypothesis of the origin of the solar system. The famous French mathematician Henri Poincaré gave an illuminating account of the difficulty when he considered the case of a cloud of particles, moving in random directions, which condense to form the solar system. As the particles combine, their angular momenta will tend to cancel out, because their motions are random.

Poincaré estimated the degree of cancellation of the angular momenta in the following manner. He imagined an initial cloud, 100,000 astronomical units in radius, all of whose particles moved around the center in the *same* direction, under the force of gravity of the cloud. The cloud's angular momentum would be about 10^{55} units according to formulas of celestial mechanics. This is about 30,000 times greater than 3×10^{50}, the present angular momentum of the entire solar system. The value today, therefore, could result only if there were a much smaller tendency of the primordial swarm to rotate in a preferential direction.

A different way of looking at the problem of the low angular momenta of stars, compared with those of the interstellar clouds from which they condensed, is by a statistical theory like that W. H. McCrea developed to explain the origin of the solar system. He supposed, as did Poincaré, that the original cloud had a radius of 100,000 astronomical units, and consisted of separate cloudlets or condensations moving in random directions at one kilometer per second. The number of these cloudlets would be very great, and can be estimated from McCrea's formulas. If several had coalesced, then others colliding head on with the more massive cloud would contribute mass to the growing protostar while adding very little angular momentum. Other blobs, which did not collide with the protostar, would escape from the cloud, carrying off angular momentum. McCrea's calculations show that most of the original angular momentum can be removed in this way. But since the cancellation would not be complete, the resulting star should rotate at a relatively slow rate. This can account for a few slowly rotating O and B stars, but not for the numbers observed. . . .

Lyman Spitzer, Jr. has recently written: "In the earliest discussions of star formation it was realized that angular momentum posed serious problems in the theory of condensation. In the absence of external torques the rotational velocity of a mass of gas varies inversely as the radius, R. Stars of early spectral type are observed to rotate at speeds of about 100 km/sec. Since the present mean density of these stars exceeds the density of interstellar clouds by a factor of at least 10^{21}, their radii are less by a factor 10^7 than they were before contraction began. Two possibilities are present: either the initial angular momentum per unit mass was very low, corresponding to the extremely low velocity of 1 cm/sec, or else the angular momentum has been decreased by some process. Since the turbulent velocities in the interstellar medium are probably at least 0.1 km/sec, in a cloud with a mass of several suns, it seems unlikely that much material can be sufficiently quiescent to condense into stars without loss of angular momentum. . . ."

Like Spitzer, most investigators have assumed that during a star's contraction a large fraction of the angular momentum of the primordial interstellar cloud is lost. C. F. von Weizsaecker in 1947 suggested that a rotating protostar forms a concentration in a gaseous medium, all in turbulent motion. As a result of the turbulent viscosity, the rotation of the star itself is retarded, and the excess angular momentum is carried away to the outer parts of the gaseous envelope. The latter could then form a rapidly rotating disk from which the planets and their satellites could develop. However, Spitzer and others have concluded that von Weizsaecker's process would not be adequate to explain the slow axial rotations of the cooler dwarf stars.

Another possibility was first suggested by the Soviet astronomer V. G. Fessenkov and later discussed in detail by E. Schatzman in France: stars of early spectral class might lose a large amount of mass from their surface layers, which carry most of the angular momentum, by a process Fessenkov termed *corpuscular radiation*. But Schatzman pointed out that a fast-rotating star of spectral type A must lose about half its mass to become a slowly rotating F star. So drastic a loss of material, if it actually occurred, would probably not escape direct observation. Furthermore, Fessenkov's theory does not explain why there is such a sharp difference between stars earlier and later than spectral class $F2$, the former rotating rapidly, the latter slowly. This discontinuity is particularly striking in visual binary stars having main-sequence components of different spectral type. A component later than F_2 invariably shows a very small velocity of rotation, while a hotter member often, but not always, rotates faster.

Several authors have advanced hypotheses based upon the interaction of the rapidly rotating equatorial layers of a star with a magnetic field—either interstellar or belonging to the star itself. The first theory of this sort was advanced by H. Alfvén of Sweden in 1942. He assumed that the interstellar medium was ionized in the neighborhood of the star, whose magnetic field turned with it around an axis approximately coincident with the rotational axis. If, at the beginning, the ionized medium did not take part in the star's rotation, induced electric currents would be set up in it. The magnetic field of the star would cause the interstellar medium to rotate more and more rapidly, while the spinning of the star itself would be retarded.

Similar hypotheses involving magnetic coupling have been explored theoretically by the German scientists R. Lüst and A. Schlüter in 1955 and by L. Mestel in 1959. Schatzman is of the opinion that these processes are too slow and inefficient. A more effective means of removing angular momentum from a star by magnetic interaction was advanced last year by R. Ebert in Germany. From an overall view of these suggestions Spitzer concludes, "While detailed proof is still lacking, we may reasonably adopt the working hypothesis that a magnetic field can effectively reduce the angular momentum and permit the contraction of clouds into stars."

As I now see the problem of stellar rotation, there are some indications that the angular momenta of the T Tauri stars [see p. 149] have been retained during the contraction process, and there are even stronger reasons for believing that early-type stars leaving the main sequence and evolving into giants retain their angular momenta. But late-type stars (including the T Tauri objects) remain in the contracting stage for billions of years, while very massive O and B stars may take only a million years to reach the main sequence. This suggests that any mechanism that removes angular momentum from rapidly rotating newborn stars is likely to have more effect on stars of later types.

All of the suggestions we have discussed for slowing down stellar rotation have failed to explain the observed break at stellar type F_2 between rapidly and slowly turning stars. This may be accounted for by a mechanism proposed by Schatzman in 1958 at the Paris symposium on the H-R diagram. He considered a star with a pair of "sunspots," 100,000 kilometers apart, each with a magnetic field intensity of 10,000 gauss but with opposite polarities. Extending outward from each spot to a great distance above the surface of the star, the lines of magnetic force would be almost radial like spokes on a wheel. A puff of rarefied gas ejected at high speed from one of the spots would be highly ionized and would therefore travel far outward along these lines of force and would be compelled by the field to turn with the star. As it moved outward the gas would acquire more and more angular momentum from the star.

The nearly radial lines of force extend to distances much greater than the radius of the star, but ultimately loop back to the other spot. In the region where the lines of force curve back, the fast-moving ionized gases can no longer be restrained by the magnetic field and continue outward to escape from the star. Schatzman has computed that angular momentum can be carried away from the star, and that it is even possible for the rotation to approach zero.

Schatzman has applied this idea to stars of different spectral types. He points out that sunspots are probably connected with the so-called convective zones in the outermost layers of stars, where turbulent motions exist. These zones are produced by the ionization of hydrogen and are located near the surface of stars of spectral class F.

Figure 69 is Schatzman's schematic H-R diagram, in which the region labeled CI is the domain of stars in which spot activity should

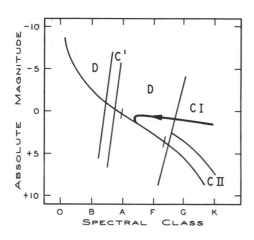

FIG. 69. E. Schatzman drew this spectrum-luminosity diagram to indicate which stars can lose angular momentum. Those in areas CI, CII and C' (but not D) should have surface activity, thus ejecting mass and losing momentum. The arrowed line is the evolutionary track of a star contracting to the main sequence, which extends from the upper left to the lower right. (Mount Wilson and Palomar Observatories diagram)

be prominent. For such stars, Schatzman's mechanism would work; rapidly rotating stars would lose angular momentum. The diagram shows the evolutionary track of a star that reaches the main sequence at spectral class A. Where the track is in region CII, the star's rotation will be braked. In region D the stars have no convective zones and presumably no spots. There Schatzman's mechanism would not operate, and the star would retain its angular momentum until reaching the main sequence.

The diagram shows another narrow strip, C', where stars can have surface convective zones produced by the ionization of helium. A star evolving through C' will also experience loss of angular momentum, but the effect is probably small because the strip is so narrow.

FIG. 70. According to E. Schatzman, contracting stars in region CI should be shaped as at the left, those in CII as at the right. (Mount Wilson and Palomar Observatories diagram)

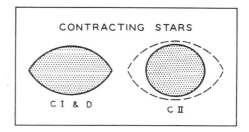

CONTRACTING STARS

C I & D

C II

From theoretical grounds, Schatzman suggests that in CI stars lose mass at their equators, while in CII mass loss occurs only through surface activity. This should influence the shapes of the stars in different parts of the H-R diagram as Figure 70 shows. His most recent work contains additional details, many of which agree with observational data.

One great unresolved difficulty is that the number of slowly rotating O, B, and A stars is greater than follows from Schatzman's theory. In other words, there are many more of these stars with small *observed* rotational velocities than we should expect. . . . Their existence does not seem to be explained by Schatzman's present hypothesis or, for that matter, by any other hypothesis advanced to date.

Stellar

Explosions

....

The most direct evidence of stellar evolution comes from observations of novae—stars that suddenly flare up from obscurity and blow
off a fraction of their mass. There can be no doubt but that such
violent outburst changes the star, and a good deal of effort has been
spent by astronomers in studying the novae, much of it discussed in
Volume 5 of this series, Starlight.

After a brief review of the observed behavior of novae and supernovae, this chapter is concerned with the physical conditions that lead
up to a nova's explosion, the full nature of changes that take place,
and what can be inferred from this about evolutionary processes in
stars.—TLP

....

New Stars

CECILIA H. PAYNE-GAPOSCHKIN

(*The Telescope*, November–December 1937)

Let us choose two scenes from the endless reels of scientific history.
A young man is walking by the sea. Highborn, wealthy, he is followed
by a suite of servants. He lifts his eyes to the starry sky, and as his
glance roves over Cassiopeia he notes a new star blazing there. It is

bright as Venus—but Venus never strayed so far from the ecliptic. He cannot believe his own eyes. He calls a halt, summons his servants, asks them if they see what he sees. He does not know it, but Modern Astronomy has been born.

We turn to a very different scene. An astronomer is scanning the heavens: not with the eye, not through a telescope. The instrument is a little magnifying glass, and the heavens are represented by a photographic negative. One star after another is examined, its image compared with another photograph of the same part of the sky, its brightness measured. Suddenly the astronomer pauses. Thousands of stars have been compared on the two photographs, and found to be similar on both; but on one plate there is a star where the other plate shows no image. Again there is a checkup; other photographs must be found and examined; the reality of the new star must be established. It is indeed a new star, and a careful study shows that it lies within the confines of a little hazy patch that is seen on all the photographs—even on those that do not show the star.

These two scenes are far apart in time; they represent the first discovery of a nova in the western world, and one of the most recent of such discoveries. In the year 1572 the Danish nobleman Tycho Brahe discovered the nova in Cassiopeia that bears his name. It is a matter of history that the discovery inspired him to found an observatory and to initiate the modern science of observational astronomy, for we may note in passing that until his day the Aristotelian doctrine that the stellar universe is fixed and immovable had held the belief of learned men, so that theoretical speculations were the only form that astronomy could take. It is difficult for us to imagine today how fundamental and startling was the discovery that a new star had appeared. Tycho Brahe, after making many observations, summarized his ponderings by stating his belief that the nova had been born from the Milky Way.

The second scene was enacted in the Harvard Observatory [in 1936]. The discovery of a new star was recently announced by Constance Boyd, who found it on several photographs of the southern sky. . . . The little hazy patch on which it lies is in reality a vast galaxy, and the nova is a member of that system, separated from our own island universe by a great gap, a gap that light takes 15 million years to span. . . .

These are not ordinary stars; they are not even ordinary novae, which are themselves most extraordinary stars. They are so much brighter than the more usual novae, so much more extreme in all their doings, that they have earned the name *supernovae*, now applied to them by almost all astronomers. The Swedish name, "upper-class novae," expresses the view that they are the aristocrats of the stellar universe; but as I hope to show in this article, they are excessively puffed up, they expend their resources with unequalled extravagance, their glory is evanescent, and they decline to a comparatively humble state, possibly even to straitened circumstances and eventual destitution.

A few figures speak more eloquently than all the flowers of rhetoric. Imagine our sun, an "ordinary" nova, and a supernova all placed side by side at a suitably large distance; the nova would shine 40,000 times as bright as the sun, and the supernova, 40 million times as brightly. If we could watch the nova come into being, we should probably see something like the following: a star about as bright as the sun would become slightly disturbed. Its light would probably fluctuate—perhaps for long periods of time—before the great spectacle began. But when the actual nova outburst started, it would go on with amazing suddenness. Most of the ordinary novae are the result of a change so tremendous and so rapid that there is scarcely anything in the stellar universe to compare with it. Within a few days the star seems to swell to perhaps 300 times the size of the sun. . . .

Tremendous as this picture is, it pales beside the spectacle of a supernova. At its brightest, a supernova would look about 30,000 times the size of the sun, and the debris of its explosion would fly into space at the rate of about 6000 miles a second. . . .

Since the beginning of modern astronomical observation, about a hundred ordinary novae have been recorded in the galactic system, and about the same number have been found during the last twenty years in one of the nearest of our sister galaxies, the Andromeda nebula. In the same interval of time, only about twenty well-authenticated supernovae have been discovered. This is interesting, for it tells us something about the relative commonness of the two sorts of nova. In astronomical terminology, the absolute magnitude at maximum of an ordinary nova is about -7, that of a supernova, about -17. In other words, supernovae are about ten thousand times as bright as normal novae, so that if the two kinds of nova really happened in equal numbers, the supernovae would be far more readily, and therefore far more commonly, observed. But that is far from being the case; the normal novae outnumber the supernovae by ten to one. Furthermore, most of the normal novae have been found more or less by accident, many of them with the naked eye; whereas almost all the supernovae have been so faint that they are discovered only after exhaustive searches. There is but one conclusion to be drawn: the normal novae are far more common than the supernovae, although, curiously enough, Tycho's nova, which started it all, was almost certainly a supernova.

All the well-authenticated supernovae, excepting Tycho's nova, are situated in other galaxies than ours. One of the most interesting blazed up in the middle of the Andromeda nebula in 1885, and all the others have fallen within or near the confines of other "island universes," usually spiral nebulae. The great luminosity attained by supernovae at maximum is shown by the fact that at their brightest they are not far from the total brightness of *the whole galaxy* in which they are situated; some few have even seemed to exceed their parent galaxy in brightness.

One of the great practical difficulties of the student of novae is the suddenness with which these stars brighten; they are seldom discovered before they reach their maximum brightness. . . .

It is in fact a huge undertaking to survey a galaxy from the inside. But to survey one from the outside is a more simple matter. With a suitable telescope it is possible to photograph hundreds or thousands of distant galaxies at once, and since supernovae are approximately as bright as the galaxies in which they appear, a photograph that will show a thousand galaxies is capable of revealing a supernova that appears in any one of them. Such a survey has in fact been maintained for some years under the joint auspices of Mount Wilson Observatory and the California Institute of Technology; and three of the known supernovae have been caught in this dragnet—two of them within the last few weeks. . . .

The spectrum of a nova is a spectroscopist's paradise—and despair. In the chaos of spectral lines we can read the story of an atmosphere set in violent motion, of matter pouring out through the surface of the star, flying off in irregular jets, obscuring, shining, absorbing by turns. There may be a dozen separable systems of lines—a dozen distinct regions or conditions visible at once. It is clear that the star has had at least a superficial explosion; the outer parts have been set in motion with speeds of hundreds of miles a second.

Beside the spectrum of a nova, the spectrum of a supernova might look simple to the uninitiated, for it is comparatively featureless. Supernovae are so distant that the spectra of only a few have been successfully photographed. . . . The spectra are not the clean-cut, complex groupings of bright and dark bands that the novae display. They show what was first taken to be a series of broad dark bands, but is now almost universally considered to be a few very wide *bright* lines. If the widening of these lines is attributed (as for ordinary novae) to a Doppler shift, which represents motion in the line of sight, the superficial layers of the star are rising with velocities of five or six thousand miles a second. This conclusion can be roughly drawn, be it noted, without a knowledge of the identity of the atoms that are moving; the width of the bright band (considered as a unit) is the only datum needed. . . .

The supernovae, the "aristocrats of the stellar system," are recognized wherever they appear; but when we look into their antecedents we find that we know very little about them. We do not know what they were before their sudden rise to glory, nor whence they derive their resources. Most of them we have recognized only during the brief era of extravagance when they were pouring out more energy in a second than any other sort of star can expend. They are so far away that we cannot follow their later careers. Tycho's nova has now fallen at least to one millionth of its maximum brightness, possibly even lower. It has been suggested that a supernova is a star that has given all it has; that the outburst has actually consumed all its substance. Even without entertaining such an extreme suggestion we can see how evanescent is the phenomenon that is so conspicuous— evanescent even in terms of human life, which is negligible in comparison with a stellar lifetime. Man may go "from shirtsleeves to shirtsleeves" in three generations; supernovae run from obscurity to obscurity in three decades, sometimes in three years. They are not the aristocrats of the stellar system; they are its *parvenus*.

Novae and Cosmic Rays

(*The Telescope*, July–August 1935)

The nature and origin of cosmic radiation are questions that have troubled scientists ever since these rays were discovered. Cosmic radiation was thought, at first, to be a form of light, a sort of super X ray, but recent experiments indicate that a large fraction, if not all, of the radiation consists of charged particles.

Recently, the California scientists Fritz Zwicky and Walter Baade suggested that novae might be the source of cosmic radiation. When a star "blows up," considerable matter is ejected with high velocity. These particles, reaching the earth and ultimately impinging on our detection apparatus, might produce effects similar to those of cosmic radiation.

Nova Herculis is the first bright nova that has occurred since the discovery of cosmic rays, and naturally, scientists were eager to test the hypothesis that these are of nova origin. Early observations indicated the possibility of a small increase in intensity of the radiation, but later and more extensive research has shown, first, that the observed increase was less than the probable error of measurement and, second, that the cosmic radiation from the direction of Hercules did not show an increase.

It may be argued, of course, that cosmic rays come only from "supernovae" and that the Nova Herculis outburst was not sufficiently intense to produce the phenomenon. The failure to secure positive results, however, casts doubt upon the theory.

Are Cosmic Rays
Swan Songs of Stars?

GERALD WENDT

(*Monthly Bulletin of the Hayden Planetarium*, December 1935)

The most important thing that can be said about cosmic rays is how much we do *not* know. But, after all, anybody who is working in

science is much more interested in the puzzles—in the unknown—
than he is in the facts that can be put into books.

So if you ask me what cosmic rays are, my first impulse is to say,
"Nobody knows, but we have plenty of clues." And that is why they
are interesting. We call these rays cosmic because *cosmos* comes from
an ancient Greek word for the universe. It implies that they come to
the earth from some remote regions of space, from somewhere far
beyond the limits of the solar system and probably far beyond our
own little galaxy, which we call the Milky Way. We know that they
come from enormous distances, and we think that they are vibrations
of the ether, just as light is, or X rays. But they cannot be seen because the human eye is not sensitive to them.

That is why they have to be studied and measured with instruments
that the astronomer has not yet used. Again and again astronomy
has advanced through the perfection of instruments by other scientists. The telescope itself was not originally an astronomical instrument. The spectroscope, which now tells us so much about the
temperature and composition of the stars, was developed by a chemist. And so cosmic ray instruments are now being developed by
physicists, and perhaps it will not be long before astronomers are
exploring distant universes by means of these invisible rays.

When the rays go through a brass box which has the correct
electrical attachments, they cause the air in the box to become a
conductor of electricity, so that a small current goes through the air
in the box. With modern means of amplification such as are used
in radio, this tiny current can be made to register or to bark on a
loudspeaker. The rays are so rare that one can sit before such an
instrument and actually count the rays one by one as they plunge
through the box. Such a complicated apparatus, with nothing to see,
means that only a very few people have ever really had any proof
that these rays exist. Nevertheless, cosmic-ray counters have been sent
up in stratosphere balloons, without any human crew, and the rays
have been counted by radio impulses sent out automatically from
the balloons and received in laboratories on the ground. The cosmic
messages captured and relayed by a balloon are recorded until the
balloon is lost or comes down.

Balloons have been used so often because the great question about
these rays is, Where do they come from? Our chief reason for thinking that they come from outer space, rather than from any point on

the earth, is that the higher you go, the more plentiful these rays become. Ten miles of our atmosphere offer much more resistance than millions of miles of empty space, and so the rays are greatly thinned out before they reach the surface of the earth. Investigations of this effect of altitude have been made on all stratosphere flights and on a great many expeditions to the peaks of high mountains, and all show that there are more cosmic rays the higher you go.

It has been suggested that the rays originate in the lightning of distant thunder storms, but R. A. Millikan [at the California Institute of Technology] disposed of this idea by devising what amounts to a perfect natural telescope. He lowered his brass box device on a cable deep into the waters of Muir Lake, just below Mount Whitney in California, which is surrounded by cliffs and high mountains. These act just like the tube of a telescope to prevent rays reaching the measuring box from the sides. Millikan thus proved that cosmic rays do, indeed, come from above. . . .

What causes them is another matter. If they are waves in the ether, they are the shortest waves known. The waves of visible light are ten thousand times as long as X-ray waves, but these in turn are a thousand times as long as cosmic-ray waves. Now, it is well known that the shorter a wave is the more energy it takes to produce it. We know that a red-hot piece of iron must be heated to a much higher temperature before it gets white hot. The red waves are longer, and it takes less energy in the wire to send them out. On the same principle it would take tremendous energy to produce waves that are ten million times shorter. Heat alone could not do it. Electrons also could not.

In fact the only conceivable source of such intense energy is the actual explosion of atoms, that is, the transformation of the material that composes the atom into radiating waves. We have no proof that this really happens, but we are quite certain that if matter could be transformed into ether waves, they would be of this type, that is, extremely short and energetic waves. This is the basis for thinking that cosmic rays are the "death rattle" of dying atoms and represent the annihilation of matter and its conversion into the energy of these waves. On this supposition cosmic rays tell us that somewhere out in space a star is dying and its material is going forth in the form of rays.

But no one can be sure what we mean by the dying of a star. There are some astronomers, like Sir James Jeans and Sir Arthur Eddington in England, who think that this is the destiny of all the stars and that ultimately they will all disappear in radiation. This would mean that the universe is gradually running down and sooner or later—i.e., after many billions of years—nothing will be left but cold dead matter and various sorts of rays.

Others, including Millikan, argue that other stars are at the same time also being formed and that the universe is thus eternal. . . .

New stars do occasionally appear in the sky. Two years ago a brilliant star flashed forth in the constellation of Hercules; this star is known as Nova Herculis. The star is so far away that it takes light 1300 years to reach us from there. Hence, the actual event took place in about A.D. 635. Astronomers do not know why a faint star suddenly becomes bright during the course of a few weeks or months. Can cosmic rays provide any evidence?

In the case of this new star in Hercules two European physicists arranged their experiments in such a way that the light from this star entered their cosmic-ray telescope once a day. They were surprised to find that whenever this happened there was a definite increase in the number of rays recorded. This would mean that the flaring up of the star involved the destruction of some of its atoms.

Probably the star had always been there, but was dark or cool so that it could not be seen. Some kind of explosion took place in which tremendous energy was released. Both cosmic rays and visible light were sent out. This gives us a hint. It is possible that only a part of the star's matter was destroyed and changed into energy, which thus heated the rest of the star to such a temperature that it became white hot and therefore visible.

Now why should any part of the star be destroyed? Here Professor MacMillan [of the University of Chicago] suggests an idea that is clever but that most astronomers cannot accept without real evidence that it is true. He supposes, first, that stars gradually grow by sweeping up particles and atoms in their path. A giant star is formed which gradually cools and gets denser. The more dense it becomes, the greater is the pressure on the material at the center. Even at the center of the earth, which is a tiny body astronomically speaking, the pressure is 22,000 tons per square inch. In a great star it is probably millions of tons. MacMillan's suggestion is that at this tremendous pressure the atom caves in: electrons at the surface of the atom are crushed into the nucleus at the center. The former are negative electrons, and the latter are positive, so that they neutralize each other. If this happens, the atom would cease to exist, being completely transformed into cosmic rays. When this point is reached, tremendous quantities of these rays passing out through the outer layers of the star heat them and vaporize them, so that the star is once more a hot, gaseous giant. In this way he explains the appearance of a nova. Perhaps such stars go through this cycle repeatedly, becoming great red giants, then cooling down to become dense dwarfs, only to explode once more.

This, however, is not the whole story, because light and cosmic rays would be constantly emitted from the stars and would be filling all of space. It is Millikan's idea that individual atoms are formed in empty space from these rays. First, electrons and protons are generated; these combine to make hydrogen atoms, and these in turn combine to make atoms of helium and oxygen and carbon. He supposes that cosmic rays are produced when this happens—in other words, that part of the material of the hydrogen atom turns into cosmic rays when such atoms combine to make helium or oxygen. Here again the cosmic rays that we count would be evidence of the formation of matter.

These far-reaching speculations on cosmic rays, at a time when the subject was very new, are interesting because they hint at much of what has since been learned: nuclear reactions synthesizing heavier elements from hydrogen in stellar interiors, the effect of high pressures, and the formation of matter from radiation. However, it is now known that primary cosmic rays from outside the atmosphere are high-speed ions (particles, not X rays), some of them coming from the sun. Distant sources of cosmic rays would be difficult to check with a cosmic-ray telescope because interstellar magnetic fields deflect the high-speed charged particles, which probably "bounce around" for quite a while in the Milky Way rather than following a straight path from each source. Undoubtedly, the supernovae and novae (as well as flare stars and many others) eject ions, but the resulting cosmic rays do not provide direct means of observing stellar explosions.—TLP

II

Spendthrift Stars

DONALD H. MENZEL

(*The Telescope*, January–February 1939)

The scale of living of the stars is in almost every respect a great exaggeration of the scales to which we are accustomed. In size, in motion, in temperature, they exhibit values that are enormous compared with those found on earth. And in changes of brightness no star exhibits greater extremes than the supernovae—those abruptly exploding objects that make even the novae appear relatively mild. . . .

It is both difficult and important to learn something about the nature of these extremely brilliant and explosive objects. For a few of them the changes in light have been followed for more than a hundred days after the explosion. One of the most recently discovered supernovae is that found in the external galaxy NGC1003 by Zwicky on Mount Palomar in September 1937. Dorrit Hoffleit has studied this star on Harvard photographs, which have revealed its explosive course for over a year, commencing from a point ten days before its discovery. Her observations confirm those recently published by Baade and Zwicky in *The Astrophysical Journal,* and include a longer period of time, both before and after the dates of their photographs.

On August 31, 1937, the supernova was apparently at its brightest, at magnitude 12.8. In October of 1938 there was visible in the same position a very faint star, of magnitude 17.4, which faded in a month to magnitude 17.8. If this faint star is really the remains of the once brilliant supernova, and not a foreground star, its light course has indeed been peculiar. For the first three months after maximum light it dropped four magnitudes—a fairly normal rate. But thereafter, as shown by the combined Mount Palomar, Mount Wilson, and Harvard observations, it varied less than half a magnitude in over two hundred days—a much slower speed than that known for any other supernova.

Light curves representing fairly long time intervals—more than a hundred days—are available for only seven other supernovae. With the exception of the curve for SS Ursae Majoris, which is also peculiar in other respects, they are similar in showing that the supernovae fade at first very rapidly and later more slowly. After the first hundred days, however, the slope of the curve of a diminishing supernova may be extremely steep, like that of S Andromedae, or very gradual, like the curve of the supernova in NGC1003. Such differences in speed of decline make it impossible to draw any inferences for those objects that have not actually been observed, or to extrapolate a curve at maximum for the stars that have been discovered—as usually happens—long after the maximum has been reached.

....

The Crab Nebula, a Probable Supernova[1]

NICHOLAS U. MAYALL

(*The Telescope*, September–October 1939)

In the year of our Lord 1054, when Omar Khayyam was a small boy, and the battle of Hastings still twelve years in the future, an unknown Chinese astronomer, perhaps weary and sleepy after working all night, was astonished to see a strange and brilliant new star appear in the graying eastern sky just before sunrise. The object was located in the Chinese stellar division of Peih, which we know as the constellation of Taurus (the Bull), a little less than halfway from the Hyades (the center of Peih), toward Pih Ho (the Twins, Castor and Pollux). Although this noteworthy astronomical event occurred on the Fourth of July, and the Chinese probably had a plentiful supply of firecrackers, it was not appropriately celebrated, so far as we know. Instead, the astronomer carefully noted the new star's approximate position with respect to a familiar star, Teen Kwan, known to us as the third-magnitude star Zeta Tauri, and during the next six months watched it fade to invisibility.

By one of those remarkably fortunate coincidences, a Japanese astronomer, also unknown, witnessed the apparition of the same strange star. In addition to describing its place among the known stars, he recorded that it was as bright as the planet Jupiter. As we shall see in

[1] Reprinted from Astronomical Society of the Pacific *Leaflet* 119, January 1939.

a later paragraph, this brightness estimate is a datum of crucial importance.

When the strange new star disappeared from view in the middle of the eleventh century, the two records of its temporary appearance likewise dropped from sight, and they remained hidden in the Oriental chronicles for nearly nine hundred years. In fact, these Chinese and Japanese observations did not come to the attention of modern astronomers until 1921 and 1934, respectively.

We now turn our attention from the apparition of the temporary star of 1054 to the discovery and history of the Crab nebula, which lies quite near Zeta Tauri. Several authorities credit its first discovery, in 1731, to John Bevis, an English physician whose avocation was astronomy. . . . The Crab nebula apparently remained unobserved until 1758, when it was rediscovered by Charles Messier, a French astronomer. . . .

The next significant observational records of the Crab nebula are those of Sir William Herschel. He carefully examined the nebula nine times between 1783 and 1809, and finally concluded, "As all the observations of the large telescopes agree to call this object resolvable, it is probably a cluster of stars at no very great distance beyond their gaging powers." Somewhat later his son, Sir John Herschel, came to the same conclusion, now known to be false, but which more than a hundred years ago seemed consistent with the best visual observations. . . .

FIG. 71. The Crab nebula. (Mount Wilson and Palomar Observatories photograph)

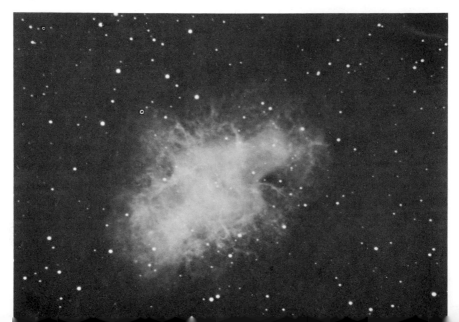

The first photograph was obtained in 1892 by Isaac Roberts, who was quick to notice that the nebula hardly resembled any of the existing drawings. Later photographs by Keeler, Curtis, Ritchey, and others then established the significant fact that the roughly oval form and peculiar filamentary structure of the Crab nebula had no faithful counterpart among the thousands of known nebulae. While examining some of the Lowell Observatory negatives, C. O. Lampland discovered, but did not measure, certain motions within the Crab nebula. The much more difficult task of determining by actual measurement the nature of these motions was soon undertaken by John C. Duncan, who used two Mount Wilson Observatory plates taken eleven and a half years apart. He selected twelve of the more conspicuous filaments distributed around the edge of the nebula and measured their positions with respect to surrounding stars on each plate. The results showed that each filament had moved in a direction generally outward from the center of the nebula. In other words, the very important fact emerged, in 1921, that the Crab nebula is *expanding*.

About the same time that the expansion of the Crab nebula became known, the Swedish astronomer Lundmark, using material extracted from existing translations of old Chinese chronicles, published a list of suspected temporary stars seen in ancient times. In this paper, he remarked, among other things, that several suspected strange stars were located in parts of the sky where there were known nebulae. One of the objects he listed was the strange star first observed by the Chinese on July 4, 1054. While Lundmark pointed out that its position in the sky agreed closely with that of the Crab nebula, he did not, in the absence of other data, suggest any closer relation between the two objects.

With the knowledge of the expansion measures and of the old Chinese observation of 1054, there was now available some tangible evidence to consider seriously the hypothesis that the Crab nebula originated as a "nova," and this possibility undoubtedly occurred to many astronomers. . . .

It is easy to see that the size of the nebula divided by its annual rate of increase gives the time interval since it began to expand, although in this case it has to be assumed that the rate of expansion has remained constant. The result of such a calculation for the Crab nebula was briefly mentioned by Edwin Hubble, who stated "the nebula is expanding rapidly and at such a rate that it must have required about nine hundred years to reach its present dimensions."

Hubble's conclusion did much to strengthen the case for an identification of the nebula with the old nova, for it was now evident, within the errors of the observations, that (1) the nebula began to expand at about the same time the old nova was seen, and (2) both objects were in the same part of the sky. . . .

The first spectroscopic observations of the nebula were made from 1913 to 1915 at the Lowell Observatory by V. M. Slipher, who found the spectrum to be of the type characteristic of an incandescent gas; that is, the light is concentrated into a few colors or bright lines, similar to, but not identical with, the radiations emitted by ordinary neon and helium advertising signs. However, the most interesting facts were (1) each bright line was split into two components, and (2) the separation between the two components was different in different parts of the nebula. . . .

When spectra of all parts of the nebula were eventually obtained—at Lick Observatory in 1937—the peculiar behavior of the double bright lines could readily be accounted for; it is merely the consequence of the expansion of the nebula. . . . It probably is expanding in all directions from its center, and if we record its spectrum at that point, the part of the nebulosity on the near side will be approaching the observer, and its spectrum lines will be decreased in wavelength, while the part on the far side will be receding, and its spectrum lines will be increased in wavelength. In other words, a normally single bright line will be split into two parts, and most important of all, the separation of them will be a measure of the linear speed of expansion. Moreover, if the slit of the spectrograph is long enough to extend entirely across the nebula, we should expect the bright lines to be bow shaped, that is, they should be double near the center of the nebula, gradually coming together at its edges. The reason for this is, of course, that at the center of the nebula the motion of expansion is mostly *in* the line of sight, while at the edges it is predominantly *across* the line of sight. The spectrum of the Crab nebula taken at the Lick Observatory shows just this phenomenon, for the bright lines are very noticeably bowed, or lens shaped. . . .

Finally, the spectrographic measures also can be used to give some very valuable information about the distance of the nebula if the assumption is made that it is expanding at the same rate in the line of sight as it is across the line of sight. This is done, in principle, as follows: the maximum separation of the components of the double bright lines, when expressed in the proper units, is the *linear* velocity of expansion (in *miles* per second), while the rate of increase in size of the nebula, obtainable from Duncan's measures, is the *angular* velocity of expansion (in *seconds of arc* per year). As soon as any quantity, in this case the velocity of expansion, is known in both linear and angular measure, a very simple calculation gives the distance. In this manner, we estimate that the Crab nebula is about 5000 light years from the earth.

The Crab nebula at once becomes a unique object, because, instead of being regarded as the product of an ordinary nova, it must be seriously considered as the "remnant of a supernova." This inference follows from the distance estimate of 5000 light years and from the Japanese brightness estimate of the object seen in 1054, the combination of the two data yielding the intrinsic luminosity of the nova. The calculation indicates that the old nova of 1054 was at least one hundred times as luminous as an ordinary nova.

In conclusion it may be said that the identification of the Crab nebula as a former supernova possesses a degree of probability sufficiently high to warrant its acceptance as a reasonable working hypothesis. Bearing this in mind, together with the fact that supernovae are very rare and puzzling objects, about which little is known, perhaps we can appreciate why the Crab nebula is one of the most interesting objects in the sky.

*Despite Mayall's cautious conclusion, there is no doubt but that the Crab nebula is in fact a remnant of a supernova explosion in our galaxy about nine hundred years ago. At 5000 light years' distance, it is a beautiful record of a violent event at a safe distance, and has provided data confirming the radioastronomers' theory of synchrotron radio emission. (Its radio emission and light are polarized.)—*TLP

....

Another Supernova
Radio Star

DORRIT HOFFLEIT

(*Sky and Telescope*, November 1952)

Tycho's nova of 1572 has been tentatively identified as the source of radio radiation at 158.5 megacycles per second observed recently at the Jodrell Bank Experimental Station, Cheshire, England, by R. Hanbury Brown and C. Hazard. They discuss the problem in *Nature* for August 30. The 1950 position of the new radio source is $0^h21^m49^s$, $+64°15'$, which compares well with the position of Tycho's star at $0^h22^m0^s.2$, $+63°52'.2$. The chief difficulty in observing the new source is its proximity to another intense radio star known as Cassiopeia I, which may account for its not having been observed before.

The intensity of this radio star is less than one tenth that of the radio source that was previously identified with the Crab nebula. This is also the difference in brightness of the two supernovae at their respective maxima (about -4.0 for Tycho's star, -6.5 to -7.0 for the Crab nebula). Their present integrated photographic magnitudes must differ by over six magnitudes; in fact, no visible remnant of Tycho's nova has even been observed.

The discovery of this new radio source supports the conclusion, previously based only on the Crab nebula identification, that "the remnant of a supernova is a source of intense radio-frequency radiation." The investigators state, "This phenomenon is of great interest, since no satisfactory mechanism for the generation of the radiation has yet been proposed."

....

A Radio Source and a
Chinese Supernova

DORRIT HOFFLEIT

(*Sky and Telescope*, September 1953)

The Taurus radio source coincides in position with the Crab nebula, the remnant of a galactic supernova recorded in the Orient in A.D.

1054. This suggested to the Russian astronomers, I. S. Shklovsky and P. P. Parenago, that further comparisons of the positions of radio stars with old records of novae should be made.

One of the most intense radio sources is in Cassiopeia at $23^h21^m.2$, $+58°32'$ (1950), where the British astronomer, D. W. Dewhirst and Walter Baade have photographed faint nebulosity. The Russians find that this is in a region where Chinese astronomers observed a new star for six months in the year 369. While the ancient record of this object is brief and vague, it appears to indicate a supernova rather than an ordinary nova.

···

Report on Supernovae

(*Sky and Telescope*, December 1960)

An international search for supernovae in distant galaxies was described in a paper [presented at the August 1960 meeting of the American Astronomical Society] by F. Zwicky, M. L. Humason, and H. S. Gates of Mount Wilson and Palomar Observatories. Participating in the program in addition to Palomar are the Steward Observatory at Tucson, Arizona, and the observatories in Berne, Switzerland, and Meudon, France. Funds for the survey have been made available by the National Science Foundation and the Swiss National Science Fund.

A first search for supernovae was conducted by Zwicky and J. J. Johnson with the 18 inch Palomar Schmidt telescope during the five years preceding World War II. They found nineteen objects, among them the brightest supernova ever observed, in the dwarf spiral galaxy IC4182. At its maximum brightness, this star was more than a billion times as luminous as the sun.

As a result of the present survey, which began in 1954, the number of supernovae detected has been raised to forty-four. Of these, about fifteen were discovered during the past two years by Humason with the 48-inch Schmidt telescope.

Several classes of supernovae have been found, with their absolute luminosities ranging from ten million to over a billion suns. The light curves of the different classes are not alike. Each type of supernovae has its characteristic spectra, bearing no apparent resemblance to the spectra of common novae. In spite of concerted efforts by observers and theoreticians alike, supernovae spectra have not yet been satisfactorily interpreted.

In presenting the paper, Zwicky pointed out that some of the bright galaxies may have supernovae occurrences at a much higher rate than the average of one every three hundred years. For instance, in each of the spirals NGC3184, 4321, and 6946, three supernovae have appeared in the past sixty years. And according to the number of remnants of probable old supernovae found in the Milky Way by radioastronomers, our own system would also seem to have a high frequency.

··

Pray for an Explosion!

DORRIT HOFFLEIT

(*Sky and Telescope*, April 1944)

George Gamow of George Washington University continues to theorize and to investigate the consequences of theories on stellar evolution. In a note on "Contractive Evolution of Massive Stars" in *The Astrophysical Journal*, he discusses such types as P Cygni and Wolf-Rayet (varieties of high-luminosity blue stars), nuclei of planetary nebulae, and supernovae.

The nuclei of planetary nebulae (not related to planets) are stars which are several magnitudes fainter than the Wolf-Rayet stars, and Gamow assumes them to represent a consequence of Wolf-Rayet evolution. The temperatures at the centers of these two classes of stars are computed to be of the order of one hundred million and 1 billion degrees centigrade, the planetary nuclei being the hotter. At such temperatures, large quantities of neutrinos are produced. "The rapid cooling of the interior through the escape of high-energy neutrinos must inevitably cause a rapid collapse of the stellar body," says Gamow. This would be observed as a violent supernova explosion, which he hopes may be seen in one of the known planetary nebulae during our lifetime.

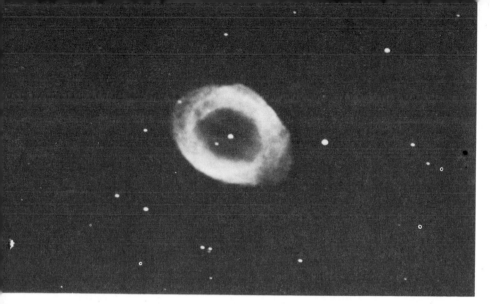

FIG. 72. The Ring nebula in Lyra. (Mount Wilson and Palomar Observatories photograph)

In addition to the nebula shot off by a supernova, there will also be a star remainder. A planetary nebula, like the one shown in Figure 72, combines these features—central star and spherical shell of gas. Such nebulae could be results of explosions, but do not show as much filamentary structure as the Crab nebula and may not have involved the violence of a supernova. Gamow assumes that a planetary nebula was formed before any supernova explosion, as the central star was becoming more and more unstable. There is separate evidence of nebular shells like planetary nebulae forming around ordinary novae. This and other details about gas ejection from Wolf-Rayet stars are covered in Volume 5 of this series, Starlight.—TLP

Nuclei of
Planetary Nebulae

GEORGE S. MUMFORD

(*Sky and Telescope*, May 1965)

Planetary nebulae are expanding shells of rarefied gas that are caused to shine by hot blue central stars. As such a nebula evolves, it grows from a tiny disk of high surface brightness to a very large object of low brightness. Hence detailed observations are easier for the nuclei of old planetaries, because of lessened interference from the nebulosity.

G. O. Abell of the University of California at Los Angeles has made a special study of the central stars of eighty-six old planetaries discovered on photographs taken with the Palomar Mountain 48-inch Schmidt telescope. In sixty-five cases the central star could be identified, and for thirty nuclei he measured magnitude and color photoelectrically with the 100-inch and 60-inch reflectors at Mount Wilson. For the other thirty-five he used photographic data.

The UCLA astronomer deduces that a typical central star from his sample of sixty-five has a photographic absolute magnitude of +5, a surface temperature of at least 50,000° Kelvin, and a radius about 0.1 the sun's. Individual stars, however, may deviate considerably from these values.

In the *Publications* of the Astronomical Society of the Pacific, Abell points out: "These data, therefore, support the conclusion of [C. R.] O'Dell that some planetary nebulae nuclei have dimensions of white dwarfs, and that the planetary nebula phenomenon may represent a stage in the evolution of certain stars to the white dwarf state."

....

White Dwarfs

OTTO STRUVE

(*Sky and Telescope,* December 1953 and January 1954)

In 1924 A. S. Eddington derived the theoretical relation between mass and luminosity for stars that obey the perfect-gas laws [see p. 57]. When he compared the theoretical relation with observational data, he found agreement not only for such diffuse stars as Capella, whose mean density is about that of air, but also for red dwarfs like the sun, whose material is denser than water, and the double star Krueger 60, which is as dense as iron.

Eddington was much surprised that so wide a variety of stars obeyed the mass-luminosity relationship. In his own words, "Something very different was being sought for," namely, the *departure* of dense stars from the theoretical mass-luminosity relation that might result from a failure to conform to the equation of perfect gases. (The pressure is proportional to the density and the temperature of the gas, and inversely proportional to the mean weight of the gas particles.)

But "the big terrestrial atoms which begin to jam at a density near that of the liquid state do not exist in the stars. The stellar atoms have been trimmed down by the breaking off of all their outer electrons. . . . Consequently we can go on squeezing ever so much more before these tiny atoms, or ions, jam in contact. At the density of water or even of platinum there is still any amount of room between the trimmed atoms; and waste space remains to be squeezed out, as in a perfect gas."[1] In other words, the perfect-gas laws remain in force for all the stars of the main sequence. . . . These considerations make it rather difficult for a star not to conform!

Yet a truly enormous number of stars in our galaxy are of the "non-conformist" type; most of these stars are white dwarfs, of which the most famous representative is the faint companion of Sirius. The following simple computations demonstrate the peculiar properties (large relative mass, small luminosity, and extremely high density) that are characteristic of this and other white dwarfs.

In 1844 F. W. Bessel found that the proper motion of Sirius is not uniform, but roughly sinusoidal, with a periodicity of fifty years in the length of the waves. Eighteen years later Alvan G. Clark first saw the faint star, Sirius B, whose gravitational attraction upon Sirius A produces the irregularity of motion detected by Bessel. The parallax of Sirius is 0.38 second of arc, and the angular size of the orbit of B around A is 7.6 seconds; therefore the linear size is $7''.6/0''.38$, or 20 astronomical units (about the distance between Uranus and the sun).

Kepler's third law tells us that the total mass of a double star, in terms of the mass of the sun, is equal to the ratio of the cube of the orbital semimajor axis to the square of the period, $20^3/50^2$, or 3.2. This total mass must be shared between Sirius A, which from its normal spectrum has a mass of about 2.2 suns, and Sirius B, for which there remains the difference, $3.2 - 2.2 = 1$ solar mass.

[1] *Stars and Atoms*, Yale University Press, New Haven, 1927, p. 39.

But Sirius B is about ten magnitudes fainter than Sirius A, making its absolute visual magnitude about +11.3. (The sun has an absolute magnitude of +4.85.) Thus Sirius B emits only about 1/10,000 the light of Sirius A, and 1/400 the light of the sun. Yet its mass is the same as the sun's, and if it obeyed the mass-luminosity relation, it would emit the same amount of light as the sun, two ergs per second per gram. In reality it emits only 1/200 erg per second per gram.

From the studies of stellar spectroscopy by W. S. Adams at the Mount Wilson Observatory we know that Sirius B has approximately the same color as Sirius A. Their surface temperatures are thus the same. The only way we can explain the 10,000-times deficiency in the total light of Sirius B is to suppose that its surface area is 10,000 times smaller than that of Sirius A. This makes its radius the square root of 10,000 or 100 times smaller than that of Sirius A, which is itself about twice the sun's radius. Thus, Sirius B has a radius about 1/50 that of the sun, and only 1/125,000 the sun's volume. The masses are the same; therefore the density of Sirius B is 125,000 times the mean density of the sun.

Even more fantastic is the mean density of the star AC +70°8247. G. P. Kuiper has estimated that this white dwarf has a diameter only about 0.005 that of the sun, or about one half of the earth's. It is believed to be of about one solar mass, and its mean density must be 10 million times the solar density. W. Krogdahl[2] has computed (with slightly different data): "At the surface of the earth a little 0.1 inch cube of average stuff from this star would weigh almost 1300 pounds. At the surface of the star, however, this same pinch of material would weigh 2,200,000 tons, for the surface gravity of this white dwarf is calculated to be 3,400,000 times the earth's. Here a 150-pound man, though his body were as strong as steel, would be crushed to tissue thinness by his own 250,000 tons of weight. The enormous compressive force of the star's tremendous surface gravity causes its atmosphere to increase in density about a billion times through a depth of just fifteen feet; consequently the whole atmosphere of this white dwarf is probably only ten to fifteen feet thick!"

The steep density gradient implied by the small size and large mass of the star has an interesting consequence, pointed out some years ago by E. Schatzman. Just as on the earth the dense metals have sunk

[2] The Astronomical Universe, Macmillan, New York, 1952, p. 393.

into the deepest core, while the lighter substances, like water and especially the gases, have risen to the surface, so in a white dwarf all available hydrogen floats on top of a dense inner mass, and gives rise to a thin atmosphere of hydrogen-rich gases. The atmosphere is under heavy pressure from the attraction of the star as a whole, so that very broad hydrogen lines are produced—about as observed under pressures of many atmospheres in the laboratory.

The broadening of the hydrogen lines in stellar atmospheres is caused by the electrical fields of ionized atoms and free electrons which happen, in their random flights, to come close to a radiating hydrogen atom. This is related to the Stark effect [broadening of spectral lines when an element is influenced by an electric field] in the laboratory. The amount of the broadening depends upon the pressure of the atmosphere, which in turn depends upon the surface gravity of the star. In an ordinary main-sequence star like the sun, the surface gravity is about thirty times greater than at the surface of the earth, but because of the very low density of the sun's reversing layer, the pressure is only a small fraction of one atmosphere. We have seen that in the exceptional case of the star AC +70°8247, surface gravity is about three million times greater than the earth's, which would make it about 100,000 times greater than the surface gravity of the sun. The corresponding pressure in the reversing layer would then be many times that of the earth's atmosphere and the hydrogen lines would be broadened to such an extent that they would flow together into a fairly uniform continuum of absorption. This might explain why there are white dwarfs with purely continuous spectra. According to Kuiper, AC +70°8247 has such a continuous spectrum.

In other white dwarfs the hydrogen lines are visible, but they are usually much broader than in main-sequence stars of spectral type A. A study by Kuiper of the line profiles of two such objects, 40 Eridani B and Wolf 1346, has given surface gravities about 10,000 times greater than the surface gravity of the sun. Assuming that these stars have masses of the order of the sun's, and about 1/100 the sun's radius, the computed surface gravity would be 10,000 times the sun's —as was found from the line profiles.

It must, however, be admitted that we have no satisfactory theory of the spectra of the white dwarfs. A few of them show fairly narrow hydrogen lines together with lines of iron and other metals. Others have strong helium lines and weak hydrogen lines. This might have been expected if the white dwarfs had consumed nearly all of their original hydrogen through nuclear reactions. L. Mestel has suggested that the hydrogen now found in the atmosphere of a white dwarf such as Sirius B may represent not the small remaining fraction of its original supply of hydrogen, but gas which this star has collected from interstellar space during its long lifetime. It is therefore possible that some stars have collected a reasonably large amount of surface hydrogen, while others have failed to do so, either because they never happened to travel through a region of space containing dense interstellar gas clouds or because their motions through such clouds may have been too fast for the process of accretion to operate.

About twenty-five years ago W. J. Luyten started a systematic search on Harvard Observatory photographs for faint stars having large proper motions. Nearly 100 million stars were examined with a blink instrument which compares two plates, in this case taken some twenty-five years apart. About 100,000 stars were found to have measurable proper motions, of which some three thousand had *large* proper motions. All these stars must be close to the sun, otherwise they would not show a measurable displacement in twenty-five years.

FIG. 73. W. J. Luyten's diagram of nearby stars of faint absolute luminosity. On the right are ordinary red dwarfs (designated by circles); to the left are white dwarfs (designated by dots). Stars identified by letter are E, 40 Eridani B; G, AC +70°8247; P, companion to Procyon; R, Ross 627; S, companion to Sirius; W, Wolf 489. The curves show the locations of stars with diameters four times, equal to, and one fourth of the earth's diameter, respectively. (University of Minnesota chart)

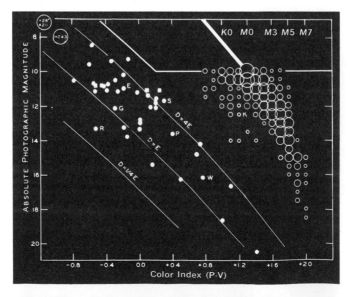

Most of them appear faint, roughly of magnitudes 12 to 15. Located at distances of ten parsecs or less, they must be very faint intrinsically —they are all dwarf stars.

From their colors, Luyten, in collaboration with E. F. Carpenter at the University of Arizona, divided the fast-moving dwarfs into two distinct classes. About 2900 are ordinary red dwarfs of spectral type M; about 100 are white dwarfs of spectral types B, A, F, and "continuous." The last named have no spectral absorption lines, not even those of hydrogen.

We can roughly compute on the basis of Luyten's work that within any large volume of space 3 per cent of all stars are white dwarfs. Ninety-five per cent are main-sequence stars. Two per cent remain for the other sequences, mostly the subdwarfs and subgiants. The giants and supergiants are exceedingly rare.

We have already seen that the white dwarfs depart from the mass-luminosity relation. According to Luyten they form a broad band in the Hertzsprung-Russell diagram, whose central line, not quite parallel to the main sequence, is about 10 magnitudes below. [That is, the white dwarfs are about 10,000 times fainter than main-sequence A stars.] The width of the band is about four magnitudes, and is thus much greater than the width of the main sequence.

The tremendous mean densities of the white dwarfs suggest that they do not obey the laws of perfect gases. If we should disregard this point and compute the central temperatures based on the gas laws, we would obtain approximately one billion degrees! With such an immense temperature the nuclear processes would be extremely active; if hydrogen were present, the star would blow up like a hydrogen bomb. But even without hydrogen there would be nuclear processes building up heavier atoms from helium—and these would supply far more radiation than is actually observed in the feeble glow of Sirius B. Its central temperature cannot be anything like one billion degrees.

In trying to find the nature of the departure from the laws of perfect gases, we are at first led to follow intuition and attribute it to the forces discovered by van der Waals in the laboratory when gases are compressed to about 100 or 1000 atmospheres. In this state of compression the atoms, whose diameters are of the order of 10^{-8} centimeter, begin to touch one another. But at the high temperature of a star's interior atoms are completely ionized. Fragments of atoms

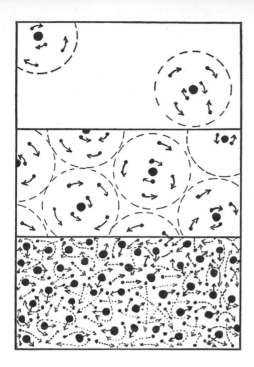

FIG. 74. A schematic representation of the gaseous, liquid, and crushed states of matter, according to George Gamow. (From *Birth and Death of the Sun*, The Viking Press, Inc. 1940)

occupy individual spheres only of radius about 10^{-12} or 10^{-13} centimeter. This kind of gas can be compressed to a density billions of times greater than that of water without encountering any difficulty from the actual bodily contact between the atomic fragments. Despite its high density, the substance of a white dwarf is gaseous. . . .

Why, then, do the ordinary perfect-gas laws not apply? The answer is found in the theory of *degenerate matter* formulated by E. Fermi and P. Dirac, and applied to white dwarfs by R. H. Fowler and S. Chandrasekhar. The properties of a degenerate gas differ drastically from those of normal gas. Of course, no one has ever obtained such a gas in the laboratory, and our conclusions rest upon theory. . . .

Ordinarily, gas pressure is proportional to the product of density and temperature, and if we reduce the temperature to zero absolute, the pressure will also be zero; . . . the normal full-sized atoms are brought to rest. But in the interior of these atoms . . . even in a completely cold hydrogen atom, the electron continues revolving around the proton, but exerts no pressure.

In the crushed state of ionized matter, however, the free electrons, squeezed off their original atomic nuclei, do not come to rest at zero temperature; they retain vestiges of what were once their orbital velocities around the nuclei. Thus the motions of electrons that were once orbital, and as such exerted no pressure upon the walls of an enclosure, are now more or less at random, and even at absolute zero they contribute an appreciable *zero-point pressure*.

Let us suppose that we start with a vessel containing a small amount of degenerate gas. From the foregoing discussion we know that even at zero temperature the gas exerts a certain pressure. Let us now add more degenerate gas to the vessel, all at zero temperature. The density will, of course, increase. But will the pressure also change? In a perfect gas at zero temperature it would remain always equal to zero.

It turns out that by adding more gas to the vessel we of necessity increase the pressure. The argument rests upon Wolfgang Pauli's exclusion principle, which tells us that the newly added electrons cannot duplicate the velocities and spatial locations of electrons already present in the gas. Thus if the old electrons have the smallest velocities consistent with their original orbital motions, then the new electrons must, on the average, move faster. They increase the zero-point pressure, which is proportional to the $5/3$ power of the density and is independent of the temperature. (Only for the largest densities found in the white dwarfs is there a modification in this law; according to Chandrasekhar the pressure then becomes proportional to the $4/3$ power of the density. But we shall not use this elaboration, even though it is essential in any accurate computation.)

A remarkable property of degenerate stars can be deduced immediately. Consider Sirius B, whose mass is equal to the sun's, and whose mean density is 200,000 times that of water. The mean pressure derived from this density by the law we have just stated is about 6×10^{15} atmospheres, if the gas is hydrogen. It is this internal pressure of the gas that prevents the star from collapsing under its own tremendous gravity, and the size of the star is determined by the balancing of the pressure against the gravity.

Let us suppose we pack an additional amount of material, also equal to the sun's mass, into the volume occupied by Sirius B. The density will become twice what it was before. Every cubic centimeter within the star will have twice its former mass, and by Newton's law of universal gravitation will attract every other cubic centimeter with a force that is proportional to the product of their masses; hence the attraction of the hypothetical star upon itself will be 2×2, or 4 times as great as in Sirius B.

Now the internal pressure will also rise; by the density law stated above, it will be $2^{5/3} = 3.2$ times as great as in Sirius B. But this is insufficient to hold the star to its original size because of the four times increase in internal gravity, and the star of twice the sun's mass must therefore contract until it becomes small enough again to establish equilibrium between pressure and gravitation.

The remarkable property we have deduced is that the size of a degenerate star depends inversely upon its mass. In other words, the heavy white dwarfs are smaller than less heavy ones. (Chandrasekhar has computed that a white dwarf that consists of pure hydrogen would have a radius of zero were its mass about five suns. Hence there can be no degenerate hydrogen star of mass larger than five suns. A white dwarf consisting entirely of helium, however, cannot have a mass in excess of 1.5 times the sun's. This results from the fact that the pressure of a crushed assembly of atoms is given by the number of free electrons. Hydrogen furnishes only one such electron per nucleus (proton, of mass 1), whereas helium has two per nucleus (alpha particle, of mass 4). Since the attraction of the star upon itself depends almost entirely on the masses of these atomic nuclei, the balance of gravitation and pressure demands a smaller radius in the case of helium than it does for the lighter hydrogen.

A recent theoretical interpretation of the white dwarfs is contained in a paper by L. Mestel in the *Monthly Notices* of the Royal Astronomical Society (112, 583, 1952), where he considers the energy sources of white dwarfs in these terms.

If we assume that a thin outer skin of a white dwarf consists of ordinary nondegenerate matter, we can compute the pressure and temperature, step by step inward from the surface, using the ordinary laws of perfect gases. At the base of this outside layer the pressure is 10^{13} atmospheres, the density about two kilograms per cubic centimeter, and the temperature about 20 million degrees. Inside this layer the density becomes so great that the gas is degenerate because the atoms are crushed.

This thin outer layer contains about 1/400 the total mass of the star, but it forms a blanket of high opacity which limits the rate of cooling of the degenerate core. This layer is subject to the star's high surface gravity, which greatly broadens the lines in its spectrum; thus the spectrum gives an important clue to the high density of the star's interior even though it arises only in the surface layer. . . . This

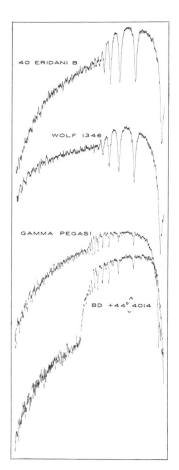

FIG. 75. Microphotometer tracings of spectra of four stars, the upper two white dwarfs, in which the hydrogen-beta line is at the right. The lines through hydrogen-zeta may be seen; the other Balmer lines are blended because of the Stark effect (see p. 325) in the dense atmospheres of the white dwarfs. BD +44°4014 shows the normal sharp appearance of hydrogen lines in main-sequence stars of this type, and the usual Balmer drop (see Fig. 22) at the limit of the series. Gamma Pegasi, which is a B-type star, has relatively weak hydrogen lines and a much smaller Balmer drop.

is illustrated by the tracings of four spectra, two of them white dwarfs, reproduced in Figure 75.

The temperature inside all but the outer 0.25 per cent of the mass differs very little from 20 million degrees. This temperature would be ample to convert hydrogen into helium—if hydrogen were present—but so long as nuclear processes are active a star cannot condense to the degenerate state. Mestel concludes that the white dwarfs contain no nuclear energy sources in their interiors, and hence no internal hydrogen.

On the other hand, we know that the interstellar clouds consist mostly of hydrogen. Therefore these peculiar stars cannot have condensed directly out of the interstellar gas into the white dwarf state; they must have been, to begin with, ordinary hydrogen-rich stars (on the assumption that all stars are formed from interstellar matter).

Since the present mass of Sirius B is the same as the mass of the sun, and since nuclear evolution causes only a negligible decrease of mass (by 0.7 per cent), we might think of Sirius B as the kind of star the sun will become after it has converted all its hydrogen into helium. This hypothesis is unsatisfactory, however, because with its slow rate of energy production, the sun will require 10^{11} years to reach the stage of hydrogen exhaustion. Yet in the Hyades cluster we find four white dwarfs and several normal G and K dwarfs. There are no intermediate types. Since all the cluster members must be approximately the same age—much less than 10^{11} years—this theory is ruled out.

Mestel therefore adopts the hypothesis suggested by F. Hoyle and previously also favored by E. A. Milne, Chandrasekhar, Gamow, and others: what we now observe as a white dwarf was once a very massive O or B star that rapidly burned up its hydrogen and then, in the final stages of its "perfect-gas" condition, blew off enough material (perhaps in a nova or supernova outburst) to reach the critical mass of 1.5 suns for helium, after which it could contract by its own gravitation, eventually reaching the white dwarf state.

A white dwarf radiates energy without replenishment. It contains no hydrogen and is thus deprived of nuclear sources. It cannot contract still further and derive heat by the Helmholtz-Kelvin process [wherein radiation takes place at the expense of potential energy lost during contraction], because, as we have seen, its radius is permanently fixed by its present mass. It can only slowly cool, as radiation from its supply of internal heat diffuses outward through its highly opaque "perfect-gas" skin, at a rate which will maintain the star's present low luminosity for 10^9 years.

Now let us turn to Luyten's H-R diagram for faint stars in Figure 73. Open circles represent ordinary dwarfs (at the lower end of the main sequence), dots the white dwarfs, and square dots are the four Hyades white dwarfs. Each white dwarf is observed at only one brief moment of its existence, but all of them taken together are believed to give a picture of the evolution (or "ageing") of these stars. The situation is far simpler than elsewhere in the H-R diagram; the surface temperature, which decreases as the white dwarf cools, is the only variable factor.

Thus the location of such a star along Luyten's sequence depends on its surface temperature, and hence on its age: the oldest and reddest stars are on the right-hand end of the band. Stars of greater mass have smaller radii and lie farther to the left and lower. Those along the lower edge of the sequence have diameters of the order of half that of the earth, and their masses are near 1.5 suns, the maximum for white dwarfs made of helium. Stars near the upper edge of the band are about four times as large as the earth, with masses about half the sun's.

It will be noticed in Luyten's diagram that the white dwarf sequence and the main sequence are not quite parallel. Theoretically, the luminosity of a main-sequence star is proportional to the 11/2 power of its effective surface temperature. But a white dwarf cools without change in radius, so that its luminosity will remain proportional to the fourth power of the temperature, in obedience to Stefan's law ($L \sim T^4$). As a result, the two sequences should have different slopes, and there is excellent agreement between observation and theory.

Adams, Luyten, Chandrasekhar, Kuiper, L. Mestel, and others have pieced together a consistent picture of these remarkable white-dwarf stars, the ashes of stellar evolution. The largest uncertainty remaining is the actual process whereby an aged O or B star blows off its outer layers to leave only its degenerate core. Recent studies (p. 243) show that helium probably enters nuclear reactions in the later stages of a B star's life, so that its core would not necessarily be pure helium.

The prevalence of white dwarfs raises another question, not fully discussed here, How much of the universe can we "see"? The many white dwarfs of absolute magnitude +10 to +14 plotted on Figure 73 are cooling at rates that can be calculated from their masses, volumes, and radii; and their further evolutionary tracks (as Struve says) slope downward to the lower right of the H-R diagram. Luyten's survey may be complete out to a distance of a few hundred light years for these white stars, but he can't have discovered all the redder ones with absolute magnitudes from +16 to +20. Mestel's argument (p. 220) that there are young white dwarfs in the Hyades cluster implies that earlier generations of B stars produced white dwarfs 5 or 10 billion years ago—dwarfs that would now be much cooler and fainter. These, and the low-mass red dwarfs at the lower end of the main sequence, might be very much more numerous than the estimate quoted by Struve (white dwarfs are 3 per cent of all stars in a large volume near the sun).

Several other lines of reasoning raise this same question about unseen matter. For instance, in many outside galaxies the measured mass of material is much too large for the observed luminosity, assuming that most of the material is in the form of ordinary main-sequence stars. In order to explain this "mass discrepancy" in elliptical galaxies, "black dwarfs" would have to be several times more numerous than ordinary stars, so that the stars we see would be only 10 per cent of the total. Such a conclusion, still highly speculative, is perhaps not too surprising. As this chapter has shown, the white, red, and black dwarfs form an end point in stellar evolution, like ashes in a burning fire. In the case of other stellar types, stars evolve in and then evolve out; in the case of interstellar matter, gas clouds are formed by ejection from stars, and they collapse to form new stars; but there seems to be no glowing future for the degenerate dwarfs, and their number must have been increasing since shortly after the first stars were formed.—TLP

7

Changes in Chemical Composition

The systematic study of cosmic abundances and nucleogenesis (the evolution of chemical elements) started only about thirty years ago. It has required cooperation between geochemists (studying the composition of terrestrial rocks and meteorites), seismologists (the interior of the earth), astrophysicists (the composition of sun, stars, and nebulae), and nuclear physicists (nuclear reactions). As this chapter shows, one of the more dramatic ideas was Gamow's—that the chemical elements were formed in a "big bang" at the beginning of the universe about ten billion years ago. The evidence for this, in observations of galaxies, and the general relativity theory, is reserved for a later volume in this series.

As more data were obtained on nuclear reactions and on the evolution of stars, it became evident that one big bang could not account for all the elements, and that stars are now producing heavier elements from hydrogen—increasing the abundance of helium, for instance, as shown in Chapter 1. The different patterns of characteristics of stars in various groups led to Baade's idea of Populations I and II, and to the differences in chemical compositions among the stars. Accurate means were developed for measuring the abundances of elements in stellar atmospheres by Greenstein, Aller, and others, including Otto Struve, who was responsible for much of the advance in this field.—TLP

...

The History of the
Chemical Elements

OTTO STRUVE

(*Sky and Telescope*, April 1953)

"The chemical constitution of the universe is surprisingly uniform; . . . about 55 per cent of cosmic matter is hydrogen and about 44 per cent helium; the remaining 1 per cent accounts for all the heavier elements, in the same proportions as we find them on the earth," writes George Gamow, in his book *The Creation of the Universe*. In other words, as J. L. Greenstein said[1] recently, "The stars are mainly hydrogen and helium, with an impurity of carbon, nitrogen, and oxygen, and only 'traces' of the other 90 elements."

Obviously, this cosmic distribution of the chemical elements does not apply to the earth, or to the other planets; nor does it apply to the meteorites, or to the particles that compose the zodiacal light and the counterglow. Both hydrogen and helium are almost non-existent in the smaller bodies of the solar system, and even the oceans of the earth, consisting of only two atoms of hydrogen for one atom of oxygen, are by weight more oxygen than hydrogen. It is reasonable to suppose that this anomaly is entirely due to the escape of the lighter gases from the smaller bodies of the solar system. Presumably these gases were ultimately driven out of the solar system by the pressure of the sun's radiation.

Yet for the heavier elements the composition of the earth closely resembles that of the sun, as may be seen in Table 6, where the num-

---

[1] In a lecture on astrophysics at Michelson Laboratory, China Lake, California, on December 8, 1952. The data in Tables 6 and 7 were also presented at the lecture.

bers listed are the powers of 10 equal to the numbers of various atoms mixed with each 10^{12} hydrogen atoms. For example, in the sun a volume containing 10^{12} atoms of hydrogen has only $10^{1.19}$ atoms of lithium—a factor of nearly 100 billion.

TABLE 6. ELEMENT ABUNDANCES IN SUN AND METEORITES*

Element	Sun	Meteorites		Element	Sun	Meteorites	
		Brown	Urey			Brown	Urey
H	12.00	——	——	Ge	2.6	3.90	3.54
Li	1.19	——	3.5	Sr	2.88	3.11	3.11
O	8.88	——	——	Y	3.2	2.50	2.49
Na	6.28	6.16	6.21	Zr	2.4	3.68	3.65
Mg	7.54	7.45	7.44	Cb	2.2	2.45	2.35
Al	6.23	5.45	5.41	Mo	1.8	2.78	2.27
Si	7.12	7.50	7.50	Ru	1.3	2.47	1.82
S	6.9:	7.04	6.49	Rh	0.1	2.04	1.35
K	5.15	5.34	5.04	Ag	0.6	1.93	1.78
Ca	6.42	6.33	6.25	Ba	2.52	2.09	2.02
Sc	3.3	2.76	2.73	La	1.4	1.82	1.82
Ti	4.96	4.92	4.76	Ce	2.0	1.86	1.86
V	4.05	3.90	3.68	Nd	1.6	2.02	2.02
Cr	5.20	5.48	5.41	Sm	1.1	1.58	1.54
Mn	5.40	5.39	5.33	Eu	1.0	0.95	0.95
Fe	7.09	7.76	7.33	W	−0.2:	2.77	2.61
Co	5.0	5.50	4.96	Pt	1.2	2.44	1.68
Ni	5.9	6.63	6.09	Hg	3.0:	——	−0.72
Cu	4.5	4.16	4.12	Pb	1.7:	<1.8	<1.8
Zn	4.53	3.70	3.76				

* Each number given is $\log_{10}$ of the number of atoms, with hydrogen normalized to 12.00. The meteorite abundances have been fitted by adding 3.5 to Brown's and Urey's data. Colons signify low accuracy.

The table gives two independent determinations of the abundances in meteorites, one by Harrison Brown, the other by H. C. Urey. They based their work upon slightly different assumptions regarding the nature of an average meteorite. The actual samples differ appreciably from one another—the iron meteorites containing more iron and nickel than the stony meteorites, which are rich in various kinds of silicates. However, for our purpose the two meteorite determinations are sufficiently similar to one another, and beginning with the element sodium (Na) they also resemble the abundances in the sun.

Table 7 lists the abundances of the elements in some of the hotter stars and in planetary nebulae. Here the observational data of A.

TABLE 7. ELEMENT ABUNDANCES IN HIGH-
TEMPERATURE OBJECTS*

Element	Stars	Planetary Nebulae
H	12.00	12.00
He	11.14	11.40
C	7.96	7.9
N	8.22	8.22
O	8.73	8.89
F	6.4:	5.5:
Ne	8.77	8.86
S	7.25	7.90
Cl	7.0	7.00
A	7.7:	6.90
Be	1.5	

* Each number given in $\log_{10}$ of the number of atoms, with hydrogen normalized to 12.00. Colons signify low accuracy.

Unsöld and L. Aller have been used extensively. This table furnishes the abundances of the lighter elements, such as carbon, nitrogen, neon, fluorine, sulphur, and so on, which are not normally observed in the sun. Yet we know that they must be present. Their spectral lines fail to appear because the temperature of the sun is too low to produce the required amount of excitation.

The two tables overlap in the case of oxygen: the solar abundance is $10^{8.88}$; the average abundance in the hot stars and nebulae is $10^{8.81}$. The agreement is perfect, and we are probably entitled to assume that both tables represent the basic "cosmic" abundances of the elements in the universe.

However, despite the large amount of work which has been done toward the determination of these abundances, the results are still uncertain by factors of the order of two or three. Even the important abundance ratio of hydrogen to helium is still quite uncertain. Table 7 gives $H/He = 10^{12}/10^{11.14} = 7$. Thus, for every atom of helium there are, supposedly, seven atoms of hydrogen. Since one helium atom weighs four times as much as one atom of hydrogen, the ratio by mass is 7:4, roughly that quoted from Gamow's book. Yet recent work by Anne Underhill at Victoria, B.C., leads to a ratio of about one helium atom to twenty or twenty-five hydrogen atoms, and her conclusion has been confirmed by the Belgian astronomer L. Neven, whose result is H/He — 30.

The uncertainty referred to has its origin in the different assumptions that have been made by different persons regarding the distribution of the temperature and pressure in a stellar atmosphere. Unsöld, in Germany, who used spectra obtained at the McDonald Observatory in Texas, assumed an average value of the temperature and pressure, as if these were the same for all layers. On the other hand, Neven has tried to compute exactly how the temperature and pressure vary with height in the atmosphere. . . .

It is particularly instructive to plot the relative abundances of the elements against their atomic weights, as in Figure 76. The abundances used by Gamow in this plot are not quite the same as those listed in Tables 6 and 7. Moreover, the abundance of hydrogen, instead of 10^{12}, is here given as about $10^{8.5}$. Therefore, if we wish to compare the diagram with the data of the tables, we must add to all the ordinates the number 3.5. For example, for helium we read from the diagram an ordinate of about 7.5. Adding 3.5 gives 11.0, which is close enough to the value of Table 7, $10^{11.14}$.

The circles in Figure 76 represent atoms of odd atomic number—hydrogen, lithium, and so on; the crosses stand for atoms of even atomic number—helium, beryllium, and so on. In a general way, the crosses correspond to larger abundances than the circles—a conclusion

FIG. 76. In this chart circles represent elements with odd atomic numbers, and crosses those with even atomic numbers. Hydrogen is represented by the filled half-circle in the upper left; helium by the cross just below it. (Adapted from *The Creation of the Universe* by George Gamow, Viking Press, 1952)

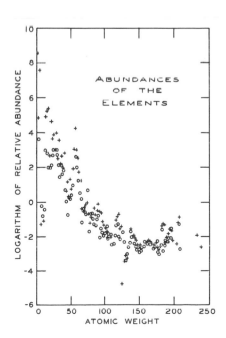

that is well known to chemists and physicists as Harkins' rule. Undoubtedly, it reflects important nuclear processes by which the elements were formed.

The diagram contains other valuable information. We notice that the distribution of the elements is not a random one. The largest abundance is that of hydrogen. This is followed by helium. These are joined smoothly by the abundances of carbon, nitrogen, oxygen, and the rest of the heavier elements. Thus, with the exception of a few very low values, which are for lithium, beryllium, and boron, the crosses and circles arrange themselves in a wide band which at first shows a rapid drop, as we pass from hydrogen to the heavier elements. After reaching atomic weights of the order of 100, the band levels off—indicating that the heavier elements all have about the same abundance.

Gamow's diagram contains far more data than are given in the tables. This is due to the fact that he has used all terrestrial abundances from the work of V. M. Goldschmidt, as supplemented by Brown's more recent measurements. Gamow has also included the abundances of the various isotopes, such as heavy hydrogen, or deuterium, most of which are not observed in astronomical sources.

The low abundances of lithium and beryllium (atomic weights 7 and 9) are the most striking evidence of nuclear processes going on in the universe. From laboratory experiments we know that both Li and Be are capable of capturing protons at relatively low temperatures, of about a million degrees absolute. A lithium atom of mass 7 becomes a new element of mass 8, which rapidly disintegrates into two normal helium atoms of mass 4.

Temperatures of the order of a million degrees are not so rare in the stars, and we need not descend into the far depths of the sun to find conditions where lithium and beryllium must be quickly converted into helium. Are the present low abundances of lithium and beryllium the result of nuclear processes going on at the present time? Or were these elements turned into helium ashes in a hot prestellar medium before stars were formed?

A partial answer to this question comes from Table 6. Greenstein and R. S. Richardson found a solar abundance of lithium equal to $10^{1.19}$. Urey obtained a value of $10^{3.5}$ in the meteorites. Thus lithium is more than 100 times as abundant in the meteorites as it is in the atmosphere of the sun. In the meteorites, nuclear processes are absent, because temperatures are not sufficiently high.[2] In the sun, an atom of lithium need only descend, by convection, to a depth of a thousand miles or so below the surface, and it will be converted into helium. The conclusion is inescapable that the original medium out of which sun, planets, comets, and meteors were formed contained at least $10^{3.5}$ atoms of lithium for every 10^{12} atoms of hydrogen. The abundance of lithium in the sun was then reduced by a factor of 100, whereas in the meteors the abundance remained the same, $10^{3.5}$.

Of course, even this abundance falls way below the band in Gamow's diagram. We must therefore suppose that the original gaseous and dusty medium out of which stars are formed was to begin with deficient in lithium and beryllium. This is supported by Lyman Spitzer's announcement that the interstellar gas contains very little lithium and beryllium; the spectral lines of these elements are too weak to be seen at all.

Even if we should find that the abundance of lithium in the interstellar gas is similar to that in meteorites, or to that in the sun, we shall still not know whether the burning-out process occurred in a prestellar state, or whether interstellar gas clouds were expelled from the surfaces of novae and other expanding stars. In the latter case, the lithium "burn out" could have taken place in these stars within the three-billion-year interval during which our galaxy has remained essentially what it is now.

A few years ago A. McKellar at Victoria discovered several stars with exceptionally strong absorption lines of lithium. Although the surfaces of these stars are cooler than the sun's surface, there can be no doubt that their internal temperatures are more than sufficient to convert all the lithium into helium. The actual lithium abundances in these stars have not been determined, but it is fairly certain that they exceed the abundance in the sun by a factor of many thousands. How, then, can we explain the presence of so much lithium in McKellar's stars and so little of it in the sun? One suggestion is that the surface material of McKellar's stars never travels much below the surface: there are no convection currents. . . .

Another possibility is that lithium is being *newly produced* in the stars. One process for such production, considered by Fermi and Turkevich [at the University of Chicago], is that a normal helium

<hr/>

[2] Struve neglects, here, the possible effects of cosmic-ray bombardment.—TLP

atom combines with an atom of tritium (the hydrogen isotope of mass 3). The result is the creation of a lithium atom of mass 7, and the production of a quantum of gamma radiation. However, to be efficient, this nuclear reaction requires a temperature much higher than the 20 million degrees in the interiors of ordinary stars. If this method of building up lithium in stars occurs at all, it must be confined to peculiar regions. Many such regions are known to exist. Even the sun, a relatively quiescent dwarf, has hot spots with flares, has regions of high magnetic activity, has tremendous up-and-down surges of material in the form of prominences, and is surrounded by a tenuous coronal envelope whose temperature is a million degrees. Is it not possible that there are localized regions, either on the surface or a short distance below it, where atoms like lithium are being formed? If so, then these newly created atoms are being constantly destroyed in the deeper layers by the conversion of lithium into helium.

An analogous question arises when we consider P. W. Merrill's recent discovery of strong absorption lines of technetium in several late-type variable stars. Technetium, which follows the normal and stable element molybdenum in the periodic table and has atomic mass 99, is neither normal nor stable. It does not exist on the earth under natural conditions, and it was first produced artificially in the year 1937 by E. Segré and several other physicists from molybdenum samples exposed to intense bombardment with deuterons in the Berkeley cyclotron. Its absence on the earth is due to the fact that its mean life is only 200,000 years. In two million years, less than 1/10 of the original amount of technetium would be left—the radioactive disintegration being independent of the temperature and pressure.

The large abundance of technetium in Merrill's S-type stars is one of the greatest mysteries of our physical universe. The physicists believe that there is a remote possibility that a stable isotope of technetium may exist, but in that case the absence of this element on the earth would remain wholly unexplained. At the present time it appears more likely that some local phenomena on the surfaces of S-type stars continuously create new technetium atoms, which are then subjected to radioactive decay and end up in the form of other, stable elements.

It seems to me that the importance of local phenomena in creating various kinds of heavy atoms in stars has not been sufficiently appreciated in the past. It is true that we have at present little, if any, information regarding the nature of these hypothetical local processes that we invoke to account for the continuous creation of lithium, technetium, and perhaps other heavy atoms. But we should remember that we are here concerned only with the production of "traces" of elements—occasional freak atoms that may happen once in a hundred billion tries. Let me use an analogy to explain what I mean.

The earth, with its low temperature, is certainly not now a "caldron" in which atoms are being brewed on a large scale. Yet if an astronomer on a hypothetical planet orbiting a nearby star should be observing the spectrum of the earth four years after the detonation of the first hydrogen bomb, he might find to his surprise that "traces" of helium had appeared where no helium was previously in existence. Since he would know that on a grand scale the creation of helium out of hydrogen does not occur on the earth (as distinct from the creation of helium by radioactive decay in the rocks), he would conclude that a localized phenomenon on the earth, though inappreciable in the grand scale of the universe, had resulted in the formation of traces of elements that should not normally be present at all. If, then, such localized phenomena can occur on the earth, is it not reasonable that much more powerful local "ovens" exist on the stars where the conditions are sufficiently different from average to permit the formation of heavy elements?

We should probably distinguish between nuclear processes in stars on a grand scale, such as the conversion of hydrogen into helium, and freak nuclear processes which only very rarely produce a heavy atom. The former must occur throughout large volumes within the stars, and must in practice be realizable under the average conditions of internal stellar temperatures and pressures. The latter need not occur at all under such average conditions. What they require is a local hot spot or other anomalous region on a star, such as a *natural* cyclotron or betatron.

The grand-scale process of conversion of hydrogen into helium is required to explain the energies of stellar radiations, and it finds a satisfactory confirmation in the theory of stellar evolution. But do we have any direct observational evidence from the spectra of the stars that the old stars are deficient in hydrogen and rich in helium? The strange thing is that we do not.

It is true that D. M. Popper and W. P. Bidelman in this country, and A. D. Thackeray and A. J. Wesselink in South Africa, have discovered some stars whose spectra are strangely lacking in hydrogen lines. But these are few in number, and they are not the ones we would have expected, on other grounds, to show low hydrogen-helium ratios. For example, we believe that the hotter stars in the Pleiades are older, and therefore more advanced in the nuclear time-scale than the hottest stars in the cluster h and Chi Persei [see p. 108]. Yet, the stars of the Pleiades have fairly strong lines of hydrogen.

We could evade this difficulty by suggesting that there is no mixing of atmospheres of the Pleiades with their interiors—in which case the compositions of the atmospheres would not reflect the changes in the stellar interiors. But the Pleiades are rapidly rotating stars, and on other grounds we believe that rapid rotation aids in the process of mixing. Conversely, we might think that the Popper-Bidelman stars are old and are subject to efficient mixing by convection. But there is no reason to believe that in these particular stars mixing is more efficient than in the hotter members of the Pleiades. Perhaps here, too, we shall have to consider departures from normal conditions in localized regions of the hydrogen-deficient stars.

One of the strangest results of stellar spectroscopic investigation is the low abundance of the metals relative to hydrogen in the stars of Baade's Population II. First announced by Schwarzschild, Spitzer, and Rupert Wildt at Princeton University this result has been amply confirmed by other workers. Yet the Population II stars are the "oldest" objects in our galaxy. Their high relative abundance of hydrogen is probably due to two causes. First, these stars are evolving slowly; they are not sufficiently luminous to exhaust a large fraction of their original supply of hydrogen in three billion years. Second, they may have had relatively more hydrogen to begin with than do the young stars in the solar neighborhood. The latter have, in part, grown out of interstellar dust clouds, and these are almost certainly deficient in hydrogen. Dust particles, like molecules, can contain only comparable numbers of hydrogen and heavier atoms. Ice crystals, for example, when impinging upon a newly formed star, would contribute only two atoms of hydrogen for every atom of oxygen.

What can we say, in general, about the origin of the elements? A few years ago, when it became apparent that under normal stellar conditions no heavy atoms can be produced, and only the process $4H \rightarrow He$ is of real importance, the tendency was to suppose that the distribution of the heavy elements could only be accounted for by

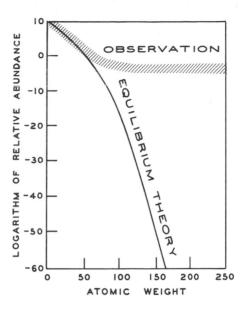

FIG. 77. The abundances of the elements as they would be established according to the theory of "frozen equilibrium" fits the observed abundances of the lighter elements but fails completely to match the relative quantities of the heavy elements. (Adapted from *The Creation of the Universe* by George Gamow, Viking Press, 1952)

assuming a prestellar state of matter at a very high temperature and pressure, in which the atoms were formed. This "equilibrium" theory resulted in a distribution of the elements that became "frozen" when the temperature dropped below 20 million degrees. This theoretical distribution can be adjusted to represent the light elements of atomic weights less than about 60, but departs violently from the observations of heavier elements (see Fig. 77).

To overcome this difficulty, one could think not of a single brewing caldron, but of successive stages corresponding to different temperatures. The earliest stage, presumably at the highest temperature, produced a distribution rich in very heavy elements. A later stage, at a somewhat lower temperature, did not disturb the first "frozen" set of abundances, but modified very greatly the abundances of the lighter elements. On this view we are now in the last stage of element brewing. Our present universe has all the abundances of the heavier elements frozen from one of the prestellar stages. But we are still converting hydrogen into helium.

A modification of this picture by Gamow and his associates has been presented in popular form in *The Creation of the Universe*. It starts with a hot nuclear gas consisting mostly of neutrons, protons, and electrons (Gamow's "ylem"). This gas had a temperature of many billions of degrees, and expanded so rapidly as to prevent the setting up of an equilibrium between different kinds of particles and

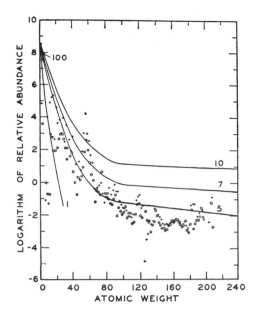

FIG. 78. Abundance curves based on the theory of atom building by successive neutron capture, calculated for different density constants by R. A. Alpher and R. C. Herman on the electronic computer of the National Bureau of Standards. (Adapted from *The Creation of the Universe* by George Gamow, Viking Press, 1952)

the prevailing temperature and pressure. The theory presents a breath-taking flight of the imagination and contains many departures from conventional ideas. It leads to a rather beautiful explanation of the abundance curve. In Figure 78, the four curves correspond to four different assumptions concerning the initial density of the primordial medium.

Opposed to this theory of a prestellar "ylem" are G. B. Van Albada and especially F. Hoyle, who believe that the abundances of the elements can be explained by especially powerful nuclear processes in the red giants (Van Albada) and in the exploding supernovae (Hoyle). In principle, their theories are similar to the ideas presented earlier in this article, except that I would be inclined to look for small atomic brewing ovens in a large variety of stars—perhaps even in the sun.

As the rest of this chapter shows, a great deal of evidence has been obtained since 1953, and much of it supports the ideas of Struve on "freak," localized nuclear reactions, and those of Hoyle on the production of heavy elements in supernovae and supergiant stars.

The chemical analysis of rocks and meteorites is beyond the scope of this book, but measuring the abundances of elements in nebulae deserves some explanation. Emission lines of hydrogen, helium, oxygen, neon, and other elements show in spectra of nebulae. Figure 79

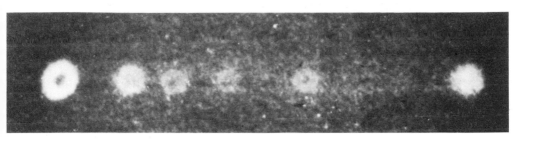

FIG. 79. Spectrogram of the planetary nebula in Lyra. The bright image at the right is due to ionized oxygen (5007 angstroms). The other images are due to hydrogen and ionized atoms of neon and oxygen. (Yerkes Observatory photograph)

*shows a spectrum made without a slit, so that the image of the ring-like planetary nebula shows at each emission-line wavelength. The difficulty in deriving abundances from measures of the strengths of these lines lies in the theory of how ultraviolet light from the small central star (Fig. 72) causes the nebula to fluoresce. This theory was proposed by the Dutch astrophysicist H. Zanstra in 1926, and refined by Menzel, Goldberg, and others in the U.S. during the 1930s. One of the first estimates of abundance ratios was by T. Page in the British journal Nature in 1937. More recent ones are summarized in the next two articles.—*TLP

Composition of Planetarics

(*Sky and Telescope*, June 1956)

The chemical composition of six planetary nebulae (NGC1535, 2022, 2165, 2392, 2440, and 7662) has been determined by Lawrence H. Aller, University of Michigan Observatory, from spectrograms he secured with R. Minkowski at the 100-inch and 60-inch Mount Wilson reflectors.

The effects of filamentary structure of the nebulae, and the distribution of atoms among different stages of ionization, introduce complications that appear particularly serious for elements, such as nitrogen, that are observed only in the lowest stages of ionization. The effects of interstellar absorption upon the measured brightnesses of the spectral lines are also troublesome.

There is no convincing evidence of variations in composition from one object to another. The average for the six planetaries gives the following relative numbers for atoms: hydrogen, 17,000,000; helium, 1,350,000; oxygen, 10,000; nitrogen, 5000; neon, 1500; sulphur, 900; argon, 130; chlorine, 34; and fluorine, 4. [On the scale of Tables 6 and 7, the logarithmic abundances are as follows: H, 12.00; He, 10.90; O, 8.77; N, 8.47; Ne, 7.95; S, 7.72; A, 6.88; Cl, 6.30; F, 5.37.]

....

Orion Nebula's
Composition

(Sky and Telescope, May 1959)

One of the most important problems in astrophysics is to determine the abundances of the chemical elements in nebulae and stars. For work on gaseous nebulae at the University of Michigan Observatory, a photoelectric spectrophotometer has been in use since December 1955, attached to the 24-inch Schmidt telescope at the Portage Lake observing station.

This device is a grating spectrograph, employing a 15,000-line-per-inch grating. The diffracted light passes through a narrow slot onto the light-sensitive surface of a photomultiplier tube. As a motor slowly turns the grating, the spectrum is scanned by the slot, and the photomultiplier output provides an intensity record, wavelength by wavelength. . . .

The system provides for scanning the spectrum at rates of 30, 90, and 270 angstroms per minute.

Reproduced in Figure 80 is a typical record obtained with this equipment, of a portion of the spectrum of the Orion nebula. Most

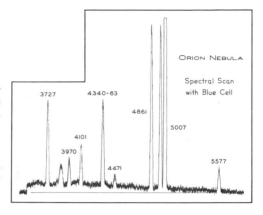

FIG 80. Part of the Orion nebula's spectrum, the peak heights indicating emission-line intensities. The strongest line, at 5007 angstroms, is of doubly ionized oxygen; 4861 is due to hydrogen, and 4471 to helium. The oxygen line at 5577 is of terrestrial origin. (University of Michigan diagram)

of the lines are due to nebular oxygen, hydrogen, and helium, but the one at 5577 angstroms originates in the earth's atmosphere. From nine similar tracings, astronomers William Liller and Lawrence H. Aller [then at the University of Michigan] have made a quantitative chemical analysis. They also used photographic spectrum measurements made many years ago by A. B. Wyse at Lick Observatory.

As a preliminary step, they deduced that there are on the average 4000 free electrons per cubic centimeter in the central part of the Orion nebula, and that the temperature of this electron gas is 9000° absolute. Then they converted the measured line intensities into the abundances of the elements. The most uncertain step in their calculations was in allowing for the distribution of the atoms of a particular element among its different stages of ionization.

Hydrogen is by far the commonest element in the Orion nebula. Also, for every 1000 atoms of oxygen, there turn out to be about 1600 of neon, 130 of nitrogen and sulfur, 40 of argon, and 2 of chlorine. [On the logarithmic scale of Tables 6 and 7, the abundances are as follows: O, 8.88; Ne, 9.08; N, 7.99; A, 7.48; Cl, 6.18.]

These relative abundances for the most part closely parallel those in early-type stars studied in this way by the Michigan astronomers. Chlorine, however, seems more abundant in the stars by a factor of 20 or 30. Earlier findings that the Orion nebula was abnormally rich in sulfur are not confirmed, although the new values for sulfur, chlorine, and argon are rather rough

■■■

Element Formation
in Stars

OTTO STRUVE

(*Sky and Telescope*, July and August 1956)

Three years ago, I wrote [see p. 230], "It seems to me that the importance of local phenomena in creating various kinds of heavy atoms in stars has not been sufficiently appreciated in the past." . . .

At that time most astronomers believed that the cosmic abundance scale of the chemical elements in the universe could only be explained in terms of a prestellar process involving something like the "ylem" of G. Gamow, R. A. Alpher, and R. C. Herman. This was thought of as an intensely hot and fantastically dense medium of neutrons, protons, and electrons, in which all the chemical elements were produced by interactions between these fundamental particles. As the medium cooled by its rapid expansion, the initial abundances remained "frozen" into the mixture. All the nebulae, dust clouds, and stars were produced from this medium, and they contained, to begin with, the same abundances of the chemical elements. All that the stars could do later to modify their composition was to destroy any small amounts of lithium, beryllium, and boron; to increase the proportion of helium at the expense of hydrogen; and perhaps to increase the ratio of the carbon isotopes, C^{13} to C^{12}, as a result of the Bethe–von Weizsaecker carbon-nitrogen cycle [see p. 43].

Only a few astronomers, among them G. B. Van Albada and F. Hoyle, dared to think, three years ago, of the creation of heavy atoms in red giants and exploding supernovae, and even they did not regard these processes as very important in the entire picture of the formation of the chemical elements.

Today the situation is very different. In the *Proceedings* of the National Academy of Sciences (April 15, 1956), W. A. Fowler and J. L. Greenstein say, "Can nuclear and astrophysical processes, now understood, be found which produce the heavier elements from hydrogen, in stars, under conditions such as exist at present? Is there any astrophysical evidence that element-building is going on now? We are not

FIG. 81. Each of the myriads of stars in this photograph of part of the great Sagittarius star cloud (not far from the galactic center) can be regarded as an atomic reactor, forming heavier atoms from hydrogen. (Mount Wilson and Palomar Observatories photograph)

committed to any speculative relativistic cosmology, nor are we excluding the possibility of a primeval, explosive phase. We wish to trace the evolution of a universe containing initially only the simplest atom, hydrogen, part of which condenses into stars, leaving an interstellar gas, out of which later generations of stars may condense. We will show that known laws of nuclear physics and known astronomical processes lead to element building in certain stars; mass loss to interstellar space, or explosion, both of which now occur, returns heavier elements, to be mixed with the interstellar hydrogen. New stars formed will have an increased proportion of heavy elements."

There can now be no doubt that the stars do serve as atomic reactors in which heavy elements are produced. But not all stars do so in the same manner or with the same efficiency. Those of the sun's type are relatively inactive, though even they "cook" the heavy elements on a small scale. The red giants and supergiants produce large atomic nuclei copiously in their interiors; the novae and supernovae do so explosively; and the magnetic stars manufacture heavy elements near their surfaces by the betatron effect [magnetic acceleration of charged particles].

The meaning of the cosmic abundance scale is now very different; there is no uniform "frozen" cosmic distribution of the elements. The Milky Way is being continuously enriched in heavy atoms, and newly formed stars start on their evolutionary tracks with greater abundances of heavy elements than did the oldest stars of Population II. Individual stars are now known to differ greatly from each other in detailed chemical composition.

Until recently, there were three reasons why astronomers believed in a uniform cosmic abundance scale. First, the leakage of matter from stars into interstellar space proceeds very slowly, even though mass is being ejected by many kinds of stars: supergiants, supernovae and novae, close binaries, and very hot main-sequence stars. Consequently, stars formed even a billion years apart will differ only slightly in initial composition. Second, most of the stars whose atmospheres have been analyzed with the spectrograph happen to be neighbors of the sun in space. Thus they all belong to the relatively young Population I, and their initial compositions would not have differed greatly. Third, in such stars there is little mixing of gas between the deep interior (where nuclear reactions are forming heavy atoms) and the surface layers. These layers therefore should still have essentially the same composition as the interstellar medium from which the stars were born; the term cosmic abundance scale is meaningful today only when we are speaking of stellar atmospheres that are free of the effects of mixing.

The new ideas on element building in stars come from the work of many astronomers: M. Schwarzschild and F. Hoyle on the internal temperatures of the giants and supergiants, Fowler and Greenstein on the formation of heavy atoms, and Fowler, G. R. Burbidge, and E. Margaret Burbidge on nuclear reactions at the surfaces of magnetic stars.

In the past few years we have come to realize that the fundamental process in stellar evolution is the gravitational contraction of a mass of gas. In its earliest stages this gas is an extremely tenuous interstellar cloud, containing some 1000 hydrogen atoms per cubic centimeter at a temperature perhaps only a few hundred degrees above absolute zero. To contain enough matter to make an average star, such a cloud must originally be about one light year, or six trillion miles, across.

As the cloud contracts, its internal temperature rises until nuclear reactions start. The first of these, at about a million degrees, consists of the destruction of the rather rare elements lithium, beryllium, and boron; it produces relatively little nuclear energy and a small amount of helium.

Because the energy release is small, the star continues to contract until its central temperature is at least five million degrees. At this stage (on the main sequence in the H-R diagram) thermonuclear fusion of hydrogen into helium sets in. Because of the great abundance of hydrogen, the star can now release an enormous amount of energy at a controlled rate, and its contraction is temporarily halted. During a long interval the star changes hardly at all in size and surface temperature. For cool dwarfs like the sun, this stage lasts billions of years, but it is only a few million years for a very luminous O-type star such as Zeta Puppis.

Eventually, when much of the available hydrogen supply has been converted into helium, the contraction resumes, and the central temperature rises rapidly until it reaches several hundred million degrees. In this stage the outer layers of the star are blown out; it becomes a supergiant of low surface temperature, like Antares or Betelgeuse. But, as Hoyle has succinctly stated, "The nuclear transformations cannot stop a star from contracting." Its internal temperature may continue to rise until it reaches several billion degrees! Ultimately the density of the core becomes so great—of the order of a million grams per cubic centimeter—that the material ceases to obey the laws of perfect gases. It becomes degenerate, and the star is then a white dwarf. But if it is more massive than the sun, it must expel some of its matter before it can settle down to its long cooling-off stage as a white dwarf. In this way, still more material is returned to the interstellar medium [see p. 220]. . . .

A hydrogen atom of mass 1.7×10^{-24} gram consists of one proton carrying nearly all the mass and possessing a positive electric charge, and of an electron whose mass is $1/1836$ that of the proton and whose electric charge is negative. At $10,000°$ absolute (the surface temperature of Sirius) hydrogen atoms have velocities of about 10 kilometers per second. At these speeds, collisions can remove the electron from a hydrogen atom; it is then ionized, and the gas consists mainly of free protons and electrons. A collision between a proton and an electron may result in capture, reconstituting a normal hydrogen atom. Two protons cannot collide because their positive electric charges repel each other very strongly whenever the particles get close together.

The temperature inside a hydrogen star gradually rises because of gravitational contraction. At 20 million degrees the velocities of the protons are about 500 kilometers per second, and two protons can approach very close to each other when they meet head on. Recent computations show that they may come within 10^{-13} centimeter, which is some 1/10,000 the size of a normal hydrogen atom. In such a near collision, the two protons stick together. Simultaneously, one of the two protons emits a positron (positive electron) and a neutrino, becoming an uncharged particle called a neutron. The results of the fusion are a deuteron, which has the mass of one proton plus that of one neutron (almost, but not exactly, the mass of two protons), and the positive electric charge of the proton. This deuteron, should it capture an electron, would become an atom of heavy hydrogen (H^2), also known as deuterium.

If the deuteron collides with another proton at the high speed of 500 kilometers per second, the proton sticks to the deuteron and does not eject a positron, but emits a powerful gamma ray of electromagnetic radiation. The remaining particle is the nucleus of a rare isotope of the element helium (He^3), consisting of two protons and one neutron, with very nearly three times the mass of a proton.

This nucleus does not interact with either a proton or a deuteron, but if enough He^3 nuclei have been produced, two of them may collide, bringing together four protons and two neutrons. This would combine six proton masses and four positive charges, but such a particle can exist only momentarily; it quickly expels two protons, leaving only two protons and two neutrons. Thus it becomes a nucleus of the abundant helium isotope (He^4), the alpha particle. It has nearly the mass of four protons, with two positive electric charges.

This "proton-proton reaction" produces deuterium and helium out of hydrogen. No other elements are generated. But as the star gradually exhausts the hydrogen in its innermost core, contraction again sets in, and when the temperature rises to about 150 million degrees a new reaction begins to function. Two alpha particles meeting with velocities of a few thousand kilometers per second fuse to form a new particle of four protons and four neutrons, an isotope of beryllium (Be^8), which rapidly disintegrates back into two alpha particles. But in some stars there should be at a given moment a considerable number of such nuclei, even though any single one decays quickly. Fowler and Greenstein have computed that at a density of 10^4 grams per cubic centimeter, such as might exist in the heavily contracted core of a supergiant, there would be at any moment one Be^8 nucleus for every billion alpha particles.

While such a beryllium isotope lasts, it can collide with another alpha particle and produce a nucleus consisting of six protons and six neutrons. Thus it has a mass of twelve and six positive charges—it is a carbon nucleus (C^{12}). In this process a gamma ray is ejected, adding to the radiant energy of the star. Fowler points out that this reaction cannot be observed in the laboratory because it is impossible under experimental conditions to maintain a supply of the unstable beryllium isotope. But he has, nevertheless, proved the existence of the process by means of the reverse reaction, the breaking up of carbon into beryllium and helium when the carbon nucleus is excited by gamma radiation.

Once carbon has been produced, building heavier elements is relatively direct. The carbon nuclei can combine with alpha particles to produce oxygen (O^{16}) and the latter, by similar collisions, can form neon (Ne^{20}). At still higher temperatures, about five billion degrees, the nuclei of carbon, oxygen, and neon can react with each other and with their reaction products. In this manner iron (Fe^{56}) might be built up by successive steps. Fowler suggests, "The marked peak in the universal abundance curve, symmetric about Fe^{56}, is due to those stars which remained stable until all nuclear energy release had terminated."

We have thus accounted for the building up of a large number of elements in first-generation stars. But notice that carbon, oxygen, and neon came into existence only at the very high temperature of 150 million degrees, when hydrogen was practically exhausted. Therefore no simple collisions of these heavier nuclei with protons could have played any role. Yet we know of stellar nuclear processes that involve just these atoms. Therefore Fowler suggests that some first-generation stars explode or expel matter into interstellar space after the creation of carbon, oxygen, and neon but before temperatures of the order of five billion degrees are reached.

The interstellar medium would thus be enriched in these elements, and new stars—of the second generation—would contain them, in addition to a large amount of the original hydrogen. At a relatively low temperature in a second-generation star's mixture, say 20 million degrees, many new processes become possible. Of fundamental importance is the carbon cycle, the first detailed nuclear reaction discovered to explain energy generation in the stars [see p. 43].

Its starting fuel consists of four protons, and the end product is an alpha particle; the slight loss of mass appears as radiant energy. Carbon atoms, used in the beginning, reappear at the end without change in their ultimate number. Incidental new particles are N^{13}, C^{13}, N^{14}, O^{15}, and N^{15}. Many of these nuclei react with protons and with neutrons, so that ultimately in these second-generation stars all elements are generated (from hydrogen, helium, and carbon) to atomic masses as great as that of lead, excepting lithium, beryllium, and boron. (However, Fowler and the Burbidges suggest that these light elements are produced at the surfaces of stars possessing spots of high and variable magnetic intensity.)

Fowler and Greenstein assume that first-generation stars expelled much of their material into the interstellar medium, from which second-generation stars were formed. We can ask, however, if this assumption is necessary, for would not the C^{12} formed in the first-generation stars allow element building by the carbon cycle? The difficulty is that C^{12} first appears at the very high temperatures of over 100 million degrees that occur only in stars largely exhausted of their original hydrogen supply. . . . However, this does not mean that the carbon cycle does not exist at all in such stars. It could produce additional nuclei in a cooler outer layer containing abundant hydrogen if carbon nuclei could migrate into the layer from a very hot stellar core.

Hence the carbon cycle can take place in such cooler outer layers of first-generation stars (as well as in second-generation stars that are cooler inside) where there is a large supply of hydrogen with a small admixture of carbon.

Now, the carbon cycle produces new isotopes: N^{13}, C^{13}, N^{14}, O^{15}, and N^{15}. There is a parallel series of reactions whereby ordinary oxygen is converted by proton capture into an isotope of fluorine (F^{17}), which decays by positron emission to O^{17}. Then this heavy isotope of oxygen, upon colliding with another proton, splits into ordinary nitrogen (N^{14}) and an alpha particle. In a somewhat similar manner, the heavy isotope of neon (Ne^{21}) is also produced.

These heavy isotopes of carbon, oxygen, and neon differ from their lighter counterparts because they each contain an extra neutron, just as the deuteron differs from the proton by its extra neutron. Such neutron-rich isotopes are especially important because they can capture alpha particles and expel the extra neutron. Thus at 85 million degrees in second-generation stars, there are such reactions as the capture of an alpha particle by C^{13}, yielding O^{16} and a neutron. Similar reactions convert O^{17} to Ne^{20}, and Ne^{21} to Mg^{24}. These processes furnish a large supply of free neutrons.

Because they have no electric charge, neutrons are not repelled by the positively charged atomic nuclei. Hence they are easily captured and thus produce, step by step, still heavier elements up to lead (Pb^{208}), or bismuth (Bi^{209}). For example, the light isotope (Au^{197}) of gold can acquire a neutron to become Au^{198}, with the release of gamma radiation. If this nucleus should next emit an electron, with one negative charge, it would form a particle of the same mass number, 198, but having 80 positive charges. This would be the fairly abundant isotope of mercury Hg^{198}. . . .

The Fowler-Greenstein theory, as it now stands, does not explain the large abundances of the third lightest element, lithium, in several late-type stars. Nor does it account for the presence of technetium, recently identified in such stars. . . .

To explain the presence of lithium, which Greenstein and R. S. Richardson have definitely identified in several stars, and even on the surface of the sun, Fowler and the Burbidges have worked out the "betatron effect" of the magnetic spots that occur on the surfaces of many stars. They also suggest such a mechanism to explain the peculiarly large abundances of the rare-earth elements in the atmospheres of magnetic and spectrum variable stars, such as α^2 Canum Venaticorum.

Although the details of this theory are fairly involved, the basic ideas are simple. The betatron is a high-energy accelerator, principally used to accelerate electrons (beta particles). It was invented in 1940 by D. W. Kerst at the University of Illinois, and is a modification of the cyclotron. Electrons are injected into the field between the poles of an electromagnet, where they follow circular paths and form an electric current. With a constant magnetic field, the electrons have constant velocities, but if the field strength is increasing, the electrons are accelerated. To prevent them from spiraling outward, the magnetic flux density also grows, and they continue moving in a circle with ever-increasing speed and energy. Several hundred thousand revolutions may be made, and betatron energies can reach 100 million electron volts.

An energy of one electron volt corresponds to a velocity of each electron of 600 kilometers per second. With this energy a proton, roughly 2000 times as heavy as an electron, would travel at a rate of only 14 kilometers per second. In the largest existing accelerators, such as the Berkeley bevatron (name derived from "billion electron volts"), the particles may be accelerated to about six billion electron volts. They then travel with velocities approaching that of light.

On the surface of a star with a temperature of 10,000°, the velocities of protons are of the order of 10 kilometers per second. This is the equivalent of about one electron volt—far below the energy required to produce any nuclear transformations. But the sun has spots which form in the course of only a few hours from the quiescent solar photosphere. Strong magnetic fields are generated in these disturbed areas, and while the fields are increasing, large accelerations will be experienced by nearby charged particles, both ions and electrons.

Fowler and the Burbidges have suggested that in some stars even stronger magnetic spots, of the order of one million gauss (which is 100 times stronger than has been observed in the sun), are built up in a few hours. This could give many particles betatron-type accelerations of 10 or even 100 million electron volts. With such enormous energies, the particles could indeed synthesize not only lithium, beryllium, and boron, but the rare earths and other heavy elements found to be abnormally abundant in some stars.

These are stimulating ideas, but the theory of nuclear processes in stars would be sterile if it were not possible to verify some of its predictions by means of observations. The following important part of our discussion is due mainly to Greenstein.

First of all, is there any evidence that the original medium out of which the earliest stars of our galaxy were formed consisted of hydrogen only? There are now no stars known that are pure hydrogen, but this is not unexpected, for even the oldest first-generation stars (which may have been once entirely hydrogen) have had some six billion years to convert hydrogen into heavier elements. Their atmospheres should contain some admixture of heavy elements, brought up from their interiors by even very slow mixing, in the form of convection currents.

Nevertheless, the very oldest stars have atmospheres relatively deficient in metals. Their spectra show hydrogen lines of normal intensity for surface temperatures of about 4500° (spectral class K), but their metallic lines are very faint. In the most abnormal members of this group, the deficiency of the metals may reach a factor of 20 (that is, metal abundance is estimated at one-twentieth of that in normal stars). As Greenstein puts it, "Such stars can be relics of the earliest days of element and star formation," when the diffuse medium of the galaxy was mainly hydrogen.

It is useful to distinguish between the absolute age of a star in years and its evolutionary stage. The latter may be defined as the fraction

$$\frac{\text{Age of the star in years}}{\text{Total life span of star}}.$$

The total life span of a star of the sun's mass may be 5×10^{10} years, or even longer if by life span we mean the interval between the formation of the star and its ultimate conversion into a white dwarf. Hence even though the sun is probably 4.6×10^{9} years old, its evolutionary stage is only of the order of $1/10$. The very old high-velocity stars and the cool giants in globular clusters are perhaps 6×10^{9} years old, but their average life span may be somewhat shorter than the sun's, say 2×10^{10} years. Their evolutionary stages should be about $1/3$. They have not completely exhausted their hydrogen supply, at least at their surfaces there is still more hydrogen in relation to heavy elements than in stars of recent origin.

What about stars whose evolutionary stages are close to $1/1$? The best objects to examine would be relatively massive stars, which expend their energy rapidly and have short life spans. Even though of considerable age, these stars could still be much younger than the sun, and they may even be second-generation stars born from a medium enriched in heavy elements. Such stars, most likely to be found in the upper regions of the H-R diagram, should not be numerous, for their evolution has taken place much more rapidly than if they were on the main sequence and still had a large supply of hydrogen fuel.

Greenstein, Münch, and others at Mount Wilson and Palomar Observatories have found a number of such objects, usually described as underluminous blue stars. Some were first discovered by F. Zwicky and M. Humason, long before anything was known about their evolutionary status. As a reasonable guess, we may now assign to them an evolutionary stage of about 0.8 or 0.9. They have substantially exhausted their hydrogen, and they are old enough in years to have experienced a considerable amount of mixing. Even their atmospheres are depleted in hydrogen and rich in helium. The spectrum of one such star, (No. 44 in the Humason-Zwicky list) has a strong line of neutral helium at 4026 angstroms, and there are many other prominent lines of helium. On the other hand, the hydrogen-epsilon and hydrogen-delta lines are very weak.

If, as seems probable, the carbon cycle was operating in such a star while its central temperature was about 20 million degrees, nuclei of C^{13}, N^{14}, and N^{15} were produced. After a long time, the equilibrium ratio of N^{14}/C^{12} should be 20/1, that is, the star should be rich in nitrogen and relatively poor in carbon. The spectrum of No. 44 verifies this, and the carbon lines that might otherwise be expected are not visible.

Another prediction from the equilibrium theory of the carbon cycle is that the abundance ratio of C^{13} to C^{12} should be 1/4. The terrestrial ratio is 1/90, and about the same value is observed in the solar atmosphere. Even though the carbon cycle may be active in the sun's interior at present, the abundant C^{13} nuclei have not had time to be carried to the surface by convection currents.

But in some late-type giant stars, A. McKellar has observed at Victoria, B.C., very strong bands produced by three kinds of diatomic carbon *molecules*. The first is made up of two C^{12} atoms, the second is a mixture of isotopes, $C^{12}C^{13}$, and the last is composed of two C^{13} atoms. Evidently in these stars mixing is more powerful than in the sun, and the C^{13} nuclei have been carried to the surface. The observed ratio of C^{13} to C^{12} is about 1/4, as predicted by theory. However, others of McKellar's stars show little if any evidence of C^{13}. These stars are either younger or they had little mixing.

As for the "betatron effect," which would produce the elements lithium, beryllium, and boron, McKellar says that to his knowledge only three out of a hundred carbon stars show the strong line of neutral lithium at 6707 angstroms. They are WZ Cassiopeiae, WX Cygni, and T Arae. Evidently for strong local magnetic fields to form on a star's surface, special conditions are required that are infrequently realized.

According to Fowler and Greenstein, the red giant stars—classes M, N, R, and S—give the most straightforward evidence for the synthesis of heavy elements. Many of them must have central temperatures of the order of a billion degrees, and their spectra are rich in molecules containing heavy atoms. . . .

The theory of an original hydrogen cloud being enriched continuously with heavy elements produced in stars, is not inconsistent with today's very limited knowledge of nuclear reactions in stars. An explosive origin of the universe, with atom building from an original "ylem," is not entirely excluded. But some difficulties are clearly recognized. One is the great age of the sun, 4.5 billion years or older. Do the abundant heavy elements in its atmosphere indicate that it is a second-generation star, formed from enriched interstellar gas? The difference between the age of the galaxy (about six billion years) and the sun's own age seems too short for this.

If the sun is a first-generation star, the atmospheric abundances indicate more powerful internal element building than is possible at 20 million degrees; also, there may be more violent mixing by convection that can be reconciled with the observed intensities of the lithium lines and the carbon isotope ratio in the solar atmosphere.

Thus there remains a suspicion, stressed especially by W. Baade, that the original interstellar medium was already enriched when the oldest stars of the spiral arms (like the sun) were produced. It is also possible that different distant regions of the original cloud—for example, near the galactic nucleus and in the halo—had different chemical compositions. If so, stars from these regions that stray into our neighborhood, RR Lyrae variables, high-velocity stars, and so on, might make us mistake a real difference of original composition for the apparent result of evolution.

▪▪

Five Stellar Populations

(*Sky and Telescope*, April 1958)

The current status of the study of stellar populations is reviewed by J. B. Oke, David Dunlap Observatory, in the February 1958 issue of the *Journal* of the Royal Astronomical Society of Canada. In an article entitled, "Stellar Populations—the Key to Our Galaxy," Oke presents the accompanying table, to show how Baade's original two Populations I and II have been revised and expanded into five groups, of different ages.

TABLE 8.   REVISION OF BAADE'S ORIGINAL POPULATIONS I AND II INTO FIVE GROUPS OF DIFFERENT AGES

Population Group	Age in Billions of Years	Examples	Heavy Elements
Extreme Population I	0–1	Hot O- and B-type stars Interstellar gas and dust Young galactic clusters	4 %
Intermediate Population I	1–3	Older galactic clusters	3 %
Disk Population	3–5	The sun	2 %
Intermediate Population II	5–6	"High-velocity" stars	1 %
Extreme Population II	6–6½	Globular clusters in the galactic halo	0.3 %

The list of examples in Table 8 is only partial, but illustrates the content of the various populations. The percentages of heavy elements (those other than hydrogen and helium) are greater for the younger stars. This indicates that the latter are formed out of an interstellar medium that has a higher content of heavy elements than the original material from which the extreme Population II stars were made.

Oke concludes his article with a bird's-eye view of the role of the interstellar matter: "When the first stars were born the galaxy must have been entirely interstellar gas. As each generation of stars formed out of this interstellar matter, some of the matter was trapped in the faint, almost unchanging stars of small mass. Thus after each generation there was less interstellar matter and more stars. At present only about 2 per cent of the mass of the galaxy is in the form of interstellar matter.* Eventually this matter will almost completely disappear. When this happens, no new stars will form, very luminous stars will rapidly disappear, and we shall be left with a galaxy composed of faint, cool stars and tiny white dwarfs. Our Milky Way system will have become a rather uninteresting place in which to live."

* Many astronomers consider 10 per cent a better estimate.—TLP

Metal Abundances in
K-Type Stars of
Population II

(*Sky and Telescope*, October 1958)

In order to explain the differences between stars of Population I and Population II, more information is needed concerning the relative abundances of elements in their atmospheres. This work requires careful analyses of detailed observations of the intensities of lines in their spectra.

To study these differences in stars of late spectral type, where the lines of metals are strong, H. L. Helfer and G. Wallerstein, Mount Wilson and Palomar Observatories, selected three stars of Population II: one each in the globular clusters M13 and M92, and one extremely high-velocity star (HDE232078). For comparison purposes they included a fourth sample star in the galactic cluster M41, which is of Population I. They carried out curve-of-growth analyses from spectrograms with a dispersion of 18 angstroms per millimeter.

Although all four stars are giants of spectral type K, the first three have extremely weak metal lines, indicating a metal abundance only 1/100 that in the sun. The fourth star, of Population I, yielded roughly the solar abundance of metals.

Lithium in K Stars

(*Sky and Telescope*, July 1959)

There are some notable exceptions to the general agreement among the earth, the sun, and normal Population-I stars in the relative abundances of the elements they contain. For example, the earth is lacking in hydrogen and helium, and lithium is far more common on the earth than in the sun.

In order to find if cool stars in general are deficient in lithium, W. K. Bonsack, California Institute of Technology, has measured the abundance of that element relative to vanadium for forty-six stars with spectra of near class K (G8 to Mo inclusive). His observations were made with the coudé spectrograph of the Mount Wilson 100-inch reflector. On high-dispersion spectrograms, he compared the intensity of the neutral lithium line at 6708 angstroms with a number of lines of neutral vanadium.

Among stars of similar surface characteristics, the abundance ratios thus found differed by as much as a factor of 100, and none had more lithium than the sun. Nevertheless, there was a tendency for cooler stars to contain less lithium relative to vanadium. Bonsack feels that this tendency is not due in any significant degree, to differences in vanadium content. Instead, he suggests that both the trend and the variations are the result of convective transport of lithium from the surface layers of cool stars into their interiors. This mechanism had earlier been proposed by J. L. Greenstein and R. S. Richardson to explain the deficiency of lithium in the outer parts of the sun.

Are Stars Alike in Different Parts of the Universe?

(*Sky and Telescope*, March 1960)

In studies of star formation and of the evolution of galaxies, the following problem is basic. Suppose a quantity of primitive material is converted into stars. The distribution of intrinsic luminosities among these newly formed stars is called the *initial luminosity function*. It tells the relative numbers of stars for each absolute magnitude, before the stars have evolved appreciably. For different stellar samples that were formed from the same amount of matter but at different times and places in the universe, will this function be the same?

Recently a number of astronomers have assumed that such a uniformity in fact exists. D. N. Limber of Yerkes Observatory has now tested whether this assumption is consistent with observation, and finds strong evidence against it.

The first step in his investigation was to derive the initial luminosity function for well-observed stars in the solar neighborhood and in galactic clusters. Then, making use of the modern theory of stellar evolution, he could predict how the mass-to-light ratio of this sample of stars would change as the stars aged.

Next, he compared this changing mass-to-light ratio with the observationally determined values of the ratio for globular clusters and for other galaxies than ours. This comparison led to two alternatives: either the initial luminosity function does differ among stellar systems, or a significant fraction of the stellar systems in the observable universe must be well over 20 billion years old. Limber prefers the first alternative.

Limber concluded his report to the December 1959 meeting of the American Astronomical Society by saying, "It thus appears that the form of the initial luminosity function depends in a marked way upon at least certain of the parameters that describe the prestellar medium from which stars form—parameters such as density, temperature, turbulent velocity, magnetic field strength, and chemical composition."

Lithium, Beryllium, and Lead in the Sun

(*Sky and Telescope*, July 1963)

J. P. Mutschlecner, now at Los Alamos Scientific Laboratory, has redetermined the abundances of lithium, beryllium, and lead in the solar atmosphere. His observational material consisted of numerous spectral scans obtained with the vacuum spectrograph at the McMath-Hulbert Observatory of the University of Michigan. To interpret these observations, he computed theoretically for each line the manner in which line intensity would grow as the abundance of the element was increased.

For each million atoms of silicon in the sun's atmosphere, there are 1.1 of lithium, 6.9 of beryllium, and 1.4 of lead, Mutschlecner finds. [The logarithmic abundances to compare with Table 6 are as follows: Si, 7.12; Li, 1.16; Be, 1.96; Pb, 1.27.] He estimates the upper limits of uncertainty as 100, 30, and 100 per cent, respectively, most of which comes from the model atmosphere assumed in the theoretical computation.

The solar abundances of beryllium and lead agree well with analyses of meteorites. Lithium, however, is only about 1 per cent as abundant as in meteorites, confirming previous results.

Lithium and Star Ageing

(*Sky and Telescope*, August 1963)

It has been known since 1957 that the lightest metal, lithium, is several hundred times more abundant in very young stars of the T Tauri type than in the sun. The usual interpretation has been that nuclear processes destroy most of the lithium after these stars have reached the main sequence. The small amount of remaining lithium in surface layers is preserved because internal mixing is too slight to carry it to the hot central regions where it would be consumed.

This explanation is now found to need some modification. O. C. Wilson (Mount Wilson and Palomar Observatories) found that the G8 star Xi Bootis A, which is very similar to the sun, has a strong lithium line. In an extensive study at Lick Observatory, George H. Herbig has used the 120-inch reflector to examine the spectra of more than sixty G0–G8 dwarf stars within 20 parsecs of the sun. They show a wide range of lithium abundances, all the way from that of T Tauri stars down to less than that of the sun.

Herbig infers that this range is an age effect, in the sense that the amount of lithium decreases with time. With George Wallerstein and Peter Conti of Leuschner Observatory, he has checked six G0–G4 dwarfs in the Hyades cluster (age 500 million years); all six of these relatively young stars have moderately strong lithium lines. The sun, with its low abundance of this metal, is about five billion years old.

Another piece of evidence is that the stars with strongest lithium lines all have low space velocities—an earmark of comparatively young stars.

If further work confirms this correlation between lithium abundance and stellar age, astronomers will have a simple spectroscopic method for sorting out main-sequence stars of different ages.

The use of velocity to estimate the age of a star results from studies of motions in the Milky Way Galaxy and of the ages of clusters like those described in Chapter 3. The galactic clusters, nebulae, dust clouds, and individual stars moving with the sun in orbits around the center of the galaxy all belong to the young stellar Population I and have fairly small velocities relative to us (although, like us, they are moving at 250 km/sec around the galactic nucleus). The globular clusters and stars of the galactic halo, on the other hand, are in very different orbits around the center of the galaxy, and therefore have high velocities relative to us. The globular clusters, and all the other Population-II halo-stars, are older—possibly as old as the galaxy itself. Moreover, there are no nebulae and dust clouds moving with them, so it is unlikely that new high-velocity stars can be formed. Hence

FIG. 82. G. H. Herbig finds much evidence to support the hypothesis that newly formed stars are relatively rich in lithium, but that this element is gradually consumed. The young T Tauri stars have about a hundred times as much lithium as the sun; the Pleiades, Coma, and a few Hyades stars have less than a hundred times. The curve passing through the sun shows the theoretical course of its lithium depletion; it is entirely independent of the stellar data. (Adapted from a Lick Observatory chart in *The Astrophysical Journal*, The University of Chicago Press)

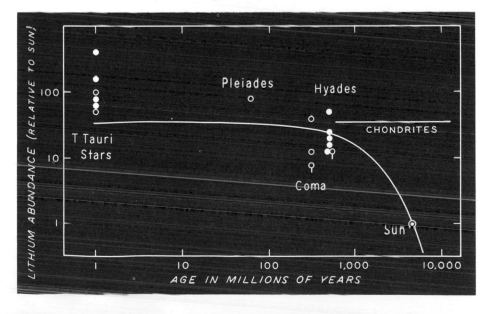

high-velocity stars are older, and low velocities are an "earmark" of youth.

A comparatively recent summary of lithium abundances is shown in Figure 82, where the abundances in chondrites (a type of stony meteorite) is linked to that in the sun and stars. The fact that meteoritic material—remains of the primordial nebula from which the sun was formed—contains more lithium than the sun shows that the sun's lithium content has decreased by a factor of 20 during the past four billion years. Before that, the surface layers of the sun probably had as much lithium as the meteorites and the youthful stars in the Hyades cluster—almost as much as in the newly formed T Tauri stars.—TLP

....

Is the Sun Metal-Rich?

(*Sky and Telescope*, August 1963)

Dutch astronomer Sidney van den Bergh has developed a new method for determining the abundance of metals in a main-sequence star of spectral type G. He has obtained photoelectric scans of the spectra of over one hundred high-velocity and low-velocity stars, using the 74-inch reflector of David Dunlap Observatory of the University of Toronto. His scanner has an effective resolution of 20 angstroms.

One of van den Bergh's two criteria is the difference in intensity of the spectral continuum on the two sides of the hydrogen line Hζ at 3889 angstroms. In each case tested, the continuum on the short-wavelength side of the line is relatively brighter in metal-poor stars than it is in metal-rich ones. . . . The second criterion is the size of the Balmer discontinuity [see p. 73] near 4000 angstroms. This discontinuity decreases with decreasing metal abundance.

Applying these criteria to sunlight, van den Bergh finds that the sun itself is a metal-rich star. However, its abundance of metals does not differ by more than 10 per cent from that of stars in the Hyades cluster, which are perhaps four billion years younger. He infers from this that the rate of enrichment of the interstellar medium in heavy elements must have been quite small since the sun was formed.

A similar scheme, applied to early-type stars, had been developed *five years earlier, for somewhat different purposes, by Strömgren, as the next article shows.*—TLP

....

The Chemical
Compositions and
Ages of Stars

OTTO STRUVE

(*Sky and Telescope*, November 1958)

On May 27, 1958, Bengt Strömgren, now a member of the Princeton Institute for Advanced Studies and previously director of Yerkes and McDonald Observatories, delivered the Halley Lecture for 1958 at Oxford University. To an audience of British astronomers, he summarized investigations by himself and his colleagues in the field of photoelectric narrow-band photometry and its applications to problems of the composition of stars and their ages.

In the introduction to his discourse, Strömgren called attention to a fact emphasized in the 1933 Halley Lecture by H. N. Russell, who said, "Stellar spectra are remarkably similar *inter se*. The variety is much less than it would be if the relative abundances of many elements varied appreciably from star to star."

Hence, argued Strömgren, "The observed uniformity suggests that the problems of the interpretation of stellar spectra may be tackled successfully, in a first approximation, on the assumption of uniform chemical composition of the stars. As the analysis progresses, deviations from this simple picture, if they exist, will become apparent."

In recent years astronomers have found it convenient to describe the evolution of a star with a given mass in terms of an "evolutionary track" in the Hertzsprung-Russell diagram. One example of such a track is pictured in Figure 83. For stars of larger masses, the tracks lie higher in the diagram, and the shapes of the curves are not quite the same. But for stars in general we can distinguish four principal sections of the track.

First comes the stage of gravitational contractions, which carries the newly condensed star from right to left in the H-R diagram, and lasts only a relatively short time. Second, during the long-lasting main-sequence stage, the amount of energy generated by thermonuclear processes in the deep interior of the star is balanced by the energy radiated from the stellar surface into space. Third, as the hydrogen available for fuel becomes exhausted, the balance between energy produced and energy radiated is no longer maintained, and the star changes its characteristics fairly rapidly from those of the main sequence to those of the upper right corner of the diagram. Fourth, there is the final stage of very high central temperature, during which the star evolves more or less rapidly from right to left, crossing the main sequence, and ultimately becoming a white dwarf.

If two stars were to have different initial chemical compositions—say one was mainly hydrogen, the other mainly helium—the same four sections would occur, but their tracks would not coincide, even for stars of the same mass. But on Strömgren's assumption that stars have approximately the same initial composition, different evolutionary tracks represent differing stellar masses. In other words, the location of each track would depend solely on the mass of the star.

Then, if it were true that the tracks of stars of differing mass do not intersect, the precise location of the star on the H-R diagram would give us at once the mass of the star and its age. In general, we cannot make this assumption, for the tracks probably do intersect, even if the initial compositions are precisely the same; but with some simplifications, the assumption of no intersections is likely to be valid.

First, suppose we can distinguish between stars in the early contracting stage and those in the much later hydrogen-exhaustion stage. Further, consider only stars within a fairly narrow range of mass that have not departed very greatly from the main sequence.

We will now consider the B-type stars, the hot blue ones at the upper end of the main sequence. For these, the early contracting stage may be disregarded because it requires only a short time. We assign arbitrarily an age of zero to those B stars that are just beginning their main-sequence stage, and we follow the third evolutionary stages of stars of different masses, moving rightward from the main sequence, as in Figure 84. These tracks do not intersect. Hence all we need to determine both age and mass from observation is the exact

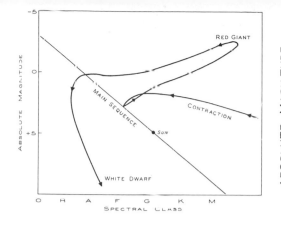

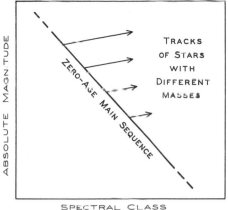

FIG. 83. Arrows trace the evolution of a star that contracts to reach the main sequence at spectral type *F*, where its thermonuclear processes begin in earnest.

FIG. 84. The more massive a star, the higher in the H-R diagram is its track on leaving the main sequence, and the more rapid is its evolution.

location of the star in the H-R diagram. That is, we need only determine the star's absolute magnitude and spectral type, or their equivalents.

Conventional spectrographic methods have been of limited precision, and Strömgren has developed a more accurate way to classify spectra two dimensionally [see p. 74]. It is used to improve the classification after a good spectral type and absolute magnitude (or luminosity class) have been secured by inspection (using the Morgan-Keenan classification) or by spectral intensity measures in the manner of Chalonge.

In the near-ultraviolet spectrum of early-type stars, there is a conspicuous drop in the brightness of the continuous background as we pass from the long-wavelength to the short wavelength side of the limit of the Balmer series of hydrogen lines. This drop is known as the *Balmer discontinuity*. From the extensive spectrographic work by D. Barbier, by D. Chalonge and E. Vassy, and by Y. Ohman more than twenty years ago, we know that in *B*- and *A*-type stars (and to some extent also in *F* stars) the depth of the Balmer discontinuity is a very good indicator of the surface temperature.

Similarly, from the work of B. Lindblad, and more recently especially of R. M. Petrie, we know that the strength of the hydrogen Balmer lines depends mostly on stellar luminosity, and only to a lesser degree upon the surface temperature. (This is illustrated for hydrogen gamma in Figure 85.) Hence it should be possible to place any star in the H-R diagram for which the depth of the Balmer discontinuity and the strength of a Balmer line are both known with high accuracy.

Strömgren's contribution is a method of measuring these two quantities with a photoelectric photometer. He makes six successive measurements, letting the star's light pass through each of six narrow-band filters (listed in Table 9).

TABLE 9.   STRÖMGREN'S NARROW-BAND FILTERS

Filter	Peak Transmission (angstroms)	Band width (angstroms)
a	5000	90
b	4861 (Hβ)	35
c	4700	100
d	4500	80
e	4030	90
f	3600	350

The brightness of the star as observed through each filter can be called I_a, I_b, and so on, respectively. Then Strömgren computes two indices: l to describe the strength of the hydrogen-beta line, and c to describe the depth of the Balmer jump (see Fig. 86):

$$l = 2.5 \ (\tfrac{1}{2} \log I_a + \tfrac{1}{2} \log I_c - \log I_b);$$
$$c = 2.5 \ (\ 2 \log I_e - \ \log I_d - \log I_f).$$

The great advantage of these Strömgren index numbers is that they describe the star alone, being virtually unaffected by interstellar reddening. (The drawback to the conventional color index, photographic magnitude minus visual, is that it depends both on the intrinsic color of the star and the reddening effects of interstellar dust). In the case of l, if the star is reddened, I_c will be depressed relative to I_a, but I_b will be depressed by an intermediate amount. The wavelengths of a and c were chosen nearly symmetrical with respect to b, to make the effects of space reddening cancel out in the formula for l. A similar argument holds for the other index, c.

Because of the extreme precision of photoelectric measurements, the probable error of one observation of l is only ± 0.004 magnitude; of $c \pm 0.008$ magnitude.

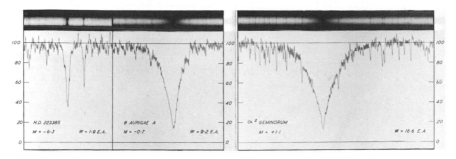

FIG. 85. The very strong dark line in each of these three stellar spectra is hydrogen gamma. Note how the width and depth of this line increase in passing, left to right, from the supergiant star HD223385 to the giant star Theta Aurigae A and then to the main-sequence star Castor (α^2 Geminorum). (Dominion Astrophysical Observatory photograph)

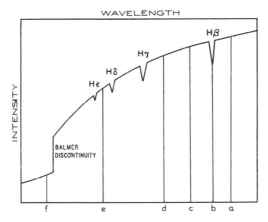

FIG. 86. In this schematic diagram of a stellar spectrum, a to f indicate the wavelengths at which B. Strömgren measures the brightness of the star. From them he deduces index numbers which describe the strength of the hydrogen-beta line and the depth of the Balmer discontinuity. These index numbers reveal the age and mass of the star.

In order to study the ages and masses of the stars, it is not necessary to convert Strömgren's l and c indices into the conventional parameters, absolute magnitude and spectral class. He simply plots each star in a diagram such as Figure 87 with l as the ordinate and c as the abscissa. To estimate the precision of his indices in terms of absolute magnitude and spectral class, Strömgren has calibrated l and c by means of W. W. Morgan's spectral types and a series of absolute magnitudes determined by A. Blaauw and by O. Eggen, D. K. Harris, and H. L. Johnson. The resulting probable error of one observation by Strömgren is only 1/100 of a spectral class and ±0.02 to ±0.03 in absolute magnitude—very satisfactory precision indeed! The departure of a star from the main sequence in the c-l diagram is usually many times larger than these probable errors.

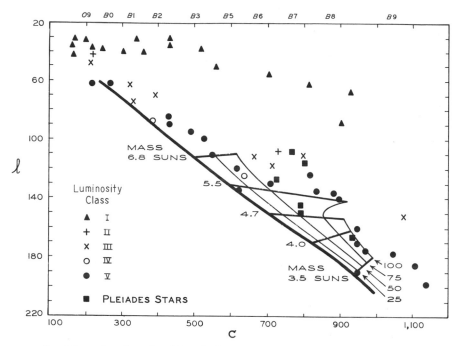

FIG. 87. Plotted points in this *c-l* diagram by Bengt Strömgren represent O- and B-type stars he has observed. The long, thin lines nearly parallel to the main sequence, labeled 25, 50, 75, and 100, are ages in millions of years since the stars left the main sequence. The luminosity class I refers to supergiants, III to giants, and V to dwarfs.

Figure 87 contains stars of five luminosity classes, with supergiants (class I) at the top, plotted as triangles. Some stars of the Pleiades cluster of early spectral type are plotted as squares. The zero-age main sequence is represented by a line, derived independently from many measurements of the *l* and *c* indices of very young stars belonging to two stellar associations in Orion and Scorpius.

We see that the supergiants of type B are easily distinguished from other B-type stars. Strömgren does not discuss their evolution. The other stars lie above the zero-age main sequence by different amounts, indicating differing evolutionary ages.

In Figure 87 Strömgren has superimposed upon the star plot a network of curves computed from the theoretical work of R. J. Taylor and R. S. Kushwaha. The roughly horizontal bars are evolutionary tracks, while the longer, thin lines approximately parallel to the zero-age main sequence represent different ages. These curves apply to stars of spectral type $B3$ and later.

Strömgren has plotted (as squares on Figure 87) the brighter members of the Pleiades that fall in this part of the c-l diagram. From the theoretical curves, we see that their ages lie between 50 and 75 million years (with one near 100 million), in good general agreement with other estimates of the age of this cluster—W. Lohmann's 100 million years and S. von Hoerner's 80 million.

Strömgren tested his assumption that all B stars had the same initial chemical composition by comparing his own measurements of l and c with the best available spectral types and absolute magnitudes for a number of stars in two associations (I Orionis and II Scorpii). If the initial compositions of these two associations had been unlike, stars with the same l and c would have different absolute magnitudes or spectral types in the two groups. However, it turns out that the compositions are the same, to within about 10 per cent in the ratio of hydrogen to helium, and about the same in the ratio of hydrogen to heavy elements.

We cannot be certain that this uniformity of initial composition applies to *all* stars. Strömgren points out that the two associations he compared both belong to the same spiral arm of the Milky Way Galaxy. It would be interesting to extend the comparison to associations in other spiral arms, and to the Magellanic Clouds.

Finally, Strömgren asks the question, Are there other physical processes in stars that might appreciably distort their evolutionary tracks? If there are, then two stars having identical values of l and c would not necessarily have equal masses and ages. He mentions differences in rotational velocities and magnetic properties of the stars, and differences resulting from the presence of hydrogen emission lines. The available evidence is not sufficient to ascertain whether these effects are appreciable. To these possibilities we might add mass exchange and mass expulsion in close binary systems like Beta Lyrae and U Cephei. There is in fact other evidence that the evolutionary tracks of members of such binary systems [see p. 181] may differ drastically from those of normal single stars.

....

Cosmic
Abundances

(*Sky and Telescope*, September 1959)

During the last few years nuclear physicists have found the semiempirical cosmic abundance table derived by H. E. Suess and H. C. Urey [both now at the University of California, La Jolla] of great value in determining the relative importance of various mechanisms of element formation in the stars. This table is based primarily on analyses of chondritic meteorites, together with Suess's hypothesis that the abundances of elements of odd mass number should lie on a smooth curve.

It has recently become apparent that certain elements are either over- or under-abundant in chondritic meteorites, for no obvious chemical reason. Not only do the abundances of some nonvolatile elements disagree with similar determinations for the sun, but they differ from predictions of the theory of nucleogenesis in stars. Therefore, A. G. W. Cameron [now with NASA] has revised the Suess-Urey table to make it consistent with his nucleogenesis calculations and, possibly, to throw additional light on abundance discrepancies in meteorites.

The most substantial changes were made in the region of the rare earths and of lead. The abundance peak for the rare earths near atomic mass 165 now appears broader, more prominent, and more symmetrical than previously, while the lead abundance has been increased to more than forty times that given by Suess and Urey. In addition, isolated changes were made in a few other cases.

The details of this work appear in the May [1959] issue of *The Astrophysical Journal*, from which Table 10 is reprinted. [In order to compare this with Table 6, multiply by 32 and take the logarithm. Note that lithium remains about 200 times more abundant than in the sun.]

TABLE 10. COMPARISON OF ABUNDANCES OF ELEMENTS IN TABLE BY SUESS AND UREY WITH CAMERON'S 1959 ADJUSTMENT (BOTH RELATIVE TO $Si = 10^6$)

Element	Suess-Urey	Cameron	Element	Suess-Urey	Cameron
1 H	4.00×10^{10}	2.50×10^{10}	44 Ru	1.49	0.87
2 He	3.08×10^{9}	3.80×10^{9}	45 Rh	0.214	0.15
3 Li	100	100	46 Pd	0.675	0.675
4 Be	20	20	47 Ag	0.26	0.26
5 B	24	24	48 Cd	0.89	0.89
6 C	3.5×10^{6}	9.3×10^{6}	49 In	0.11	0.11
7 N	6.6×10^{6}	2.4×10^{6}	50 Sn	1.33	1.33
8 O	2.15×10^{7}	2.5×10^{7}	51 Sb	0.246	0.227
9 F	1600	1600	52 Te	4.67	2.91
10 Ne	8.6×10^{6}	8.0×10^{5}	53 I	0.80	0.60
11 Na	4.38×10^{4}	4.38×10^{4}	54 Xe	4.0	3.35
12 Mg	9.12×10^{5}	9.12×10^{5}	55 Cs	0.456	0.456
13 Al	9.48×10^{4}	9.48×10^{4}	56 Ba	3.66	3.66
14 Si	1.00×10^{6}	1.00×10^{6}	57 La	2.00	0.50
15 P	1.00×10^{4}	1.00×10^{4}	58 Ce	2.26	0.575
16 S	3.75×10^{5}	3.75×10^{5}	59 Pr	0.40	0.23
17 Cl	8850	2610	60 Nd	1.44	0.874
18 A	1.5×10^{5}	1.5×10^{5}	61 Pm	----	
19 K	3160	3160	62 Sm	0.664	0.238
20 Ca	4.90×10^{4}	4.90×10^{4}	63 Eu	0.187	0.115
21 Sc	28	28	64 Gd	0.684	0.516
22 Ti	2440	1680	65 Tb	0.0956	0.090
23 V	220	220	66 Dy	0.556	0.665
24 Cr	7800	7800	67 Ho	0.118	0.18
25 Mn	6850	6850	68 Er	0.316	0.583
26 Fe	6.00×10^{5}	8.50×10^{4}	69 Tm	0.0318	0.090
27 Co	1800	1800	70 Yb	0.220	0.393
28 Ni	2.74×10^{4}	2.74×10^{4}	71 Lu	0.050	0.0358
29 Cu	212	212	72 Hf	0.438	0.113
30 Zn	486	202	73 Ta	0.065	0.015
31 Ga	11.4	9.05	74 W	0.49	0.105
32 Ge	50.5	25.3	75 Re	0.135	0.054
33 As	4.0	1.70	76 Os	1.00	0.64
34 Se	67.6	18.8	77 Ir	0.821	0.494
35 Br	13.4	3.95	78 Pt	1.625	1.28
36 Kr	51.3	42.0	79 Au	0.145	0.145
37 Rb	6.5	6.50	80 Hg	0.284	0.408
38 Sr	18.9	61.0	81 Tl	0.108	0.31
39 Y	8.9	8.9	82 Pb	0.47	21.7
40 Zr	54.5	14.2	83 Bi	0.144	0.3
41 Nb	1.00	0.81	90 Th		0.027
42 Mo	2.42	2.42	92 U		0.0078
43 Tc	----	----			

■■■

Symposium on
Abundances of
Elements in Stars

BANCROFT W. SITTERLY

(*Sky and Telescope*, January 1965)

Knowledge of the relative amounts of different chemical elements in a star's atmosphere, and their variation from star to star, is important to the astrophysicist. The composition of a star has a large influence on its dynamic and thermal structure. Differences in composition among stars may be due to differences in composition of the prestellar material in the regions where the stars were formed. And since we are now well aware that the elements evolve in stellar interiors, the composition of a star should be related to its age.

I deally, it should be simple to determine the abundance of an element in the atmosphere of a star. Light coming from the more dense lower layers of the star as radiation in all frequencies (the *continuum* of the star's spectrum) is absorbed by free atoms of the element at frequencies dictated by the atomic structure, producing the dark spectrum lines. If the element is abundant, the lines are strong; if scarce, they are weak. The strength may be measured by comparing the radiation in the line (which is not wholly dark) with that in a neighboring region of the continuum that is equal in breadth to the line. The amount of radiation absorbed may be expressed as an *equivalent width* —the breadth of a wholly black line that would absorb this much.

The ratio of this observed absorption to the number (N) of atoms of the element concerned, contained in a unit column of the absorbing layer, is given by a complicated mathematical expression involving several factors. One of these is the *f-value*, depending only on the structure of the atom. It expresses the relative probability of the electronic transition giving this absorption, compared with other possible transitions.

Other factors involve the physical state of the atmosphere of which these atoms are a part, including its temperature, pressure, and state of ionization. Given a set of measurements of lines of an element in a star's atmosphere, together with knowledge of the physical state of this atmosphere and of the detailed structure of the atom, every observed spectrum line will yield a value of N. For one element these N's should all agree; if not, the assumed atmospheric parameters are varied until they do.

This way of determining abundances is called the *curve of growth* method, since it is especially adapted to graphical treatment. A somewhat more sophisticated method uses the observed *profiles* of lines— the variation of absorption from the deep line centers out through the shallow wings. A third, very laborious procedure is to give up the unrealistic but useful approximation that absorption is due to a homogeneous atmospheric layer under uniform physical conditions, and instead to assume a complete atmospheric model, compute the theoretical spectrum (line intensities or profiles) that it should produce, and compare this with observations, amending the model until correspondence is achieved.

Of course, the ideal has not been reached. The observed quantities are affected by serious errors difficult to evaluate, and our theories, both of atomic transitions and atmospheric structure, are far from complete. We have learned a great deal about the atmospheric composition of the sun and stars, and several sessions of this symposium [held at the University of Utrecht in Holland] were devoted to what we now feel is fairly well established knowledge. But at least as much time was taken up with methods of observation, sources of error and evaluation of corrections, and establishment of reliable atomic and atmospheric parameters.

In the five days of the symposium, five topics were discussed, beginning each time with a detailed review of the subject's present state and a summary of recent work. Reports of individual investigations were followed by discussion and questions from the floor. All these discussions were lively and occasionally even acrimonious.

The first day began with a brief and happily worded welcome by the rector of the University of Utrecht, who pointed out that the observatory stands on the old city fortification of Charles V, named by him Sonnenborgh, the Castle of the Sun. Then we took up observational data, our first topic.

J. B. Oke, of Mount Wilson and Palomar Observatories, reviewed photoelectric methods for obtaining profiles of spectrum lines and the continuous absorption. In particular, he spoke of high-dispersion work (two angstroms per millimeter) with scanning spectrometers attached to large reflecting telescopes. Then K. O. Wright described recent high-dispersion spectrograms that were taken with the Dominion Astrophysical Observatory's 73-inch reflector.

Both speakers emphasized that high-precision measurements give correspondingly reliable knowledge only if correction has been made for systematic errors. One troublesome systematic error is the depression of the apparent continuum below the true level of surface brightness between absorption lines. In the later-type stars and in the ultraviolet of almost all stars the lines overlap so much that virtually no unobscured regions are found over long sections of the spectrum. Another source of error is scattered light from reflection and diffraction in the optical system, the amount of which can be determined by instrumental tests.

The depression of the continuum, however, is not primarily an instrumental effect, though high dispersion may help detect it. Since it distorts the shapes of line profiles, it may be estimated by comparing observed and theoretical shapes, or by some other, more indirect methods. . . .

The chairman of the second session was Charlotte Moore Sitterly of the National Bureau of Standards, who pointed out that well-observed and calibrated spectra are needed to determine abundances reliably. In addition, however, correct line identifications and accurate ionization potentials and f-values are needed.

The latter are contributed by laboratory spectroscopists and theoretical physicists. Unfortunately, laboratory data on the elements most interesting to astrophysicists are much less complete and less reliable than is generally believed.

Roy Garstang, University of London Observatory, then surveyed recent laboratory progress, especially in the experimental determination of f-values and other atomic constants. . . .

Much attention was devoted to the problem of translating observational data into numerical values for the abundances of chemical elements in a stellar atmosphere. L. H. Aller and Armin J. Deutsch described methods in which a simple model of the atmosphere is used in constructing curves of growth. A Canadian astronomer, Anne Underhill, on the other hand, presented methods in which an elaborately computed detailed model is the basis for the determination of line intensities and profiles. She posed the question, echoed frequently in subsequent discussion, of whether unusually prominent lines of an element in a stellar spectrum indicate that the element is anomalously abundant, or that the star has an anomalously stratified atmosphere.

The third conference day was devoted to analyses of early-type stars and the sun, the next day to solar- and later-type stars. . . . Our primary standard of relative abundances is of course the sun, and recent investigations, presented by Edith Müller of Geneva, are not at variance with earlier work.

Analysis of the solar corona, described by S. R. Pottasch of Groningen, discloses a relatively large proportion of helium (roughly a sixth) and a rather puzzling excess of iron, something like twenty times the photospheric abundance, along with lesser excesses of other common metals. G. Traving, of Kiel, and others discussed early-type stars. The probability that very extended atmospheres or shells exist complicates analysis, but the rapid evolution in these very luminous stars might be indicated by anomalous helium-hydrogen ratios, and some evidence for this has been obtained.

George Wallerstein of the University of California distinguished three groups of solar-type stars that show some differences in composition from the sun. Two of these groups are the metal-deficient main-sequence stars and the hydrogen-poor supergiants; the third is the so-called metallic-line stars, where evidence of atmospheric turbulence in many spectra suggests that the abnormality may be mainly in the structure of their atmospheres.

Those remarkable objects, the magnetic stars, were discussed by W. L. W. Sargent of the Royal Greenwich Observatory, and also by Margherita Hack of Merate, Italy. Sargent noted that in many respects these stars' spectra seem normal. But they generally show abnormally high abundance of some of the rare earths, and also of some metals. Helium or oxygen may be deficient. There is a correlation between spectral line intensity and the strength of the magnetic field. When the magnetic field is variable, line intensities vary with it. It seems reasonable to suppose that the magnetic field is in some way responsible for the anomalous abundances. Building of heavy elements in the stellar atmosphere by collisions with ions accelerated by the field has been suggested [see p. 245].

Low-temperature stars were considered by B. E. J. Pagel, Y. Fujita, and several others. It has long been recognized that the division of their spectra into three groups—M, R and N, and S—is due to differences in the elemental abundances. Here the carbon-oxygen ratio seems to be the most significant feature. Also evident among these stars are variations in the ratio of the isotopes carbon 12 and carbon 13. Some barium-rich and lithium-rich stars are found.

The final session, on the formation of the elements, was particularly stimulating. Marshal Wrubel of Indiana University led off with a masterly summary of present ideas on how the evolution of the elements *should* proceed in stars. A particular problem—to account for the large observed abundance of the iron group of elements—was discussed by W. A. Fowler of California Institute of Technology. This is assumed to be due to a statistical equilibrium maintained over a long period among competing, relatively rapid thermonuclear transmutations. These involve the concentrations of nuclei, free neutrons and protons, and alpha particles. The equilibrium conditions depend on temperature, and Fowler showed that, at a temperature of three billion degrees, theory and observation are not far from agreement.

Another Caltech astrophysicist, Jesse L. Greenstein, discussed relations between stellar composition, stellar ages, and evolutionary tracks. A major difficulty is that the transmutations occur primarily in the superhot core of a star, while the only part of the star we can observe is its atmosphere. Therefore the rate at which core material mixes with atmospheric material is of critical importance. In the best-understood stellar models, this mixing seems to be extremely slow. Catastrophic redistribution of matter is believed to occur in late stages of evolution. Perhaps noncatastrophic mixing may occur in the red-giant stages. It is to be remembered that some interstellar matter must be much older than most bright stars, and that much of the material in present stars may have passed through one or more previous stellar cycles.

The question of different abundances in various parts of our galaxy, and of differences between disk and halo populations of stars, was raised by Pagel. The impression left by the vigorous discussion of these papers was one of notable progress and immense complexity. . . .

Clearly, our knowledge of stellar constitution has entered a third stage of advancement. The first began about 1860, when it was realized that the spectroscope could analyze even celestial light sources.

A. Secchi and others quickly found that there were at least four kinds of stars. The second stage extended from Norman Lockyer's acute intuitions in the 1890s to the 1926–7 Russell-Vogt theorem.[1] Astronomers realized that the differences between stellar spectra were due primarily to the wide range in temperature and electron pressure in stellar atmospheres; only precise observation and refined theory could reveal true abundances. Now, in the third stage, we are beginning to master the necessary techniques, and it has become clear that there are real differences in the mix of elements from one star to another. A reasonable pattern of the distribution of the chemical elements in the cosmos begins to emerge. But it is still far from clear.

[1] The Russell-Vogt theorem states that the structure of a star is uniquely determined by its mass and chemical composition, provided that at each point inside the star the pressure, opacity, and energy-generation rate depend only on the density, temperature, and chemical composition.

8

Peculiarities in
the Lives of
the Stars

Before the day of variations in cosmic abundances, catastrophic collapse, surface-layer nuclear reactions, and the like, studies of stellar evolution seemed to lead toward a neat routine in the life of a star. This routine started with gradual contraction of a cold interstellar cloud, which was accompanied by a predictable rise in its internal temperature. When the temperature reached about ten million degrees nuclear reactions would start in the compressed hydrogen, and the energy released would slow down, then stop the gravitational contraction by building up the interior gas pressure. The star so formed would be stable because the rate of nuclear reactions increases with the density and temperature of the hydrogen gas; if the density increased above the equilibrium level, the increase in energy generation would heat the gas further, causing it to expand and lower its density. Because gravitation depends on mass, and the density of a gas depends on pressure and temperature, the equilibrium level would depend on the whole mass of the star—observed to be between a twentieth of and fifty times the sun's mass.

The "life" of a star in this well-regulated equilibrium state on the main sequence of the H-R diagram would depend on the amount of hydrogen available to convert into helium plus energy (6×10^{18} ergs for each gram). The rate of this nuclear energy generation would just equal the luminosity of the star—the rate of energy lost by radiation. Slow changes would take place as the central core was converted to helium; these would involve slow contraction, increasing the core density and temperature, so that the rate of nuclear-energy generation would be maintained in spite of the decreasing abundance of hydrogen.

When the temperature of the core reached 100 million degrees or more a new set of nuclear reactions would begin, releasing energy at a higher rate. The star would then evolve to the red-giant stage, becoming hundreds of times larger. It would have a lower surface temperature because its increase in surface area would more than match its increase in luminosity. Loss of mass from the low-density outer layers then would take place in some way—by corpuscular radiation, or a supernova explosion—and the degenerate core, no larger than 1.4 solar masses, would remain as a white dwarf. Without any energy source, this small star of extremely high density would cool to oblivion as a "black dwarf."

As Chapters 1 to 4 have shown, such a "life story" provides a simple conceptual basis for organizing the wealth of observational data on stars. Equilibrium in the main-sequence stage does account for the mass-luminosity law and H-R diagram; the initial contraction relates star formation to the interstellar medium; and the later evolutionary tracks account for giant stars and the differences in H-R diagrams for clusters. However, there are many departures from the normal life story: rotating stars, flare stars, close binaries, and emission-line stars are losing mass more rapidly; convection in some stars is mixing deep layers with outer layers; strong magnetic fields may be producing high-energy protons that start nuclear reactions in surface layers; and the material from which stars were formed may have differed widely.

This chapter collects a number of such deviations from the norm, starting with an early problem of the variable stars. Those of one type (the Cepheid variables), which pulsate periodically, have been useful in measuring distances because their luminosities are correlated with the period of pulsation.—TLP

•••

Variable Stars and
Stellar Evolution

OTTO STRUVE

(*Sky and Telescope*, April 1950 and May 1950)

It has long been known that the globular clusters are rich in variable stars; Helen Sawyer Hogg has listed 1300 objects in sixty clusters. Most of them are Cepheid variables of periods shorter than one day, designated as cluster-type variables or RR Lyrae-type stars. But sixty-seven of the globular cluster variables do not belong to this group, because their periods are longer than one day, and their luminosities are greater than those of the normal short-period Cepheids. Among these stars of longer period, Alfred H. Joy discovered a considerable number whose periods range from thirteen to nineteen days, and whose light curves closely resemble the light curve of the galactic Cepheid variable W Virginis. . . . Joy's investigation shows that the Cepheid variables in globular clusters appear to duplicate closely the spectrum of W Virginis. . . .

This conclusion leads us to suspect that the Cepheid variables are not a homogeneous system of pulsating stars, all of approximately the same physical characteristics, but consist of at least two different groups. Furthermore, the origin of the stars in globular clusters and their subsequent evolution may have been very different from that of stars which were formed in the spiral arms of our Milky Way system, where interstellar dust and gas abound even at the present time and may influence the manner in which the stars of the solar neighborhood develop. . . .

Apparently, we observe in the Milky Way a relatively small number of peculiar Cepheid variables which have unusual spectra and light curves, rapid motions directed toward one hemisphere of the sky, and which occur far from the central plane of the galaxy. These characteristics are typical for stars that Walter Baade has classified as Population II, which represents objects that are most numerous in globular clusters, elliptical galaxies, the nuclei of spiral nebulae, and the nucleus of our own Milky Way system. The ordinary high-velocity stars are believed to be members of Population II that we see in the sun's neighborhood because they are temporary visitors from the nucleus of the galaxy. . . .

It is of particular interest to consider the cosmogonical consequences of this division among the Cepheid variables. All recent studies lead us to believe that the objects of Population II are old, while many objects of Population I—those that are characteristic of spiral arms in galaxies and of the solar neighborhood in our Milky Way system—are relatively young. There is an intimate relation between the spiral arms and the existence of dust and gas. The stars of Population I exchange matter and energy with interstellar clouds, and it is even possible that out of these clouds stars are being formed.

Among the Cepheid variables we find two distinct classes, one of which—the W Virginis type—belongs to the group of old stars (Population II), while the other—the ordinary Cepheid—is closely associated with the young stars of the solar neighborhood (Population I). We must remember that W Virginis is . . . a very brilliant object compared to the sun. Consequently it cannot continue in its present condition for billions of years. If the globular clusters are that old, their long-period W Virginis variables can have existed as Cepheid variables only during a short fraction of their entire lifetimes.

It is certainly very surprising that we should find among the old stars of Population II and the relatively young stars of Population I objects which are so similar in their properties as the variables of the W Virginis type and the corresponding cluster Cepheids of the same period. It is reasonable to suppose that they had a similar origin and evolution, and that the origin of the rest of the galactic Cepheids was somehow quite different.

In recent years the Russian astrophysicist B. V. Kukarkin has made a concerted attack upon this problem. A recent book by him, *The Structure and Evolution of Stellar Systems Based upon the Study of Variable Stars*, is entirely devoted to this aspect of the physical variable stars. The foundations of his work rest in part upon the results obtained during the past fifty years at the Harvard Observatory.

He excludes the eclipsing binaries and those somewhat hypothetical stars that may change in light because of variable obscuration produced by clouds of interstellar dust. Among the physical variables, those of the "great sequence" present the greatest interest because they are better known and are more numerous than the other groups of variables. All the variables of the great sequence obey two statistical relations: the period-luminosity relation and the period-spectrum relation. Both have been known for a long time, but Kukarkin has rediscussed the latest observational data.

Figure 88A shows his period-luminosity relation. The ordinate is

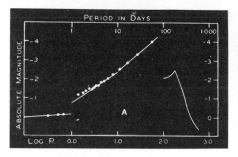
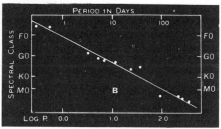

FIG. 88. A. The period-luminosity relation of three groups of variable stars. The cluster-type variables are on the left; the classical Cepheids form the middle section; the Mira Ceti stars are on the right. B. The period-spectrum relation for the same kinds of variables.

the absolute photographic magnitude of the stars (which measures the intrinsic luminosity) and the abscissa is the logarithm of the period. The intermediate group of classical (Cepheid) variables represents a fairly homogeneous system ranging in period from slightly more than one day to slightly less than one hundred days. This sequence is not immediately joined by the cluster-type (RR Lyrae) variables on the one side and by the long-period (Mira Ceti) variables on the other side. The discontinuity is especially pronounced between the long-period Cepheids and the Mira Ceti variables at about a hundred days. Since there are also pronounced differences in the forms of the light curves, the velocity curves, and the spectral characteristics of these three groups, we have for many years been treating them as three distinct systems of variable stars.

No such discontinuity is apparent in the period-spectrum relation in Figure 88B. Here the cluster-type variables have the earliest spectral types and consequently the highest photospheric temperatures; the Cepheid variables have intermediate spectral types and also intermediate temperatures; and the long-period variables have the latest spectral types and the lowest temperatures.

It should be noted that the points plotted in these diagrams are the mean values of large numbers of stars. The scatter of the individual values is not quite negligible. In Figure 88A approximately one half of the individual dots would have been included in a band having

FIG. 89. The Cepheid-variable region is plotted by Allan R. Sandage on this composite color-magnitude diagram for galactic clusters. The two groups of Cepheids (called C and AB by O. Eggen) have very different period-luminosity relations. (Mount Wilson and Palomar Observatories chart)

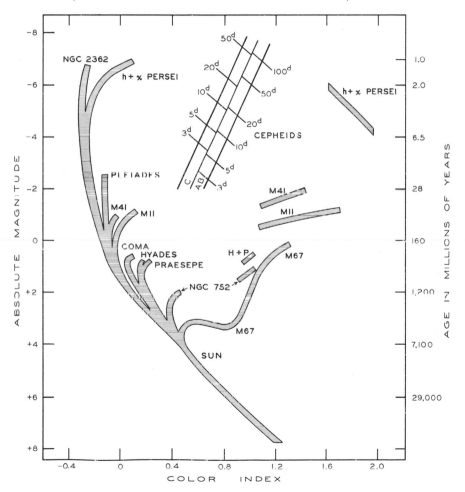

a vertical width of one stellar magnitude, while the other half would be distributed outside this band. . . .

All of this seems to suggest that the separation into two populations must be regarded as a statistical phenomenon, and that there are all sorts of transitions between them. . . . From the evidence from the variable stars, we conclude that there is no complete absence in the globular clusters of objects normally attributed to the "young" sequence of Population I. Similarly, in regions usually attributed to Population I we find representatives of the "old" sequence of spherical distributions. As Shapley remarks, this difficulty is encountered also among the red giants of the globular clusters: their large luminosities indicate rapid energy generation. By any of the known nuclear transformations, the available supply of energy would be sufficient to maintain them in their present condition for not more than 100 million years—they are "young" stars, even though they occur in formations that are mostly composed of "old" stars.

In some respects Kukarkin's book poses more questions than it solves. We must recognize that the problem of the ages of the stars is not as simple as it looked a few years ago. It is still tempting to think of the spherical distributions in our galaxy as representing objects having a different origin and evolution than the members of the flattened distributions. But it is no longer possible, without qualification, to attribute to them vastly different ages.

In addition to these problems of age, the Cepheid variables are interesting because they lie in a region on the H-R diagram crossed by many of the theoretical evolutionary tracks from the main-sequence to red-giant stage. This implies that periodic pulsation lasts only during a brief interval in the life of a star. The region, called the "Hertzsprung gap" (see p. 116), is shown by Allan R. Sandage's H-R diagram, Figure 89.—TLP

. . . .

Cepheid Symposium

(*Sky and Telescope*, April 1958)

At a special session on variable stars of the classical Cepheid type [during the December 1957 meeting of the American Astronomical

Society] five astronomers told of current researches, including work in the southern sky. The moderator of the symposium was Allan R. Sandage, Mount Wilson and Palomar Observatories.

The best-known Cepheid variables in the sky are Delta Cephei (after which the class is named) and Eta Aquilae. At David Dunlap Observatory, J. B. Oke has been using a new photoelectric spectrometer to measure their light intensities at 21 wavelengths between 3400 angstroms in the ultraviolet and 5200 angstroms in yellow. . . .

An important object for distance-scale calibration is the Small Magellanic Cloud, at present believed to be about 230,000 light years from us. Over a thousand Cepheid variables in it have been studied photographically by Halton C. Arp, Mount Wilson and Palomar Observatories. He first established a sequence of photoelectric magnitudes containing twenty-seven stars, to as faint as blue magnitude 20.1. . . .

Early in 1955 John B. Irwin of Indiana University's Goethe Link Observatory was on an expedition to South Africa to measure photoelectrically the brightnesses and colors of Cepheids in the southern sky. Altogether, about 1700 three-color observations of 145 Cepheids were secured with the 24-inch refractor of the Cape Observatory and the 74-inch Radcliffe Observatory reflector. Irwin was able to deduce photometric distances of 123 of these stars.

Another Indiana astronomer, Robert P. Kraft, discussed the classical Cepheids that are members of galactic star clusters. This subject has aroused widespread interest since Irwin's discovery during his South African work that two stars of this type, U Sagittarii and S Normae, are members of the open clusters M25 and NGC6087, respectively.

The importance of this finding is twofold. First, the distances of galactic clusters can nowadays be measured with some precision, so the existence of Cepheids within them provides a new method for determining intrinsic Cepheid luminosities. Kraft has made use of four such cluster members to ascertain that classical Cepheids average 1.2 magnitudes brighter than given by Harlow Shapley's historic period-luminosity curve.

In the second place, new information about the evolution of Cepheid variables is made available. Three of the galactic clusters containing Cepheid variables (including M25 and NGC6087) appear to be about 100 million years old, a fourth cluster about 200 million. Thus it seems that the age of the typical Cepheids is also about 100 or 200 million years. Kraft believes that the variables with shorter periods may be older stars than those with longer periods.

Charles A. Whitney, Smithsonian Astrophysical Observatory, the fifth symposium speaker, described his theoretical studies of pulsating gas spheres, such as Cepheids are believed to be. Pulsation may be maintained by varying of nuclear energy generation in the stellar interior; another mechanism might be the setting up of a "heat engine" in the external layers through the action of varying opacity of the star's material and heat storage.

....

Evolutionary Changes
in Single Stars?

DORRIT HOFFLEIT

(*Sky and Telescope*, June 1955)

Evolutionary changes in brightness or temperature are too gradual to be detected in individual stars, even in the youngest, hottest ones of spectral types O and early B. Among such stars, however, are the Beta Canis Majoris variables, pulsating stars with periods of about three to six hours. Those with the longer periods are the brighter. Otto Struve, Leuschner Observatory, suggests that these differing periods may indicate evolutionary trends among these stars.

At the Berkeley meeting of the Astronomical Society of the Pacific in December [1954], he pointed out that the mean density of a B-type star would decrease if it evolves with constant mass in such a manner as to describe an evolutionary track away from the main sequence. Furthermore, such a progressive decrease in mean density with age for the star should result in a measurable lengthening of its period.

Of the ten best-observed Beta Canis Majoris stars, three indeed have changing periods. They are Sigma Scorpii, with a period of 5 hours 55 minutes increasing at the rate of 2.3 seconds a century; HD199140, 4 hours 49 minutes, 3.0 seconds per century; and Beta Cephei, 4 hours 34 minutes, 1.2 seconds per century. These stars have

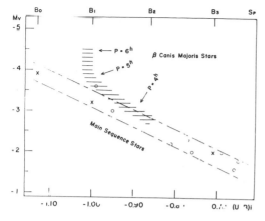

FIG. 90. In this small region of the spectrum-luminosity diagram, the dashes show the area occupied by the pulsating stars of the Beta Canis Majoris type. The data are from a 4½-year program at the Leuschner Observatory, University of California at Berkeley, carried on by D. McNamara and A. D. Williams. The main sequence is after W. W. Morgan and H. L. Johnson. Note the relation between period of pulsation and location on the diagram.

been under observation for thirty-six, twenty-eight, and fifty years, respectively.

At a rate of one second a century, a star like Gamma Pegasi, with a period of 3 hours 36 minutes, would require about one million years to evolve into a star like Beta Canis Majoris, which has a period of six hours. This corresponds well with the accepted age of one to ten million years for ordinary stars of the same spectral class.

Struve stated, however, that it may be more probable for the period changes in these stars to be irregular in character. Nevertheless, the possibility that they are evolutionary must not be ignored. He also noted that many years ago A. S. Eddington had considered the changing-period-evolution idea in reference to Delta Cephei.

:::

Some Possible Evidence
of Evolution in
Individual Stars

OTTO STRUVE

(*Sky and Telescope*, December 1958)

Modern astronomical research puts much emphasis on problems of stellar and galactic evolution. Astronomers are generally agreed that the broad picture of the life history of a star is along the following lines:

The star is born somewhere inside a normal galaxy, which contains about equal amounts of material in the form of stars and tenuous gas, with a slight admixture of solid particles—dust or crystals—whose diameters are of the order of 10^{-5} centimeter. The stars originate within the gaseous nebulae as a result of contraction. Against the faintly luminous background of a diffuse nebula we often observe dark *globules* (as in Figure 91), cloudlets dense enough to be gravitationally stable against the disrupting tidal forces of the galaxy as a whole or of nearby stars.

Each globule continues to contract, and becomes a *protostar* when it is visible by its own radiation. How long this contraction stage lasts depends on the mass of the globule. For a mass equal to the sun's, about 500 million years are needed, whereas stars twenty times as massive as the sun have a contraction stage lasting only about half a million years.

The contraction stops when the nuclear processes in the star's interior generate enough energy to balance the escape of radiation from the surface. The star is then of such a temperature and luminosity that it is on the main sequence of the Hertzsprung-Russell diagram, where it remains as long as there is an adequate supply of nuclear fuel, in the form of hydrogen. For the sun, this equilibrium condition may last about 10^{10} years, while for a very massive star it may be of the order of one million years or even less.

After the hydrogen fuel has become partially exhausted by conversion into helium, the isothermal core of the star again begins to contract. The energy released by this process tends to inflate the outer layers of the star, which grows in radius while its surface temperature and mean density decrease. Thus, the star becomes a red giant. Its evolutionary track in the H-R diagram runs from the main sequence toward the right. As the center of the star grows hotter, helium begins to fuse into carbon and more nuclear energy becomes available.

Finally, the radius of the star begins to shrink, and its surface temperature and mean density increase. In its evolutionary track in the H-R diagram, the star approaches the main sequence, crosses it, and ultimately drops into the region of the extremely dense white dwarfs. In this change all massive stars undergo more or less catastrophic explosions, resulting in loss of material.

FIG. 91. In 1946, on this photograph of the diffuse nebulosity Messier 8, Bart J. Bok found numerous globules—compact dark dust clouds that are stars in the making. Some of them are indicated by the arrows. (Lick Observatory photograph)

Most of these results have been obtained from observations of star clusters of different ages. It is reasonable to assume that a young star group, like the Double Cluster in Perseus, will after a long interval be similar to the Pleiades or Hyades, which we now recognize as old.

We have not actually observed evolutionary changes in individual stars, however, for decades or centuries are too short to reveal measurable changes in luminosity or surface temperature.

Evidently the detection of evolutionary changes in single stars would mark a great advance. There are three kinds of phenomena that give some promise in this respect. First, there are catastrophic or rapid continuous changes in mass, occurring in supernovae, novae, SS Cygni variables, P Cygni stars, or the central stars of planetary nebulae. Second, there may be evolutionary changes in the orbital periods of close binary stars. Third, and of interest to us in this article, there may be changes in the periods of pulsation of certain variable stars, such as those of the Beta Canis Majoris type.

These are hot blue stars with small rhythmic changes in brightness and radial velocity Their periods of pulsation range from roughly three and a half hours for Gamma Pegasi to six hours for Beta Canis Majoris itself. The spectral types range from B3 for the shortest periods to Bo for the longest. The location of this sequence in the H-R diagram is shown on Figure 92, together with several other sequences of pulsating variables.

Stars of this type almost certainly form a sequence of objects with different masses. Gamma Pegasi, near the bottom of the sequence, has a mass of about five suns; Beta Canis Majoris, at the top, almost ten. Since we believe that stars in this stage of evolution are developing without significant change in mass, it is unreasonable to suppose that Gamma Pegasi will in time resemble Beta Canis Majoris. In other words, the sequence is *not* an evolutionary track [as assumed on p. 280]. Instead, the evolutionary tracks of individual Beta Canis Majoris stars run nearly horizontally from left to right in the H-R diagram.

The most famous member of the sequence is the sixth-magnitude star BW Vulpeculae (also known as HD119140). Its variability in radial velocity was discovered by R. M. Petrie, and the spectrum has been investigated by him and G. J. Odgers at Victoria, and by me at Mount Wilson Observatory. In 1938 C. M. Huffer found photoelectrically that the range of the star's light curve is about 0.2 magnitude, large for a variable of this sequence.

According to Petrie and all more recent observers, the period of BW Vulpeculae is increasing steadily by about three seconds per

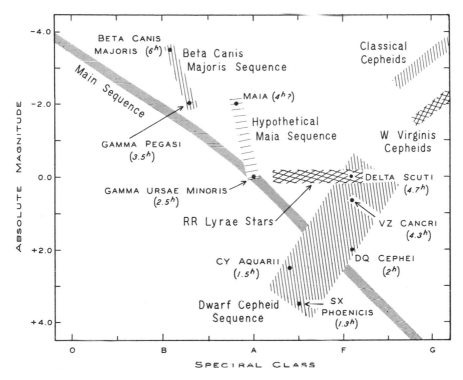

FIG. 92. In this schematic Hertzsprung-Russell diagram, the ordinary non-variable dwarf stars populate the main sequence, which runs diagonally across the figure. Several sequences of pulsating variable stars are indicated, and the names and periods of some of the individual variables.

century. Although this is a small change, it is well established by about thirty years of observation. The average period of BW Vulpeculae is 4 hours 49 minutes, or roughly 1.7×10^4 seconds, so the star runs through about 2000 cycles annually. We can time individual maxima with a precision of about one minute. Hence observations during a single year can fix the period to within $60/2000 = 0.03$ second. Thus, a rate of change of 3 seconds in 100 years is relatively easily obtained from observations stretching over a few decades.

Several others of the Beta Canis Majoris stars have been found to have increasing periods, though at smaller rates. The period of Sigma Scorpii is lengthening by 2.3 seconds per century, and that of Beta Cephei by 1.2 seconds. For some other stars of this type, the periods are growing by only 0.1 or 0.2 second in 100 years. Perhaps we may assume that a typical variable of the Beta Canis Majoris class has a period increasing by one second per century.

To interpret this fact, let us first consider Figure 93, in which are drawn a number of slanting curves representing equal stellar radii. These are obtained from the relation between the luminosity of a star and its surface area and energy output per unit area, in the following manner:

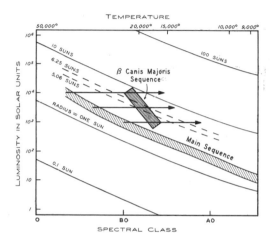

FIG. 93. In this portion of a schematic H-R diagram, arrows mark the evolutionary tracks of three massive stars, which temporarily become pulsating Beta Canis Majoris variables as they cross the shaded rectangle. The curves slanting toward the lower right represent different stellar radii; all the Beta Canis Majoris variables are larger than the sun.

If the radius of a star is R and its surface temperature is T, its area is $4\pi R^2$, and each square centimeter of this area radiates into space σT^4 ergs per second, in accordance with Stefan's law. The bolometric luminosity (that is, the radiation summed over all wavelengths) is

$$L = 4\pi R^2 \sigma T^4.$$

It is convenient to express L in terms of the sun as unity; similarly, $R = 1$ for a star of the same radius as the sun.

Consider first only stars the same size as the sun. If such a star had a temperature of 10,000°, its luminosity would be

$$L = 4\pi\sigma (10,000)^4,$$

while for the sun, whose temperature is 6000°,

$$1 = 4\pi\sigma (6000)^4.$$

Dividing the first expression by the second gives for the star

$$L = (10,000/6000)^4.$$

In this manner we find a series of points for different values of T but all for $R = 1$, giving the curve with this label in Figure 93.

The corresponding curve for stars with 10 times the sun's radius is easily obtained, since the luminosity is proportional to R^2. We simply displace every point of the original curve upward by a factor of 100 in the value of L.

On drawing such curves in the H-R diagram, we see at once that the stars at the upper end of the main sequence are four or five times larger than the sun, slowly decreasing to the solar radius at spectral type G0. The Beta Canis Majoris sequence consists of stars whose radii are about five suns at the lower end, for periods of around 3.5 hours, and about 10 suns for the six-hour stars at the upper end. Therefore, the stellar *volumes* at top and bottom are in the ratio of $(10/5)^3 = 8$.

As we have already seen, the masses at the upper and lower ends of the Beta Canis Majoris sequence are 10 and 5 times the sun's, respectively—a ratio of two to one. The mean density of a star is its mass divided by its volume. Hence the mean densities at the top and bottom of the sequence are in the ratio

$$\rho_t/\rho_b = 2/8 = \tfrac{1}{4}.$$

This is very nearly equal to the inverse square of the ratio of the corresponding periods:

$$(P_t/P_b)^{-2} = (3.5/6.0)^2 = 1/3.4.$$

We can draw a very important conclusion from this: the variables of the Beta Canis Majoris sequence obey the fundamental law of pulsating gas spheres, $P^2\rho = $ Constant. In other words, the periods of the individual stars of this type are inversely proportional to the square roots of their densities. This law has been found to apply to all other known groups of periodic intrinsic variable stars. Thus we see that as a star moves along the evolutionary track shown by an arrow in Figure 93, it begins to pulsate when it enters the left edge of the domain of the Beta Canis Majoris stars, and continues to pulsate until it passes the right edge of this region.

It is true that we have tested the application of the pulsation law only by comparing stars of different masses. We do not know enough variables of the same absolute magnitude but different surface temperatures to determine the width of the sequence. We know only that the width is small.

The evolution we are considering—a horizontal track across the Beta Canis Majoris domain—occurs without any significant change in mass. (Even converting all available hydrogen in a star to helium would reduce the mass by less than 1 per cent.) The radius does change, however; it is 5.06 suns when the star enters the band of variables and 6.25 suns when it leaves. This changes the volume of the star by a factor $(6.25/5.06)^3 = 1.86$. Since the mass stays the same, the density decreases by the same factor of 1.86.

How much does this alter the period of the variable? The fundamental pulsation law $P^2\rho =$ Constant, which we have seen holds for the Beta Canis Majoris stars as a group, may also be applied to an *individual* star whose density is changing. At the point of entering the band, the period is P' and the mean density ρ', and at the exit point they are P'' and ρ'', respectively. Writing the pulsation formula twice, for each of these points, and eliminating the constant, we find

$$P''/P' = (\rho'/\rho'')^{\frac{1}{2}} = 1.86^{\frac{1}{2}}, \text{ or nearly 1.4.}$$

Suppose that the period of the star when near the central line of the sequence is 17,000 seconds. The final period would be a little longer than this, the initial period a little shorter. Computation shows that at the entrance point the period is about 14,000 seconds, or roughly 3.75 hours, while at the end point it is 21,000 seconds, or 5.75 hours.

Hence if the band is as wide as we have assumed, there should be a considerable spread in period, not only along the central line of this sequence but across it. This effect has not been observed yet, and perhaps the sequence is narrower than we have supposed. Photoelectric observations of the kind made by B. Strömgren [see p. 260] should give us that information.

But the actual width of the band need not be known to calculate the rate of evolution suggested by the increase in period. We merely state that *if* the stars pulsate as they cross the band, their periods would increase by about 7000 seconds in the meantime. Then, if the period of a typical Beta Canis Majoris star is increasing by one second per century, it takes 7000 × 100 years—on the order of a million years—for the star to traverse the band. If the band is narrower, the change in stellar volume is smaller and so is the total change in period; the star would need less time to run across the band.

Our result—somewhat less than a million years for an average Beta Canis Majoris variable to evolve from type $B1$ to $B3$—can be compared with the theoretical time scale obtained by R. J. Tayler in 1954, about 60 million years. The discrepancy is large, but perhaps not insurmountable.

In the first place, Tayler's figure is for time starting at the main sequence, while our variables are already well off the main sequence when they first enter the Beta Canis Majoris domain. The evolution must proceed more rapidly after the star has departed one or two spectral subdivisions from the main sequence.

Furthermore, we are concerned with more massive stars than those discussed by Tayler, and the rate of evolution is faster the more massive the star. Finally, we have assumed that the evolutionary track is horizontal in the H-R diagram. If it actually curves slightly upward, as Tayler thinks, this would increase the interval of time during which the star would pulsate. . . .

Thus we cannot yet be certain that the observed changes in the periods of the Beta Canis Majoris stars are truly evolutionary in character. Nevertheless, if they are, they give us an exceedingly sensitive method of detecting evolutionary changes in individual stars. Direct measurements of a star's mass, radius, or luminosity are so crude in comparison that they offer no hope of revealing evolutionary changes within intervals of hundreds or thousands of years.

....

The Changing Spectrum
of Deneb

(*Sky and Telescope*, September 1964)

Is it possible from existing observational records to detect evolutionary change in an individual star? This question has been raised in a new form by Martha H. Liller and William Liller of Harvard Observatory.

They point to a recent theoretical finding by C. Hayashi and A. G. W. Cameron, who calculated the evolutionary track of a model star of 15.6 solar masses. Such a star should evolve very rapidly during the last stages of helium burning, so that its spectral type would change from early A to M in some 20,000 years. The star's surface temperature would thus be dropping at an average rate of a third of a degree per year during this critical interval.

If this analysis is correct, small progressive changes in the spectra of certain supergiant stars should be detectable over the course of a century or less. The Lillers selected Deneb as their first test object. This highly luminous A2 supergiant has a visual absolute magnitude of about −7, and its mass is estimated at 25 suns.

For this study twenty-nine Harvard spectrograms were used. The earliest are objective-prism photographs going back as far as 1887; the latest are slit spectrograms taken in 1962–3 with the 61-inch reflector. To fill in the years 1910–30, when Harvard plates of Deneb were few, the Lillers also used thirty-one low-dispersion slit spectrograms taken with the 37½-inch University of Michigan reflector.

One test for a progressive change in Deneb's temperature gave negative results. The 4481-angstrom ionized magnesium line's strength is quite sensitive to temperature differences. As no measurable change was found in the intensity of 4481 relative to three neighboring iron lines, the Lillers concluded that Deneb probably did not change as much as 250° Kelvin between 1887 and 1963. (According to W. Buscombe, the effective surface temperature of this star is 9700°.)

But spectral change of another kind was found. Since the earliest observations, the H line of ionized calcium has become stronger relative to the neighboring Hϵ line of hydrogen. Even an eye comparison of old and new plates reveals this change, which was verified by measurement. Although the two absorption lines overlap considerably, since they differ only 1.6 angstroms in wavelength, their cores are separated on the spectrograms.

The Lillers suggest that the calcium absorption line looked weaker in the 1890s because of a superimposed central emission, presumably originating in the star's chromosphere. Was there strong prominence activity on Deneb at that time, an activity that varies in a manner somewhat like the eleven-year solar cycle, but more slowly?

Probably the strengthening of the calcium line should not be regarded as an evolutionary change, for that interpretation would involve a temperature change contradicted by the negative conclusion from the 4481 magnesium line.

To explore these alternatives, other supergiant stars will be studied, beginning with Delta Canis Majoris, for which there are many early Harvard spectra.

Helium Flash in
Giant Stars

(*Sky and Telescope*, May 1961)

After a star of Population II has evolved away from the main sequence of the Hertzsprung-Russell diagram and become a red-giant star, a remarkable "thermal runaway" occurs deep in its interior. This had been predicted by L. Mestel, and is now confirmed in step-by-step calculations of helium burning in giant stars by R. Härm and M. Schwarzschild at Princeton University Observatory.

They traced the development of a model star, with a mass 1.3 times the sun's, through the phase of its evolution when the thermonuclear consumption of helium begins. Forty per cent of the mass is in a central core of helium, the atoms being in a degenerate state—stripped of their outer electrons and packed together to a density of a million grams per cubic centimeter. The burning of hydrogen continues in a shell of nondegenerate matter just outside the helium core.

The helium burning sets in when the temperature in the contracting core reaches about 80 million degrees Kelvin. The energy released can only raise the temperature further, as the high pressure on the degenerate matter prevents its expansion. The helium burning thus becomes more and more rapid, with the temperature continuing to rise to a maximum of about 350 million degrees! At that time, the core is liberating as much energy as 10^{13} suns, but practically none of this escapes, because of the high opacity of the hydrogen shell.

At such a high temperature, the core is finally forced to expand,

and only when it becomes nondegenerate does the thermal runaway terminate, with subsequent helium burning causing rapid expansion and cooling. On a cosmic time scale, the duration of the helium flash has been very brief, lasting about 3000 years.

During the peak of the helium flash, the star moves downward to the left along the giant branch of the H-R diagram, according to the Princeton astronomers, physical changes taking place with great rapidity. The normal time step in their calculations on an IBM 650 computer was 100,000 years, with shorter steps used when the evolution took place faster. However, at one stage of the helium flash the star's state had to be recalculated for two-second intervals. Schwarzschild pointed out that such a star would actually be evolving at a faster rate than even his high-speed computer could operate!

In this work certain assumptions had to be made that may require adjustment of the calculation if they later prove incorrect. Hydrostatic conditions were assumed to hold, with dynamical effects neglected. The validity of this simplification must be tested further.

*The "runaway" of nuclear reactions leads to very high temperatures. Under such extreme conditions a star may be expected to emit far-ultraviolet light, X rays, and gamma rays. One of the dramatic discoveries of the last few years is the X-ray source.—*TLP

X Rays from the
Milky Way

(*Sky and Telescope*, October 1962)

Discovery of what apparently is an intense cosmic source of X rays in the Scorpius region of the sky has been announced by Riccardo Giaconni of American Science and Engineering Corporation, Cambridge, Massachusetts. X-ray sensors carried in an Aerobee rocket fired

June 18, 1962, to a height of 140 miles above White Sands, New Mexico, were intended to measure fluorescence of the moon's surface under solar illumination. This experiment had been suggested by Bruno Rossi, Massachusetts Institute of Technology, as a means of analyzing lunar material.

As it turned out, the anticipated lunar X-ray flux could not be detected, even if present, because of interference from the Scorpius X-ray source, which was some 30 degrees west of the moon at that time. The sensor data indicate that the cosmic radiation is in the form of soft X rays that do not penetrate the atmosphere lower than fifty miles above the earth's surface.

The information from this first flight is insufficient to exclude completely other forms of radiation. According to press reports, a second rocket is to be sent up on October 2 to investigate the new source further. [This, and other later flights, have confirmed the X-ray source and measured its intensity at several wavelengths.] The lunar research program is sponsored by the Air Force Cambridge Research Laboratories.

....

A Satellite for
Gamma-Ray Astronomy

MARSHALL MELIN

(*Sky and Telescope*, June 1961)

To look at cosmic radiation within our galaxy in a new way is the main purpose of the gamma-ray-astronomy satellite Explorer XI, sponsored by the National Aeronautics and Space Administration. It was successfully launched from Cape Canaveral on April 27, 1961, at 14:16:38 Universal time.

The origin of primary cosmic radiation is one of the underlying riddles of the universe. As yet, too little is known about these very fast-moving protons to decide whether they come chiefly from nuclear processes in supernovae, are accelerated as in a giant synchrotron by galactic magnetic fields, or are being continuously generated throughout the galaxy by conversion of energy into matter. An effective study of primary cosmic rays should provide valuable insight into cosmogony.

Even from artificial satellites that travel well above the earth's dense atmosphere, the primary cosmic rays of galactic origin are hard to measure. Fast-moving protons trapped within the Van Allen belts interfere with observations. Also, since these primaries are charged

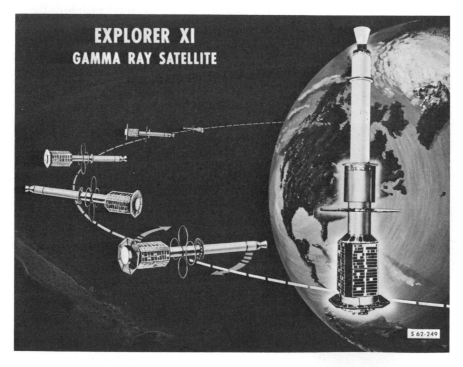

FIG. 94. Immediately after launching, Explorer XI began to spin around its long axis. The satellite's tumbling motion, sketched here, was needed so that its telescope could scan both earth and sky. To add inertia around a transverse axis, the fourth stage was left attached. A hollow doughnut containing liquid mercury was mounted above the rocket's nozzle to dissipate rotational energy. The small aluminum disk shown leaving the payload is a meteoritic-bombardment shield, removable by ground command. The 88-inch-long package weighed 95 pounds. (National Aeronautics and Space Administration picture)

particles, the direction from which they seem to approach the earth may bear little relation to the region where they originated, as their paths are warped by the magnetic fields of the galaxy, solar system, and the earth itself. However, the true direction of origin can be found for gamma rays, which are high-energy electromagnetic waves. . . .

The high energy of the gamma rays indicates that their wavelengths are very short . . . less than 1.3×10^{-12} centimeter (0.00013 angstrom). The payload of Explorer XI is designed to make a map of the sky at these wavelengths. While the crude chart will require several months of observing, it will be the first ever obtained.

The gamma-ray "telescope" carried in this satellite was kindly described to the writer by William Kraushaar, who designed it with George Clark, another Massachusetts Institute of Technology scientist. The heart of the device is a number of solid masses that scintillate when penetrated by radiation, together with eight photomultipliers to detect these flashes, and a circuit that can distinguish the wanted forms of radiation from the much more frequent flashes of other kinds.

Stacked on one another are five polished crystalline plates, three of cesium iodide alternating with two of sodium iodide, each about 0.2 inch thick and three inches in diameter. Underneath is a photomultiplier to detect flashes in this pile. Any incoming gamma ray that impinges on a nucleus produces a pair of electrons, one positive and one negative, which leave bright trails in the stack. If the ray enters at an angle of less than 12 degrees with the axis of the instrument, the two electrons encounter a lucite block several inches behind the crystal layers, where they induce bright trails viewed by a pair of photomultipliers. Both of the latter must be activated within 10^{-7} second of one another, and while the first photomultiplier is still illuminated by the flash, for the instrument to have any further interest in the event.

When this does occur, a further test must be met—nonillumination of all of five additional photomultipliers. These are arranged to see flashes originating in a plastic shield surrounding the top and sides of the telescope. Two of the detectors are at the upper end of this shield, three below. A trapped cosmic ray from the Van Allen belts would cause scintillation in the shield before activating the inner assembly, and these flashes are carried by internal reflection in the plastic to one or more photomultipliers.

The instrument must also discriminate against neutrons, which can imitate the expected behavior of gamma rays, but give rise to short "prongs" of radiation within the iodide crystals. These paths are so short that in the great majority of cases they lie in a single crystal plate, not in two. The duration of scintillations is some five times longer in the cesium salt than in the sodium one. Thus if the event satisfies other criteria, the manner in which the light intensity inside the stack changes with time will allow gamma rays to be distinguished from neutrons. . . .

Data stored in Explorer XI's tape recorder will be telemetered to earth on command in a selected two-minute period during each orbital revolution. Alternatively, the satellite may be commanded to transmit data as it is gathered without using the recorder. . . .

As the gamma-ray telescope scans the heavens, the orientation of the satellite has to be known at all times. Hence two photocells, operated with different sensitivities, serve as earth detectors. The natural tumble of the satellite is expected to provide adequate scanning for the mapping.

This shows the complexity of equipment in satellites or rockets necessary to observe X-ray sources (although the longer-wave X-ray detectors are somewhat different). By mid-1967 it was not possible to say how many X-ray sources there are or what their structure is. Herbert Friedman at the Naval Research Lab considers that there are many clouds of high-speed electrons and ions in the Milky Way, each emitting X rays for a limited period of time. At least one outside galaxy (M87) has been detected as an X-ray source. One possible explantation is that the remnants of old supernovae are X-ray sources.

—TLP

Oriental Records of Novae and Supernovae

JOSEPH ASHBROOK

(*Sky and Telescope*, January 1967)

In 1966 a major advance in the new science of X-ray astronomy was the identification of the intense cosmic source Scorpius X-1 with a faint, very blue star that is evidently a former nova. The story was detailed by Herbert Gursky in the November issue of this magazine, and in the November *Astrophysical Journal* Hugh M. Johnson and C. B. Stephenson have reported their independent recognition of this star as an ex-nova.

Can we identify this object with a "new star" observed in Japan in May of A.D. 891, said to have been east of the stars ϕ, χ, ψ, and ω Ophiuchi? This description fits the modern coordinates of the Scorpius X-ray source: right ascension $16^h17^m.1$, declination $-15°31'$ (1950).

The new star of A.D. 891 is one of about a hundred listed in "Ancient Oriental Records of Novae and Supernovae" by Xi Ze-zong and Po Shu-jen. Their article, published in Chinese in 1965, has now become available in English translation by K. S. Yang (University of Illinois), in *Science* for November 4, 1966.[1]

The two Chinese scholars have made a wholesale reexamination of the references to possible new stars in the historical writings of China, Japan, and Korea. Because of the loose terminology of the ancient annalists, much care was needed to differentiate between novae and comets. After the screening of almost a thousand possible cases, ninety were accepted as probable novae or supernovae. A few objects known only from western records have been added for completeness.

---

[1] The 1965 catalogue is a revision of an earlier list by the same authors, published in English translation as *Smithsonian Contributions to Astrophysics*, 2, 6, 1958.

In this catalogue appear such well-known stars as the supernovae of 1604 (Kepler), 1572 (Tycho), 1054 (the parent of the Crab nebula), and 1006 (in Lupus). The two earliest entries go back to the fourteenth century B.C., and refer to cryptic inscriptions on ox bones from burial mounds of the Yin dynasty. The latest is a new star seen in China on September 29, 1690, east of Epsilon Sagittarii.

In the old Oriental records, sky positions are usually vague, and any attempted conversion to right ascension and declination gives a misleading appearance of accuracy. Yang tells us:

"Under the Chinese system of dividing the sky, there were three general broad regions called *yuan* (Enclosures)! the Tzu Wei or Tzu Kun formed by stars in Ursa Major, Draco, and Camelopardalis; the T'ai Wei, by stars in Virgo, Leo, and Coma Berenices; and the T'icn Shih, by stars in Hercules, Serpens, Ophiuchus, and Aquila. In addition, there were twenty-eight *hsiu* (Lunar Mansions) distributed approximately along the equator. Other stars were designated according to their positions relative to the three Enclosures and the twenty-eight Lunar Mansions."

Clearly, much caution must be used in trying to match X-ray or radio sources with ancient records from the Far East.

Xi Ze-zong and Po Shu-jen conclude that a total of fourteen supernovae in our galaxy have been recorded in the last two thousand years. Making a plausible allowance for objects missed because of interstellar absorption, they estimate that the average rate of occurrence is one supernova per fifty years in the Milky Way.

··

X Rays and Neutron Stars

(Sky and Telescope, April 1964)

A strange and exciting new chapter in observational astronomy has been opened by the discovery of intense sources of X rays in the Milky Way. The U.S. Naval Research Laboratory has been particularly active in this novel field, and an account of its results was presented by Herbert Friedman of NRL's Hulburt Center for Space Research.

FIG. 95. The rocket-borne X-ray
detector. Note the honeycomb
channels added to narrow the
viewing field to 10 degrees.
(Official United States Navy
Photograph)

The sun's corona is a strong source of X rays, hence astronomers
had anticipated that coronas of other stars might produce measurable
X-radiation. In such observations, only X rays shorter than 10 or 20
angstroms offer hope of detection. Those of longer wavelength will be
blocked at stellar distances by the minute quantities of heavy atoms in
the interstellar medium. But the NRL observations showed sources
of quite unexpected character.

On April 29, 1963, an Aerobee rocket was sent aloft with a large
X-ray detector (see Fig. 95) looking out its side through a hexagonal
honeycomb collimator that restricted the field of view to 10 degrees.
At fifty miles, the Aerobee had reached a level at which the earth's
atmosphere was no longer opaque to radiation of one to eight angstroms. As the rocket spun, the X-ray detector scanned the entire sky
above the horizon during the four minutes of flight between altitudes
of 50 and 130 miles. In all the accessible sky, there appeared only
two sharply defined X-ray objects—a very strong source in Scorpius
and a weaker one at the Crab nebula.

On eight different scans through Scorpius, the telemetered count-
ing rate rose sharply as the detector passed over the region between
Nu and Chi Scorpii. The position of this source was right ascension

FIG. 96. Eight different times during the Aerobee flight of April 29, 1963, the rocket's gyrations caused the X-ray detector to sweep across the Ophiuchus-Scorpius region of the Milky Way.(A).Record of the photon counts in 0.03-second intervals for each sweep, lettered to correspond with the scan lines plotted on map (B). The peak count during each scan is labeled, as are a few of the other high counts. Circular contour lines surround the position of this strong X-ray source, but because of limited resolving power, its diameter is uncertain. (Charts adapted from Official United States Navy Photograph)

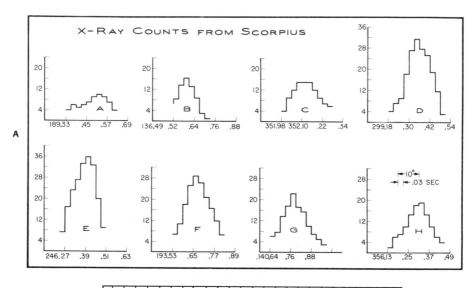

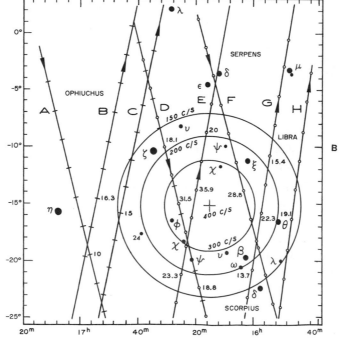

16^h15^m, declination $-15°$. The measurements are consistent with a point source, but because of the limited resolution of the detector an angular diameter of up to two degrees is not ruled out.

No unusual optically prominent features mark this place in the sky. One conjecture is that the X rays come from an invisible cloud of very hot gas, but how such a cloud might occur is by no means obvious. A second possibility is that the source is a *neutron star*.

As early as 1934 Walter Baade and Fritz Zwicky had suggested the possibility of stars composed entirely of neutrons. From theoretical considerations, the properties of neutron stars have been predicted in some detail. Produced by a supernova collapse, a neutron star would have about as much mass as the sun, yet be only five to ten miles in diameter! The enormously dense object would have a central temperature of several billion degrees. It would be an intense source of X rays, yet be so faint optically as to escape visual detection unless much nearer than even Alpha Centauri.

If the Scorpius X-ray source is indeed a neutron star, it is tempting to suppose that it is the remnant of a supernova said to have been observed in this sky area by Chinese and Arab astronomers in A.D. 827.

The other source observed by the NRL scientists was the Crab nebula in Taurus. Its X-ray intensity was about a seventh that of the Scorpius feature. The Crab nebula is famous as an exceptionally intense radio source, and for the strong polarization of its visible light. Both properties are customarily attributed to synchrotron radiation from electrons with energies up to about 100 million electron volts. But if the measured X-ray flux were to be ascribed to synchrotron radiation, electrons of 10^{14} electron volts would be required!

"Clearly, the observed X rays cannot be synchrotron radiation," say Friedman, Bowyer, Byram, and Chubb. "We suggest that the X rays are a thermal emission, as in the Scorpius case, from the neutron star remnant of the supernova explosion of A.D. 1054."

In addition to the two localized sources in Scorpius and Taurus, the NRL group found indications of a diffuse background of X-radiation. This was recognized by comparing signals recorded by the rocket looking upward with those looking earthward. If this diffuse flux is of galactic or extragalactic origin, important cosmological deductions can be made. For example, the hot-universe version of F.

Hoyle and T. Gold's steady-state theory predicts a background X-ray intensity, which would be, however, about a hundred times stronger than observed.

Nevertheless, it is difficult to decide whether the observed X-ray sky background is truly galactic or produced in the earth's high atmosphere by energetic trapped particles. The problem is still unsolved.

The NRL group is not the only team that has been working in X-ray astronomy. In fact, the first indication of the Scorpius source appears to have been obtained in a 1962 Aerobee experiment by R. Giacconi and his coworkers at American Science and Engineering Corportion and Massachusetts Institute of Technology.

A third organization investigating X-ray sources in the night sky is the Research Laboratories of Lockheed Missiles and Space Company, Palo Alto, California. P. C. Fisher and A. J. Meyerott of Lockheed have analyzed results from Aerobee-Hi launchings on September 30, 1962, and March 15, 1963. The radiation counters carried aloft covered several wavelength intervals between 0.6 and 20 angstroms.

The Lockheed results refer to the opposite side of the sky from Scorpius, but do include detection of the Crab nebula. In all, about a dozen high-count regions were found, at least half regarded by Fisher and Meyerott as real.

••

Can Neutron Stars
Be Observed?

GEORGE S. MUMFORD

(*Sky and Telescope*, June 1965)

When a normal star has totally exhausted its nuclear fuels and reaches the terminal stage in its evolution, all that remains is a neutron star, according to some astrophysicists. The hypothetical neutron star is visualized as only about ten miles across, but massive as the sun and with an internal temperature of about a billion degrees.

Radiating strongly at X-ray wavelengths, it would be invisible optically at stellar distances.

However, new calculations reported in *Physical Review Letters* indicate that neutron stars cool so fast they may not be observable. This work was done at California Institute of Technology by J. N. Bahcall and R. A. Wolf.

Depending upon the manner by which energy is carried away from a neutron star, the cooling rate is 100 or 1,000,000 times faster than indicated by previous studies. If the second alternative is correct, the time during which a neutron star would be hot enough to produce X rays would be on the order of weeks rather than thousands of years.

According to the authors, "The fast cooling rates are also inconsistent with the hypothesis that a hot neutron star exists in the Crab nebula," a strong source of X rays.

....

More About X Rays
from the Crab Nebula

(*Sky and Telescope*, September 1964)

Can neutron stars be the sources of the intense X rays discovered last year in Scorpius and Taurus? Fantastically dense and hot, these very small stars should be powerful emitters of X rays, yet unobservably faint optically. The hypothesis seemed attractive for the Taurus source (which is about 1/7 as strong as the Scorpius one) for it is centered on the Crab nebula, the remnant of a supernova explosion in A.D. 1054. It had been suggested that such outbursts produce neutron stars.

To test the neutron star conjecture for the Taurus source, Naval Research Laboratory scientists sent a rocket-borne X-ray detector aloft from White Sands, New Mexico, on July 5. It attained an altitude of 144 miles at the right time and place to observe an occultation of the Crab nebula by the moon.

A point source such as a neutron star would have disappeared abruptly when the moon's edge reached it. Instead, the X-ray intensity diminished gradually during the five minutes of measurement. Evidently the radiation is coming from a source of considerable angular extent, probably associated with the gas clouds that form the nebula.

This experiment under Herbert Friedman, of NRL's Hulburt Center for Space Research, was reported by John W. Finney in *The New York Times* for July 18.

Epilogue

The evolution of stars, as this book is intended to show, is a subject that developed almost entirely in the past thirty years. From the recent articles reproduced here, it is clear that a great deal more will be learned in the next decade or two. X-ray sources, supernova explosions, and possible neutron stars are all receiving a great deal of attention; we have much more to learn about them, and also about faint red dwarfs at the lower end of the main sequence. How small a star can form? Recent work with infrared detectors shows the promise of discovering many stars so cool (or so reddened by interstellar smoke) that most of their light is at wavelengths longer than 10,000 angstroms. Infrared surveys may also locate old white dwarfs that have cooled beyond visible detection.

There is more work to be done on nuclear processes, so that we can be sure of the changes that can go on in stellar interiors. These were summarized in an excellent article, "Chemical Evolution of Stars" by G. R. and E. M. Burbidge in Volume 51 of the Handbuch der Physik (Berlin: Springer Verlag, 1959). There are many possibilities for peculiar conditions where nuclear reactions can go on in regions outside the core of a star and even in interstellar clouds that have not yet condensed to recognizable stars. A topic barely mentioned here is that of the "superstar," of 100 million solar masses, that may form at the nucleus of a galaxy, cook up heavy elements from hydrogen, and provide explosive energy to account for various aspects of galactic structure. (The topic will, however, be covered in a later volume of this series.)

The order of equilibrium stellar models described here will undoubtedly be retained, although many modifications—some of them mentioned in the articles which make up this book—may be necessary. It represents a synthesis of laboratory findings with observations of distant stars and nebulae in a consistent theory that is the major achievement of twentieth-century astrophysics.

THORNTON PAGE

LOU WILLIAMS PAGE

Appendix I
The Origin of
Sky and Telescope

In March 1931 publication of a small quarterly magazine, *The Telescope*, began at Perkins Observatory of Ohio Wesleyan University in Delaware, Ohio, with the director of the observatory, Harlan T. Stetson, as editor. By July 1933 the magazine had become a larger, bimonthly periodical. After Stetson moved to the Massachusetts Institute of Technology, the Bond Astronomical Club, a society of Cambridge amateur astronomers, and Harvard College Observatory assumed sponsorship of the magazine. Loring B. Andrews became editor, and in 1937 Donald H. Menzel succeeded him. *The Telescope* carried stories of important astronomical discoveries, reviews of current astronomical work, and articles on the history of the science.

In the meantime, the first issue of the small *Monthly Bulletin of the Hayden Planetarium* (New York City) appeared, in November 1935, edited by Hans Christian Adamson. In addition to a review of the current show at the planetarium, it contained other astronomical notes and articles. The interest and encouragement of its readers led, in October 1936, to the enlargement of its size and scope. Its name was changed to *The Sky*, and while retaining its planetarium ties, it became the official organ of the Amateur Astronomers' Association in New York City, replacing the magazine *Amateur Astronomer*, which had been published from April 1929 to the spring of 1936.

The Sky grew in reputation and circulation. In February 1938 Clyde Fisher, curator-in-chief of the planetarium, became editor. On November 1, 1939, the Sky Publishing Corporation was formed, owned by Charles A. Federer, Jr., who for four years had been a planetarium lecturer. He and his wife, Helen Spence Federer, edited and published *The Sky* through its fifth volume.

Then, encouraged by Harlow Shapley, director of the Harvard College Observatory, Sky Publishing Corporation moved to Cambridge, Massachusetts, and combined *The Telescope* and *The Sky*, into *Sky and Telescope*, born with the November 1941 issue. The ties with Harvard have been strong. Until the middle 1950s the magazine's offices were in the observatory—now they are located less than a mile away.

The present editorial staff includes Mr. Federer as editor-in-chief, Joseph Ashbrook as editor, and William Shawcross as managing editor. Observers' material is handled by Leif J. Robinson, books and art by Mollie Boring. Unsigned material in the magazine is prepared by this group.

During its twenty-six years, *Sky and Telescope* has been a distinguished and increasingly well-received publication, with two overlapping purposes. It has served as a forum where amateur astronomers can exchange views and experiences, and where they are furnished with observing data. It has brought to an ever-widening circle of scientists and educated laymen detailed and reliable information on new astronomical developments, and through its pages, has introduced them to the important figures of modern astronomy.

•••

Appendix II
Astronomy through the
Ages: A Brief Chronology

ca. 3000 B.C.:	Earliest recorded Babylonian observations of eclipses, planets, and stars.
ca. 2500 B.C.:	Egyptian pyramids constructed, oriented north-south by the stars.
ca. 2000 B.C.:	Babylonian story of creation: *Enuma Elish.* Stonehenge built in southern England with stones lined up by the stars.
ca. 1000 B.C.:	Beginnings of Chinese and Hindu astronomical observations.
700–400 B.C.:	Greek story of creation: Hesiod's *Theogony.* Hebrew story of creation: *Genesis.* Greek philosophers Thales, Pythagoras, and Meton note regularity of celestial motions.

400–300 B.C.:	Greek philosophers Plato, Eudoxus, and Calippus develop the concept of celestial motions on spheres.
	Aristotle develops the idea of four elements and the concept that heavy things fall, light ones rise.
300–100 B.C.:	Aristarchus proposes that the earth moves.
	Eratosthenes measures the size of the earth.
	Hipparchus makes accurate observations of star positions.
ca. A.D. 150:	Ptolemy's *Almagest* summarizes the geocentric theory; the planets' motions are explained by epicycles and other motions in circles.
ca. 1400:	Ulugh-Beg, in Samarkand, reobserves star positions.
1530:	Copernicus, in Poland, postulates that the earth and planets move around the sun because this involves fewer circular motions. This revolutionary idea later rouses strong opposition.
ca. 1600:	Tycho Brahe measures the motions of the planets accurately; Kepler uses these measurements to show that the orbits of planets are ellipses rather than combinations of circles.
	Galileo uses the first telescope to observe the moons of Jupiter and the crescent shape of Venus, supplying strong support for the Copernican idea. Galileo also establishes that falling weights would all be accelerated in the same way if there were no air to hold the lighter ones back.
1680:	Newton combines Kepler's and Galileo's findings, together with observations of moon and comets, into the fundamental laws of mechanics and gravitation. He also studies light, its color and spectrum. By this time, accurate pendulum clocks are in use.
1690:	Halley notes the periodic reports of a large comet every seventy years and concludes they refer to one object moving in a long, thin ellipse around the sun.
1755:	Kant postulates that the sun and planets were formed by the coagulation of a cloud of gas like the spiral nebulae.
1780:	William Herschel builds large telescopes, discovers the planet Uranus, and explains the Milky Way as a flat disk of stars around the sun.
1700–1800:	Mathematical astronomy flourishes, involving many Europeans—Cassini, Bradley, d'Alembert, Laplace, Lagrange, and others—who apply Newton's mechanics to celestial motions with remarkable precision.
1840:	The first astronomical photograph (of the moon) ob-

tained by J. W. Draper. By 1905 photography is well established for accurate observations with telescopes ranging up to 40 inches in aperture, photographing stars 100,000 times fainter than those visible to the naked eye.

1843:   Doppler explains the effect of motion on the spectrum of a light source.

1877:   Schiaparelli observes "canals" on Mars.

1800–1900:   Navigation has become a precise and important practical application of astronomy. The accurate observations of star positions show that annual parallax is due to the earth's orbital motion around the sun, confirming the Copernican idca and providing a method of measuring distances to the stars. Other small motions show that the stars are moving.

1850–1900:   The laboratory study of light together with physical theory shows that spectrum analysis can be used to determine temperature and chemical composition of a light source.

1900:   Chamberlin and Moulton speculate that the planets were formed after another star passed close to the sun.

1904–20:   Einstein establishes the theory of relativity.
Large reflecting telescopes are built at the Mount Wilson Observatory in California.

1910–30:   Russell and Eddington establish the theory of stellar structure.

1917–30:   Shapley and Oort establish the size, shape, and rotation of the Milky Way Galaxy.

1930:   Discovery of Pluto.

1910–40:   Slipher and Hubble find that other galaxies are moving away from ours. De Sitter, Eddington, Lemaitre, and others explain this recession by application of relativity theory.

1930–60:   Bethe, Gamow, and others in the U.S. apply the results of nuclear physics to explaining the source of stellar energy. This is followed by the work of many astrophysicists on evolution of the stars from large interstellar gas clouds.
Von Weizsäcker, Kuiper, Urey, and others develop a theory of the origin of the solar system from a large gas cloud.

1947–60:   Instruments are shot above the atmosphere in the U.S. for astronomical observations.

Large radiotelescopes are built in the U.S., Australia, and England. Many radio sources are located.

1957:   Sputnik I, the first artificial satellite of the earth, is launched by Soviet scientists.

1959:   First space probe to hit the moon is launched by Soviet scientists.

1961:   First manned space flight around the earth by Soviet astronaut Yuri Gagarin.

1961–66:   Radiotelescopes locate quasi-stellar sources ("quasars"), found to have large optical red shifts like the most distant galaxies.

1962–67:   X-ray sources detected by rocket-borne equipment above the earth's atmosphere.

1964–65:   First close-up photographs of the lunar surface obtained by U.S. space probes Ranger 7 and Ranger 8.

1965:   Photographs of Mars, taken at about 11,000 miles distance by Mariner 4, show a cratered surface.

1966:   First soft landing on the moon (by the Russian Luna 9). Photographs of the surface taken from a few feet show no loose dust.

1967:   Physical analysis of moon's surface carried out by Surveyor 3.

■■■

Appendix III
Notes on the
Contributors

ALLER, LAWRENCE H. (1913–   ), chairman of the astronomy department at the University of California, Los Angeles; from 1948 to 1962 at the University of Michigan; visiting professor at Australian National University, 1960 and 1961; his greatest contributions have been in studies of gaseous nebulae, stellar atmospheres, and cosmic abundances of elements; author of *Astrophysics* (two volumes); coauthor of *Atoms, Stars, and Nebulae*. ("The Energy of the Sun and Stars," "The Source of Energy in the Fainter Stars")

ASHBROOK, JOSEPH (1918–   ), astronomer specializing in variable stars; on the Yale faculty from 1946 to 1953, when he joined the editorial staff of *Sky and Telescope*. ("Oriental Records of Novae and Supernovae")

BOK, BART J. (1906–   ), Dutch-born astronomer; director of Steward Observatory, the University of Arizona; from 1957 to 1966 director of the Mount Stromlo Observatory, Canberra, Australia; author of *The Astronomer's Universe* and *The Distribution of the Stars in Space*, coauthor of *The Milky Way*. ("Stellar Evolution")

EGGEN, OLIN J. (1919–   ), astrophysicist; director of the Mount Stromlo Observatory, Canberra, Australia; at the Royal Greenwich Observatory, Herstmonceux Castle, Sussex, England, from 1953 to 1962. ("Color-Luminosity Arrays")

FEDERER, C. A., JR. (1909–   ), editor-in-chief of *Sky and Telescope*; at the Hayden Planetarium in New York, he lectured on opening day in October 1935; in 1936 he was made a staff assistant, and in 1939 became editor and publisher of *The Sky*, which later moved from the planetarium to Harvard College Observatory and merged with *The Telescope*. ("What's Inside the Stars?")

GOLDBERG, LEO (1913–   ), director of Harvard College Observatory; from 1946–1960 chairman of the astronomy department at the University of Michigan and director of the observatory there; expert on solar physics, spectroscopy, and atmospheric physics; editor of *Annual Review of Astronomy and Astrophysics*, coauthor of *Atoms, Stars, and Nebulae*. ("The Spendthrift Bright Stars")

HOFFLEIT, DORRIT (1907–   ), conducted the "News Notes" page of *Sky and Telescope* from 1941 through 1956, while an astronomer at Harvard College Observatory; since June 1957 director of the Maria Mitchell Observatory, Nantucket, Massachusetts, and astronomer at Yale University Observatory. ("Origin of Binary Stars," "Red Giant to White Dwarf," "Tycho's Star," "Recession from Orion," "Another Supernova Radio Star," "A Radio Source and a Chinese Supernova," "Pray for an Explosion!," "Evolutionary Changes in Single Stars?")

HUANG, SU-SHU (1915–   ), Chinese-born astrophysicist who came to the United States in 1948; at Goddard Space Flight Center (NASA) 1955–1965 working on the theory of stellar atmospheres; now at Dearborn Observatory, Northwestern University. ("Jeans' Criterion of Gravitational Instability")

KUIPER, GERARD P. (1905–   ), Dutch-born astronomer; formerly director of Yerkes and McDonald Observatories and now head of the Lunar and Planetary Laboratory at the University of Arizona; editor of *The Atmospheres of the Earth and Planets, The Solar System,* and *Stars and Stellar Systems.* ("Double Stars")

MAYALL, NICHOLAS U. (1906–   ), director of the Kitt Peak National Observatory, Tucson, Arizona; at Lick Observatory from 1933 to 1960; his chief fields of study are galactic nebulae, globular clusters, and red shifts and internal motions of galaxies. ("The Crab Nebula, a Probable Supernova")

MELIN, MARSHALL (1917–   ), biochemist, amateur astronomer, and expert on visual observations of artificial satellites; conducted the department "Observing the Satellites" in *Sky and Telescope* from 1958 to 1962; member of the Bond Astronomical Club, Cambridge, Massachusetts. ("A Satellite for Gamma-Ray Astronomy")

MENZEL, DONALD H. (1901–   ), astrophysicist; at Harvard College Observatory, where he was director from 1954 to 1966; an authority on the sun, planetary atmospheres, and stellar and nebular spectra; editor of *The Telescope* from 1937 to 1941; author of *Stars and Planets, Story of the Starry Universe, Our Sun, Flying Saucers,* and *The Universe in Action.* ("Source of the Sun's Energy," "Spendthrift Stars")

MORGAN, W. W. (1906–   ), an authority on stellar spectroscopy; since 1926 at the Yerkes Observatory of the University of Chicago at Williams Bay, Wisconsin, where he was director from 1960 to 1966; an editor of *The Astrophysical Journal* for many years. ("Some Uses of Spectral Classification")

MUMFORD, GEORGE S. (1928–   ), astronomer on the faculty of Tufts University; since January 1965 he has conducted the "News Notes" department of *Sky and Telescope.* ("Nuclei of Planetary Nebulae," "Can Neutron Stars Be Observed?")

PAYNE-GAPOSCHKIN, CECILIA H. (1900–   ), British-born astronomer; retired in 1966 from Harvard University, where she had been since 1923; chairman of the Astronomy Department there from 1956 to 1960; an authority on variable stars, stellar evolution, galactic structure, and novae; author of *Introduction to Astronomy, Stars in the Making.* ("New Stars")

PRUETT, J. HUGH (1886–1955), popularizer of astronomy, associated with the University of Oregon from 1920 until his death; his "Terminology Talks" appeared in each issue of *Sky and Telescope* from 1947 to 1952. (*Spectral Classification*)

SHAPLEY, HARLOW (1885–   ), professor of astronomy at Harvard University from 1921 to 1956; director of the Harvard College Observatory from 1921 to 1952; famed for his work on star clusters and galaxies;

author of *Galaxies, Star Clusters, Source Book in Astronomy*. ("Dean of American Astronomers")

SITTERLY, BANCROFT W. (1895–   ), professor of mathematics and physics at American University, Washington, D.C.; astronomer at Wesleyan University, Middletown, Connecticut, from 1923 to 1945; his chief astronomical interests are navigational astronomy and eclipsing binaries. ("Symposium on Abundances of Elements in Stars")

STRUVE, OTTO (1897–1963), director of the Yerkes Observatory of the University of Chicago from 1932 to 1949; founder and director from 1938 to 1949 of McDonald Observatory; the last of a family that produced four generations of renowned astronomers in Russia; one of the leading figures in American astronomy in this century, he was widely known for his research on stellar spectra, and the author of many research papers and books, his last book being *Astronomy of the 20th Century*. ("Ages of the Stars," "The Two Fundamental Relations of Stellar Astronomy," "The Internal Constitution of Some Stars," "Quantitative Spectral Classifications," "Color-Magnitude Diagrams and Stellar Evolution," "What Happens to Star Clusters?" "Old and Young Star Clusters," "The Oldest Star Clusters," "Interstellar Matter," "The Interaction between Stars and Nebulae," "T Tauri Stars and Associated Nebulosities," "Axial Rotation and Stellar Evolution," "Some Problems of Stellar Rotation," "White Dwarfs," "The History of the Chemical Elements," "Element Formation in Stars," "The Chemical Compositions and Ages of Stars," "Variable Stars and Stellar Evolution," "Some Possible Evidence of Evolution in Individual Stars")

WENDT, GERALD (1891–   ), educator, writer, and lecturer; from 1916 to 1930 on the faculty of Rice Institute, then at the University of Chicago, then at Pennsylvania State College; editor of *Chemical Abstracts* from 1917 to 1921; director of the American Institute, New York, from 1931 to 1937; science editor of *Time* from 1942 to 1945. ("Are Cosmic Rays Swan Songs of Stars?")

The Greek Alphabet

	Capital	Lower Case		Capital	Lower Case
Alpha	A	α	Nu	N	ν
Beta	B	ß	Xi	Ξ	ξ
Gamma	Γ	γ	Omicron	O	o
Delta	Δ	δ	Pi	Π	π
Epsilon	E	ε	Rho	P	ρ
Zeta	Z	ζ	Sigma	Σ	σ
Eta	H	η	Tau	T	τ
Theta	Θ	θ	Upsilon	Υ	ν
Iota	I	ι	Phi	Φ	φ
Kappa	K	κ	Chi	X	χ
Lambda	Λ	λ	Psi	Ψ	ψ
Mu	M	μ	Omega	Ω	ω

Glossary

Powers of ten are used to save space in writing very large or very small numbers: 10^9 means 1,000,000,000, or one billion; 10^{21} is 1 followed by 21 zeros; 10^{-6} is $1/10^6$, or 0.000001, or one millionth; and so on.

absolute magnitude A measure of luminosity; the magnitude a star would have if observed from a distance of ten parsecs. See **magnitude**.

absorption lines See **spectrum**.

abundances The relative amounts of various chemical elements constituting the materials of a star or nebula or other object. See p. 264.

acceleration Speeding up or slowing down; more precisely, a change in amount or direction of velocity.

angle Angular distance measured in degrees, minutes, and seconds of arc. All the way around the sky is 360°; 1° = 60′ (minutes of arc), 1′ = 60″ (seconds of arc).

angstrom Unit of length used to measure wavelengths of light, abbreviated A; 1 centimeter (about 0.4 inch) is 100 million A.

angular momentum A measure of spin (or rotary motion) which remains constant in an isolated set of massive bodies. See p. 164.

association A loose grouping of stars moving together and held together by gravitational forces. See p. 104.

astronomical unit The distance from sun to earth (about 93 million miles), abbreviated A.U., and used as a unit of distance in the solar system.

astrophysics Study of physical conditions in planets, stars, nebulae, galaxies, and regions between them.

atmosphere The outer, gaseous layers of a star (or planet) through which light can pass and where the absorption or emission lines in the spectrum are formed.

atomic energy Energy released in nuclear reactions that change the total mass of material by packing nuclear particles in a different arrangement.

Balmer lines   A series of spectral lines produced by hydrogen atoms. The first (red) line at wavelength 6563 A is called Hα (H–alpha), the second (green, 4861 A) Hβ, the third (4341 A) Hγ, and so on, ending at the Balmer limit at 3650 A.

BD (followed by a number)   The *Bonner Durchmusterung* catalogue number, which serves to identify a star.

binary   A double star, or pair of stars close together in the sky. *Visual* binaries can be seen as two separate stellar images in a telescope. An *eclipsing* binary looks like one star but varies periodically in brightness. A *spectroscopic* binary varies periodically in radial velocity (measured by Doppler shift in its spectrum).

brightness   A measure of how bright a star appears in the sky; a result of the star's intrinsic luminosity and distance; commonly measured by the apparent magnitude. See **magnitude**.

calorie   A unit of energy; the amount of heat energy necessary to warm up 1 gram of water 1°C; equal to 4.185×10^7 ergs. (Food analysts use the word for a larger unit, 1000 of these "small calories.")

carbon cycle   A series of nuclear reactions involving carbon, nitrogen, and hydrogen at very high temperature. It results in four hydrogen atoms forming one helium atom and releasing energy. See p. 39.

catalogue   A list of stars or other celestial objects, giving their positions on the sky and some other characteristic; such as brightness (BD and CD catalogues), spectral type (HD catalogue), parallax, proper motion, and color.

CD (followed by a number)   The Córdoba catalogue number, similar to the BD number but referring to stars in the southern sky.

chromosphere   A layer of the sun's atmosphere just above the visible surface or photosphere.

color index   Difference between photographic and visual magnitude, ranging from —0.5 for blue stars to +1.5 and more for red stars.

comet   A small body moving around the sun in an orbit generally of high eccentricity. Comets generate an atmosphere (coma) and a tail as they come close to the sun but are virtually invisible while they are 10 to 50 astronomical units from the sun.

constellation   A group of bright stars in one region of the sky or the area on the sky occupied by such a group, named, in most cases, for ancient Greek mythological figures.

coordinate   A distance or angle characterizing the position or location of an object. Coordinates x and y are generally used on a plane surface; longitude and latitude on the earth's surface; right ascension and declination or galactic latitude and longitude on the sky. Three coordinates are needed in space.

corona A faint haze and streamers around the sun, visible only during total solar eclipse.

correlation When one quantity depends on another, they are said to be correlated. The correlation can be shown by a plot of one against the other. In a good correlation all the points lie close to a sloping line (not necessarily straight); in a poor correlation there is a large scatter of the points.

coudé focus The place where a large telescope with extra mirrors forms an image that remains fixed when the telescope is moved.

declination Angle in the sky north or south of the celestial equator; a coordinate analogous to latitude on the earth's surface.

degenerate Material highly compressed and highly ionized which, even though fluid, does not behave like an ordinary gas, is called *degenerate*. See p. 216.

degree A unit used to measure angle (1/360 of a full circle) and temperature; 18 degrees on the Fahrenheit scale is equal to 10 degrees on the Centigrade scale or on the absolute (Kelvin) scale. The zero points all differ, so that $212°F = 100°C = 373°K$.

diffraction The bending of light around an obstruction of any size, such as the edge of the moon or the edges of small particles.

distance modulus Difference between apparent magnitude and absolute magnitude; a measure of the ratio of luminosity to brightness or of the distance of an object (on the assumption that space is "clean," so that brightness is proportional to 1/distance^2.)

diurnal motion Daily apparent motion of celestial objects westward due to the eastward rotation of the earth.

Doppler shift A slight shift in wavelength in the spectrum of a light source moving toward or away from the observer. The shift is toward shorter wavelength (more violet color) for an approaching source and toward longer wavelength (redder color) for a receding source.

dyne A very small unit of force, about 1/1000 the weight of a gram, the force necessary to speed up 1 gram by 1 cm/sec in 1 sec.

eclipse When one object comes between us and another object, obscuring the first, or reducing its brightness, the first is eclipsed (not necessarily totally). In eclipsing binaries, one star eclipses another.

electron A fundamental particle of small mass and negative charge; found in the outer regions of all atoms, sometimes pulled out of an atom to move independently. Many free electrons form an "electron gas" with a density and temperature of its own.

element A chemically pure substance consisting of only one type of atom.

ellipse An oval-shaped closed curve, precisely defined by the equation, in rectangular coordinates, $x^2/a^2 + y^2/b^2 = 1$.

emission line   A sharp excess of one color (one wavelength of light or radio waves) in a spectrum; generally characteristic of low-density gas.

emulsion   The light-sensitive coating on film or glass plate which is "developed" to show a negative image of the light falling on the film or plate.

energy   Capacity for doing work—that is, exerting a force through some distance. In many processes energy is changed from one form (radiation, heat, chemical energy, potential energy) to another without being created or destroyed. In nuclear reactions mass can be converted into energy.

equilibrium   When conditions in a material (or in a set of bodies) do not change with the passage of time, it is in stable equilibrium. When conditions do change, or will change after a small disturbance, the material (or system) is unstable.

equipartition of energy   The condition in a set of moving particles or bodies with various masses when the system has reached equilibrium. On the average, each kind of particle (atoms or ions or electrons) or body (giant or dwarf stars) has the same amount of energy.

erg   A unit of energy; the work done in pushing 1 gram so that it speeds up from rest to 1.414 cm/sec.

flux   The amount of energy (usually in the form of radiation: light or radio waves) passing through 1 square meter area per second. Flux on a telescope mirror from one celestial object is a measure of the brightness of that object.

focal ratio   The "speed" of a lens or telescope mirror, expressed (inversely) as the ratio of focal length, f, to aperture (lens size). A telescope of focal ratio $f/4$ has an aperture equal to one quarter of its focal length and can photograph a nebula or other extended object in one ninth of the exposure time required with an $f/12$ telescope.

frequency   Number of periodic changes (cycles) per second. The *period* is the reciprocal of the frequency. Radio waves have frequencies of thousands of cycles per second (kilocycles per second) to many millions (megacycles per second, or Mc/sec) and wavelengths of c/f, where c is the velocity of light and radio waves, 3×10^{10} cm/sec.

galaxy   A vast disk-shaped assemblage of stars, gas, and dust. The sun is located in the Milky Way Galaxy.

gamma rays   Light of even shorter wavelength than X rays is called gamma radiation; it usually results from nuclear reactions.

gauss   A unit of magnetic-field strength; the force on a unit magnetic pole is 1 dyne where the field is 1 gauss.

giant star   Highly luminous stars are called giants; they have radii hundreds of times larger than the sun's radius, particularly if they have lower surface temperature, as do red giants of spectral classes K and M. Supergiants are about 100 times brighter than giants.

grating A set of parallel narrow slits that deflect light passing through them by the process of diffraction. A coarse grating used in front of a telescope lens gives several images of each bright star. A fine diffraction grating produces the spectrum of colors in light passing through it, or reflected from a reflection grating.

HD (followed by a number) The Henry Draper catalogue number, referring to stars with spectral type determined at the Harvard College Observatory.

helium A gas formed of single atoms each about four times the mass of the hydrogen atom, and consisting of two protons, two neutrons and two electrons.

H-R diagram A plot of brightness versus color (or temperature, or spectral type), both on a logarithmic or magnitude scale, the brightness adjusted for distance. Each star appears as a point on the H-R diagram, and many of these points (for a group of stars) fall near a diagonal line called the main sequence.

inertia The tendency of massive bodies to remain at rest or continue moving in a straight line.

infrared The "color" of invisible light with longer wavelength than red light and shorter wavelength than radio waves.

intensity The energy received per second, usually in the form of light or radio waves, but also as sound waves or such particles as cosmic rays. The intensity of an absorption line measures the gap in energy near one wavelength or frequency in a spectrum.

interference filter A filter used in astronomical photography or with a photoelectric photometer to select a very narrow band of wavelengths (just one color).

ion An atom or group of atoms with one or more electrons removed (positive ion) or added (negative ion).

ionization The process of forming ions, or the number of ions in a given region (usually the number per cubic centimeter).

isotopes Two atoms of the same type (element) with masses differing by one or more neutron masses. Unstable isotopes undergo *radioactive decay*. Atoms of stable isotopes normally remain unchanged.

kinetic energy Energy of motion, $\frac{1}{2} mv^2$, equal to the work done in pushing a mass, m, until it moves at speed v.

light year A large unit of distance, about 10^{13} kilometers or 6×10^{12} miles. It is the distance that light travels in one year (3.17×10^7 sec) at a speed of 3×10^5 km/sec.

lines Gaps in the spectrum of sunlight (colors missing) are called *Fraunhofer lines*; gaps in the spectra of light from other stars are called *absorption lines*. The stronger ones are known by letters, such as H and K lines; all of them can be designated by wavelength. Nebulae and some stars have *emission lines*, brighter patches in their spectra. See **spectrum**.

luminosity The inherent brightness of a star in terms of the sun's brightness, as would be observed if the two were at the same distance from us.

Lyman alpha A line in the far ultraviolet part of the spectrum (1215 angstroms), strongly absorbed and easily emitted by hydrogen atoms. Lyman beta, Lyman gamma, and others, as well as Lyman continuum are similar to the Balmer lines but at shorter wavelengths.

Magellanic Clouds Two small galaxies of irregular type close to the Milky Way Galaxy, easily visible in the southern sky (from latitudes south of 15° N), about 25° from the south celestial pole.

magnetic field A region near a magnet where another magnet would be acted upon by a force; also a region near moving electric charges where a magnet or other moving charges are affected similarly.

magnifying power Magnification of an image by a telescope-eyepiece combination. "Power 50X" means that an object like the moon appears 50 times larger in the eyepiece than to the unaided eye.

magnitude An indication of the brightness of a celestial object. The brightest stars are "of the first magnitude" and the faintest stars visible to the naked eye are of the sixth magnitude. With telescopes the scale has been extended to over 20 mag. Every 5 magnitudes corresponds to 100 times fainter. The brightness can be measured in visible light, photographic light, infrared light, etc., and the resulting magnitude is called visual, photographic, infrared, etc. Bolometric magnitude is based on total radiation of all wavelengths.

main sequence See **H-R diagram**.

megacycle One million cycles, a unit of radio frequency abbreviated Mc/sec.

microphotometer An instrument that measures the blackening on a photographic negative, usually designed to show on an enlarged "tracing" the differences in blackening from one region to the next—an indication of the different amounts of light that fell on the negative.

minute of arc An angle equal to 1/60 of a degree; therefore an angular distance in the sky which is 1/(60)(360) of a circle; written 1'.

nebula A vast cloud of gas between stars. Dark nebulae also contain dust and obscure the stars behind them.

neutrino A small particle with no electric charge and almost zero mass, produced in some of the nuclear reactions inside stars.

neutron A neutral particle with approximately the same mass as a proton; a component of atomic nuclei.

NGC (followed by a number) The *New General Catalogue* number which serves to identify clusters, nebulae, and galaxies.

nova A star that increases its light output 10,000 times and then fades slowly.

nuclear processes Interactions between the nuclei of atoms that generally release vast quantities of energy as one kind of atom is changed into another.

orbit The path followed by one body (satellite or planet or star or cluster) moving around another under its gravitational attraction. In the absence of any other influence, such an orbit is an ellipse.

parallax The very small change in direction of a star caused by the motion of the earth around the sun. It can be measured only for the nearer stars, on photographs taken six months apart, and is used to obtain the distance (1/parallax = distance in parsecs; 3.26/parallax = distance in light years).

parsec A large unit of distance equal to 3.26 light years; the distance at which a star has a parallax of 1 second of arc (1″).

period The time interval of one complete circuit of an orbit or one complete rotation of a rotating body or the complete cycle of any periodic change.

photodiode and photomultiplier Photoelectric cells.

photometer An instrument designed to measure the brightness of light falling on it. It is described as visual, photographic, or photoelectric, depending on the detector used.

planet A nonluminous body moving around the sun or a star in a nearly circular orbit, shining by reflected light.

planetary nebula A shell of gas ejected from and expanding around an extremely hot star; may appear as a ring because we are viewing it through the thin dimension on the front and rear parts of the shell. See Figure 72.

polarized light Light which consists of waves that vibrate across the beam of light in one direction. Ordinary light is generally unpolarized and the vibrations are in all directions. The polarization may be partial or complete (100 per cent).

pole of the galaxy A point 90° from the center line of the Milky Way. There are two such poles at opposite points in the sky, analogous to the two poles of the earth, each 90° from the earth's equator.

polytropes A set of similar gas spheres, all with the same concentration of gas near the center (corresponding to one value of the polytropic index). See p. 54.

Population I   Consists of young stars usually in the outer parts of the disk of a spiral galaxy. **Population II** consists of older stars near the nucleus of a galaxy or in globular clusters.

position angle   The direction of a line in the sky, measured from 0° (direction north) through 90° (direction east).

profile   The plot of intensity versus wavelength of a line in the spectrum of the sun or of a star from which motions of the gas producing the line can be inferred (such as the rotation of a star).

prominence   A flamelike cloud of luminous gas, usually photographed in light of one emission line of that gas near the edge of the sun.

proper motion   The very small change in direction of a star due to its velocity across the line of sight as seen from near the sun. It is expressed as a fraction of a second of arc per year, and can be measured on photographs of the star taken many years apart.

proportional   Two variable quantities, such as the pressure (p) and density (ρ) of a gas at constant temperature, are said to be proportional if one always equals a constant times the other. This is written $p \sim \rho$. There is an *inverse* proportion if $p \sim 1/V$, as in the case of pressure and volume (V) of a constant mass of gas at constant temperature.

proton   A hydrogen atom with its one electron removed. In the proton-proton reaction (see p. 242), protons stick together on collision and start a chain of nuclear reactions producing helium plus energy.

quantum   A discrete amount of energy; the smallest amount that can be radiated or absorbed by matter. The size depends upon the wavelength and is larger for the shorter wavelengths.

radial velocity   The motion of a star or other light source along the line of sight, detected by *Doppler shift* of lines in the spectrum; red shift indicates recession (positive radial velocity).

radioactive decay   The spontaneous nuclear reaction that continues at a predictable rate—resulting in decomposition of a heavy element into a less heavy one—such as uranium decaying to radium and then to lead.

radio astronomy   The study of astronomical bodies by use of radiotelescopes.

radiometer   A radio receiver designed to measure the radio energy received per second by the antenna.

resolving power   The ability of a telescope to distinguish two stars very close together in the sky; the ability of a spectrograph to distinguish two lines very close together in a spectrum.

right ascension   One coordinate of a star in the sky, measured eastward like longitude on earth, starting from a point called the vernal equinox.

Schmidt camera   A telescope or camera consisting of a spherical mirror with a "correcting plate" (thin lens) in front of it, generally with large focal ratio and able to take a wide-angle photograph.

seeing Changing fuzziness and a slight jumping of a star image in a telescope is caused by air currents in the earth's atmosphere and is called "poor seeing."

shear A tendency to break or "slice" an extended body or cloud.

solar flare A short-lived bright patch on the sun's surface which causes extra ionization in gases such as the earth's upper atmosphere due to ultraviolet light from the flare.

solar mass A large unit of mass, about 2×10^{33} grams (the mass of the sun).

spectral type One of the designations O, B, A, F, G, K, M, based on the pattern of lines in a star's spectrum. Surface temperature is high in "early-type," O and B, stars and lower in "late-type," K and M, stars. See p. 70.

spectrogram Photograph of a spectrum.

spectrograph An instrument attached to a telescope to obtain photographs of stellar spectra.

spectrum The various colors of light from a source spread out in the sequence from red to violet (long wavelength to short wavelength) as in a rainbow. Invisible wavelengths extend from the red to infrared to radio waves, and from blue-violet to ultraviolet and X rays. The spectrum of the sun is often called a Fraunhofer spectrum which, like the spectra of most stars, lacks certain colors in gaps called Fraunhofer lines or absorption lines.

spiral arm Stars, gas, and dust in the outer parts of our Milky Way Galaxy (and in other spiral galaxies) are concentrated in arms spiraling outward from a central nucleus. Our sun is in one such arm, and segments of two others can be seen in the Milky Way.

Stark effect Broadening of spectral lines caused by strong electric fields on the absorbing atoms. In stellar atmospheres electric fields are usually produced by ions and electrons. Stark broadening is proportional to the ion density or ion pressure, and is a good indicator of total atmospheric pressure and of the star's luminosity.

sunspot A region on the sun's surface about 1000° cooler than its surroundings. Spots usually occur in pairs, one with north-magnetic polarity and the other with south-magnetic polarity.

tide The bulge in liquid (water on the earth) or gas (atmosphere) produced by the gravitational attraction of another nearby mass (such as the moon).

turbulence Whirls or vortices in a fluid (liquid or gas).

ultraviolet The "color" of invisible light with wavelengths shorter than visible light (less than about 4000 angstroms).

variable A star with changing brightness (magnitude) or spectrum. Cepheid variables (p. 276) are pulsating stars; eclipsing binaries also vary periodically in brightness. Other variables show changes in magnetic field strength.

wavelength The distance between the crests (or troughs) of regular waves. Visible light of various colors has wavelengths ranging from about 1/10,000 inch to about twice that length. See **spectrum.**

white dwarf A small hot star of high density and low luminosity, the remains of a large bright star that blew up. See p. 210.

width of a spectral line Both absorption lines and emission lines are not at exactly one wavelength and often have a spread of several angstroms. See p. 213.

X rays Light of too short a wavelength to be visible, which can penetrate some distance into most materials. X rays from the sun and other distant sources are entirely absorbed in the earth's ionosphere.

Suggestions

for

Further Reading

INTRODUCTORY

Abell, G. O. *Exploring the Universe*. New York: Holt, Rinehart, and Winston, 1964.

Baker, R. H. *Astronomy* (8th ed.). Princeton, N. J.: Van Nostrand, 1964.

Bok, B. J. *The Astronomer's Universe*. Cambridge, England: Cambridge University Press, 1959.

Goldberg, L., and L. H. Aller. *Atoms, Stars, and Nebulae*. New York: McGraw-Hill, 1943.

Inglis, S. J. *Planets, Stars and Galaxies*. New York: Wiley, 1961.

Page, T. (ed.). *Stars and Galaxies*. Englewood Cliffs, N. J.: Prentice-Hall, 1962.

Page and Page (eds.), The Macmillan *Sky and Telescope* Library of Astronomy Series (Volumes 3, 4 and 5 have particular bearing).

Payne-Gaposchkin, Cecilia. *Stars in the Making*. Cambridge, Mass.: Harvard University Press, 1952.

Payne-Gaposchkin, Cecilia. *Introduction to Astronomy*. Englewood Cliffs, N. J.: Prentice-Hall, 1954.

Rapport, S., and H. Wright. *Astronomy*. New York: New York University Press, 1965.

Struve, O., and V. Zebergs. *Astronomy of the 20th Century*. New York: Macmillan, 1962.

ADVANCED

Chandrasekhar, S. *Stellar Structure*. New York: Dover, 1957.

Eddington, A. S. *Internal Constitution of the Stars*. New York: Dover, 1959.

Gratton, L. (ed.). *Star Evolution*. New York: Academic Press, 1963.

Menzel, D. H., P. L. Bhatnagar, and H. K. Sen. *Stellar Interiors*. New York: Wiley, 1963

Schwarzschild, M. *Structure and Evolution of the Stars*. Princeton, N. J.: Princeton University Press, 1958.

Stein, R. F. and A. G. W. Cameron. *Stellar Evolution*. New York: Plenum Press, 1966.

Struve, Otto. *Stellar Evolution*. Princeton, N. J.: Princeton University Press, 1958.

Index